PROTECTING PERSONAL HEALTH INFORMATION IN IRELAND

LAW & PRACTICE

PETER LENNON

www.oaktreepress.com

Published by

OAK TREE PRESS

19 Rutland Street, Cork, Ireland

www.oaktreepress.com

© 2005 Peter Lennon

A catalogue record of this book is
available from the British Library.

ISBN 1 904887 02 3

Printed in Ireland by ColourBooks.

ABOUT THE AUTHOR

Peter Lennon graduated from Trinity College, Dublin, with a First Class Honours degree in Business Studies. Subsequently, he carried out research in Employment Law. He joined the Department of Justice's Law Reform Division in 1985, where he worked on the Data Protection Act 1988. He has since worked in the Department of Finance and the Department of Health & Children.

In 2001, he was appointed Director of the National General Practice Information Technology Group, which promotes awareness of the value of information management and technology in Irish healthcare. The Group also emphasises the importance of meeting privacy standards and published a *Data Protection Information Guide for General Practitioners* in 2003.

Peter Lennon has lectured widely in Universities and Colleges on finance and management, generally, and health service management, in particular. He has had a number of articles published, ranging from employment law to health service structures. He also has helped to devise distance education programmes in Management Information Systems and is chairman of HL7 Ireland.

CONTENTS

ACKNOWLEDGEMENTS

This book was prepared as part of the National General Practice Information Technology Group's efforts to promote greater awareness of information management and privacy issues in the Irish health system.[1] Accordingly, it is only fair to start with my two colleagues, Nessa Feehan and Gregg Palmer, who worked hard not only on helping with this publication but in all the endeavours of the GPIT Group. I am indebted to them for their efforts.

The officers in the Office of the Data Protection Commissioner and the Office of the Information Commissioner were always extremely helpful and courteous. Their knowledge and expertise steered me in the right direction on numerous occasions.

There were many other individuals who took the time to read parts of the book and offer positive suggestions for improvement, together with constructive criticisms for amendment.

It is important also to acknowledge that the book would never have been written if General Practitioners, Hospital Consultants and other healthcare professionals had not contacted us and raised so many practical queries about how data protection law impinged on their records. Their interest in this area provided not only the necessary stimulus to write a guide that would help their compliance, but it also demonstrated that health professionals in Ireland already apply very high standards to managing and safeguarding patient records.

I would like to thank Brian O'Kane and his team at Oak Tree Press for their support and patience. They made sure the book was finished.

A special acknowledgement must go to Professor Eoin O'Brien who has been gracious enough to write the *Foreword*. I am delighted that he agreed to do so, as I admire greatly his enthusiasm and commitment to

---

[1]   The GPIT Group is funded by the Department of Health & Children.

using information and new technology to best effect for both patients and the health system generally.

The good that is in the book owes a great deal to all of the above persons. However, final responsibility is my own and nothing in the book should be taken as representing the views of any other person or office unless clearly indicated.

Peter Lennon
June 2005

FOREWORD

I approached my task of writing the *Foreword* to this book with considerable trepidation. I was concerned that the author had made the wrong selection – I have a fleeting appreciation of the complex issues covered in *Protecting Personal Health Information in Ireland: Law & Practice,* but no practical expertise with which to explore the vast canvas that Peter Lennon has so painstakingly created with erudition, skill and a customary attention to detail and scholarship.

However, having read the book, I can now discern a certain method in what might appear at first glance to be misguided judgment. I suspect he wanted to force his book upon a novice, such as me – after all, the health service, his ultimate readership, is staffed by such when it comes to issues of information technology law. Moreover, he may have known, or at least suspected (after working closely me with me for some years on ways of forwarding electronic information between a teaching hospital and primary care), that whereas my enthusiasm for developing innovative ways of harnessing computer technology to halt the epidemic of cardiovascular disease was without question, there was a need for some education in a broader sense, if for no other reason than to temper enthusiasm with the restraint that is now inevitably and increasingly being imposed on all healthcare personnel by government in the interest of the individual in society.

If one seeks a point of commencement in *Protecting Personal Health Information in Ireland*, it has to be an appreciation of the right of the individual in society to that most precious ideal – the right to personal privacy and the right to be, within certain constraints, master of how that privilege is used and protected from abuse. All that follows, be it confidentiality, consent (implied, explicit but always informed and voluntary), security, use of databases, transfer of information, the definition and obligations of a data processor or data controller, anonymisation and pseudo-anonymisation, the intricacies of establishing an unique identifier, data protection, data retention, freedom of information, or the need for data protection law and data commissioners to enforce those laws, all stem from the individual's right to privacy.

If we move from the starting point of privacy, we suddenly find ourselves having to grapple with the protection of privacy in a healthcare system in the throes of momentous change. Much of this change has little to do with information and communication technology, but an example illustrates the power of government to influence radically how we practice medicine. The closure of hospital beds in the 1980s was an act of political expediency that spawned to-day's crisis in the Accident & Emergency departments across the country. The way in which doctors practiced medicine had to adapt accordingly; if beds were not available, patients had to be discharged prematurely or inappropriately to make way for others with more acute problems. In the same way, but hopefully with more discussion and consideration, in protecting the right of the individual to privacy, government will influence traditional practice by forcing us to abandon, or at least adapt rather drastically, the traditional method of recording our consultations with patients. In passing, it is not untimely to admit that the old system was far from ideal – records scattered on shelves and floor (or in the boot of the consultant's car), illegible entries by numerous personnel, frequent failure to locate records, duplication of investigations because of inability to retrieve the original results, and inability to co-ordinate care, introduce safety alerts or perform even the most rudimentary audit of practice. This chaotic state of affairs has to end and while, on the one hand, we must be willing to embrace change, we must also be ever-cautious of the consequences of change. For example, who would think that the traditional method of taking a family history from a patient potentially could be compromised by the right to consent of a living family member about whom we are going to record (with the potential to disclose) sensitive personal details?

The significant use of the Internet by business and individuals in Ireland is consistent with the Government's public commitment to developing the Information Society by delivering public services over the Internet – what is known as eGovernment, of which eHealth is an integral part. But, and this is a big but, has the Government invested in information technology in the healthcare system as have, for example, banks and businesses? The answer has to be a resounding "No!". The budget for information technology for the current year for the Irish healthcare system is small by international comparison, especially with the UK. A recent major study on eHealth found that Ireland currently spends less on information and communication technology in healthcare than other comparable countries and than other economic sectors within the country, and recommended a significant increase in Government spending. If Ireland hopes to compete in the field of bioinformatics and, more importantly, if government is intent on transforming our health service radically, the newly-established Health Service Executive will have to persuade the Department of Finance to make a major investment in eHealth.

So who will be the beneficiaries of *Protecting Personal Health Information in Ireland: Law & Practice* or, put another way, who will read it and why? The answer is dependent quite simply on where you stand in the healthcare system. With the possible exception of our legislators, it is not a book that will be read from cover to cover, but a diverse corpus of personnel will find invaluable information within it for their individual needs. Administrators, be they officers in the Health Service Executive or the Department of Health & Children, must have the book within easy reach to ensure that they and their employees are acting within the law. The same consideration applies to the chief executives of all hospitals and many of their administrative personnel; to general practitioners, who constitute the core of the Irish health system – some 1,600 individual centres that effectively are independent private sector business entities, and who can be both data processors and controllers, have many obligations relating to consent, processing, and, importantly, security, that call for a knowledge of the subject as it pertains to them; to consultants, whose responsibilities may differ (as indeed is also the case in general practice) as between private and public patients, must be familiar with the data protection laws, disregard for which can be a criminal offence; to doctors, nurses and scientists involved in medical research; to members of ethics committees and statutory bodies, such as the Health Research Board, Science Foundation Ireland, the Irish Medicines Board and others; to sponsors and promoters of medical research, be they universities, bodies such as the Irish Heart Foundation or the Dublin Molecular

Medicine Centre, or indeed the pharmaceutical industry, who must be conversant with the pitfalls of misusing data in research; and one could go on. I suspect also that this book, which presents so much comparative national information demonstrating different approaches to privacy protection, will attract a substantial international readership.

I have said that this is a complex book dealing with a fundamental issue – personal privacy – from which arise a myriad of related topics, some of which have been resolved but many of which are under on-going debate. Many of the problems within this discipline of health data management (it probably does now justify such categorisation) have been dealt with by the legislators in Ireland and the European Union. Many others, such as the need to obtain consent for recording the history of a living family member, are presently being studied. We can anticipate, therefore, that the rules governing the practice of medicine will change. We should be grateful to Peter Lennon for providing us with awareness as to where we are today – hopefully, he will continue to chart our passage into the future.

As a practicing doctor with a particular interest in research, I carry away two important messages that will guide my practice in both these areas in the future. First, regardless of what information I seek to hold electronically in my day-to-day practice, or propose to enter onto a database for future research, I will err on the side of caution by obtaining consent – explicit, where possible – from my patients. This may not be as difficult as might appear at first glance, if we adapt computer technology to assist us and remember that our patients are generally more than willing to comply with such requests, given that it will ultimately improve their management and treatment. Second, if I am in doubt, I will approach the Data Protection Commissioner for advice, simply because one of the recurring themes in *Protecting Personal Health Information in Ireland* has been the desire of successive Commissioners in this country, and also of those in other countries, to make the provision of healthcare more efficient and to facilitate and encourage research and audit so as to enhance scientific endeavour. This was expressed aptly by one Irish Commissioner, who urged that the data protection law should not be seen as:

"... an obstacle to progress, even if its prescriptions sometimes seem irksome to those enthused by what information technology can do. On the contrary, it exists to ensure that this technology is used properly and to create the climate of public confidence in which application of the technology can flourish."

Eoin O'Brien
Professor of Cardiovascular Pharmacology
Beaumont Hospital, Dublin.

PREFACE

Around the world, people share an appreciation of the value of privacy when it comes to information relating to them. We live in an Information Age and enjoy its benefits, but we believe that our basic right to privacy and our personal liberties should not be compromised by the advent of new technologies. We worry about the Internet, and hackers intercepting and hijacking our details, and even our identities. We are especially anxious about the dangers that modern information technology poses for children. We are concerned too about monitoring at work and on our streets. We recognise the threat of global terrorism and the need for police and other law enforcement bodies to have access to information to combat it effectively, but we have a growing fear that the very response to the problem might itself become a serious threat to the personal privacy normally associated with living in a liberal democratic society. As the *Economist* magazine put it in 1999, the sinister concept of "Big Brother is watching you" is being replaced by the more paternalistic and reassuring "Big Brother is watching out for you".

Notwithstanding all of this, we expect Government, business and anyone else holding our personal information to treat it with care. We believe that our information should be used only for the purposes for which it was provided. We consider it proper that it should be collected from us directly rather than from third parties, and that it should not be disclosed to anyone else either without our consent or with good reason. We place particular importance on protecting certain types of personal information – especially our personal health information.

Accordingly, the focus of this book is on raising awareness of the legal and practical issues involved in managing and protecting personal information in the modern Irish healthcare system and beyond. It represents an opportunity to articulate a balanced approach to protecting the privacy of the patient and, at the same time, to meeting the legitimate information needs of management.

In that regard, this book has been written at an opportune time because the Irish health system is now undergoing a period of major structural reform. For many years, very little happened to disturb the traditional way in which Irish health services were planned, managed and delivered. Now, healthcare is centre-stage in terms not only of public expenditure but, even more importantly, in terms of patients' expectations and pressures on management to deliver better services. While the final outcome of the reform programme is impossible to predict, there is no doubt that enhanced information systems are seen as crucial to success. This will heighten the need for an informed debate on the extent to which traditional relationships between patients and their healthcare providers may need to be re-defined, especially in terms of concepts such as privacy, confidentiality and security.

This book, therefore, is only a starting point.

STRUCTURE OF THE BOOK

Privacy is the claim of individuals, groups or institutions to determine for themselves when, how and to what extent information about them is communicated to others.

Professor Alan Westin, *Privacy & Freedom*, 1967

The scope and aim of this book are straightforward. The scope is concerned with placing the development of contemporary data protection law, as it relates to personal health information, within the broader context of:

- ◆ The modern Information Society
- ◆ The future development of the Irish health service, and
- ◆ The longstanding international and national perspectives on privacy, confidentiality, ethics and information security.

The aim is to demonstrate that the implications of data protection law for managing healthcare information in Ireland are best appreciated through an understanding of the culture and organisation of our health system and the place it occupies in contemporary Irish society.

Accordingly, **Chapter 1** sets the scene by looking at Ireland in the Information Age and the implications this has for the health service, in particular the increasing emphasis on better information management. It also highlights public awareness of, and concerns about, information privacy issues.

Chapter 2 deals with privacy, both as a moral and a legal concept in a democratic society. It looks especially at what privacy means in terms of protecting information relating to us as individuals.

That theme is further developed in **Chapter 3**, which traces the evolution of data protection law as a distinct privacy area in its own right. As the term suggests, the origins of data protection come from the power of computerisation to store and process massive amounts of information and to share that information with many others. However, the data protection concept is now increasingly seen as applicable to all information systems, whether electronic or manual.

Chapter 4 then elaborates the introduction, in Ireland, of data protection legislation in 1988 and 2003. The Data Protection Act 1988 – introduced primarily to allow ratification of a 1981 Council of Europe Convention on Data Protection – was minimalist and directly concerned with assisting the development of the International Financial Services Centre in Dublin. The Data Protection (Amendment) Act 2003 was also driven by international requirements and business considerations: namely, a 1995 European Union Directive and the completion of the Internal Market. However, the 2003 Act significantly raised the level of information privacy safeguards in Ireland, by placing new obligations on persons who keep personal information (data controllers) and by enhancing the rights of individuals about whom information is kept (data subjects).

Chapter 5 outlines two important supervisory aspects of data protection law: namely, registration and enforcement. The first data protection statute, in 1988, created a supervisory authority known as the Office of the Data Protection Commissioner. It also introduced a system of public registration with the Commissioner for certain specified data controllers. The second statute, in 2003, increased the powers of the Commissioner and provided for an extension of the registration system.

In **Chapter 6**, attention is turned to the conditions necessary for the fair processing of personal information. For personal health information, the key requirement is consent of the data subject to the collection, use, retention and disclosure of his or her information. The elements of informed consent are identified, as are the permissible exceptions to the consent principle.

Fair obtaining of personal health information goes to the heart of fair processing, since, if the information is obtained unfairly, it taints all subsequent actions. **Chapter 7** examines the issues associated with the fair obtaining principle, particularly the information that must be provided to the data subject to make the obtaining fair.

Chapter 8 deals with quality and practical issues associated with keeping and securing personal information. Given the sensitive nature of personal health information, medical practitioners, hospitals and any other data controllers keeping such information must take material steps to protect the information they hold from misuse, loss, unauthorised access, modification or disclosure.

Chapter 9 covers the issues surrounding the use and disclosure of personal health information. **Chapter 10** then looks at these issues from a health service management and research perspective, and has due regard to the extent to which these issues have already been considered in the National Health Information Strategy (2004).

Chapter 11 looks at the complex and conflicting issues associated with introducing a Unique Health Identifier (UHI). The arguments for, and benefits of, a UHI are outlined and then set against the privacy concerns associated with such an identifier.

Chapter 12 is devoted to considering the various rights that Irish data protection law gives to individuals. The most important of these rights is that of subject access. The matter of giving an individual access to his or her personal information is straightforward, in principle, but, in practice, persons keeping personal health information should handle access requests with a sound knowledge of the specific obligations imposed (and exceptions allowed) under the Data Protection Acts. The value of a commonsense approach is also explored.

Data protection legislation is not the only statutory information law applicable to health information. The Freedom of Information Acts 1997 to 2003 have had major implications for records management in the public health system and for rights of access by individuals to records held on them by public bodies. Accordingly, **Chapter 13** examines the relationships between data protection and freedom of information legislation.

Chapter 14 is a short chapter setting out some conclusions.

1
THE INFORMATION AGE &
THE IRISH HEALTH SYSTEM

INTRODUCTION

In order to achieve a sense of perspective on the particular information and privacy issues associated with the Irish healthcare system, it is useful to first consider the wider Information Age picture in Ireland today. Indisputably, Ireland has embraced the Information Age revolution. In particular, the emergence of a knowledge-based economy, combined with technological progress, has intensified pressures to collect information and has made the means of doing so ever easier. Successive governments have been at the forefront of pushing the Information Age agenda and, without doubt, the Irish economy has benefited tremendously from the prioritisation given to this area. The associated forces have impacted dramatically over the past decade across the whole economic, societal and political spectrum. They are manifest, not just in the commercial side of the economy and the public service, but also in homes throughout the country.

THE INFORMATION AGE IN ACTION

The EU Commission has reported that, since 1995:

> "... there has been an exponential growth in the number of [EU] households and businesses connected to the Internet and thus in the number of people leaving an increasing amount of personal information of all kinds on the Web. At the same time, the means of collecting personal information has become increasingly sophisticated and less easily detectable: closed circuit TV systems monitoring public

places; spyware installed in PCs by websites to which they have been connected, which collect information about users' browsing habits, information that the sites often sell to others; or the monitoring of employees, including the use of emails and Internet, at the workplace".[2]

The Internet in Ireland

The extent of Internet usage, especially in the home, can be gauged from a Central Statistics Office report published in December 2004.[3] The report on Information Society statistics contained survey results[4] on how information and communications technologies (ICT) are being used in Ireland today, in the home and in business. It found, *inter alia*, that an estimated:

- ♦ 649,400 households (or 46.2% of total households) had a home computer in June 2004. This compares to a figure of 582,800 (or 42.2%) in 2003 – an increase of 66,200 households.

- ♦ 537,000 households (38.2% of total households) had an Internet connection, which represented an increase of 73,800 over the same 2003/2004 period.

- ♦ 1,489,200 people aged 16 to 74 have used a computer at some time while 1,198,800 have used the Internet.

- ♦ 727,300 people use a computer every day or almost every day and 373,300 people in Ireland use the Internet at least once a day.

It also found that:

- ♦ Virtually all businesses in Ireland use computers and have access to e-mail and the Internet.

---

[2]   European Commission (2003).

[3]   Central Statistics Office (2004).

[4]   The findings are based on the ICT module of the Quarterly National Household Survey, which examined household and individual use of computers. This is a continuous survey in which 3,000 households are interviewed each week to give a total sample of 39,000 households each quarter. These surveys (households and enterprises) will be undertaken annually to provide information to monitor progress on the e-Europe 2005 Action Plan, and will be the source for harmonised statistics at EU level in this area.

♦ The most common Internet purchases are travel and holiday accommodation.

♦ Most people use the Internet at home, followed by the workplace.

According to MORI Ireland, 36% of the adult population aged 16+ in the Republic of Ireland used the Internet during the period between July and September 2004 – up from 32% during the period from April to June 2003.[5]

In the midst of all this Internet usage, a study from the Data Protection Commissioner indicates that Irish Internet users are increasingly concerned about privacy issues, with approximately 56% of Irish adults agreeing with the statement that "if they use the Internet, their privacy is threatened".[6] This compares with just 37% in 1997. (Other findings from the study are discussed later in this chapter.)

Most Government Departments and public bodies (including health agencies and hospitals) already provide a wide range of (non-personal) information to the public about their services or performance, via websites. There are also a range of specialised health-related websites that vary significantly in terms of content and quality. The trend, as much in public services as elsewhere, is to make greater use of the Internet as a point of tangible interaction between services providers and individuals (see below, where some eGovernment initiatives are outlined.)

Growing Internet use for personal transactions raises the profile of general privacy concerns. It also increases the importance of education and awareness as a means of protecting the individual, and highlights the need for international co-operation in influencing the directions that legitimate operators should take. In his *Annual Report* for 2002, the Data Protection Commissioner welcomed an initiative by the Irish Internet Association to promote privacy awareness:

> "… the Irish Internet Association is to be complimented for devising, with co-operation from my Office, a template for privacy statements to be carried on its members' websites.

---

5   MORI Ireland (2005).

6   Data Protection Commissioner (2003), *Appendix 2: Market Research Survey on Awareness of Data Protection.*

This "public / private partnership" is an indication that business is aware of the competitive advantage it can enjoy if it clearly indicates how personal data is collected and used."[7]

Internet Privacy Statements & Organisational Privacy Policies

In his *Annual Report* for 2004, the Data Protection Commissioner examined the nature and role of website privacy statements.[8] In particular, he distinguished between the latter and an organisation's privacy policy. In his view:

> "A Privacy Policy documents an organisation's application of the eight data protection principles to the manner in which it processes data organisation-wide. Such a policy applies to all personal data processed by the organisation, including customer data, third-party data and employee data. The Privacy Policy can, in some instances, be a very complex document, having to apply the data protection principles to its own operating environment. The Privacy Policy is fundamentally a document for internal reference ... A Privacy Statement is a public declaration of how the organisation applies the data protection principles to data processed on its website. It is a more narrowly-focused document and by its public nature should be both concise and clear."

He went on to express concern about privacy standards in the online environment and pointed out that his website (www.dataprivacy.ie) contains guidance notes for preparing a privacy statement. He concluded that, at a minimum, there is an obligation on persons controlling websites to provide information about the use of such technical features as cookies or the collection of IP addresses. He added that a properly constituted privacy statement is a means by which a data controller can demonstrably comply with the

---

[7] Data Protection Commissioner (2003).

[8] Data Protection Commissioner (2005), *Appendix 7: Absence of Privacy Statements on Websites.*

requirements of section 2D of the Data Protection Acts 1988 to 2003.[9] The details of a 2004 survey on privacy statements in Ireland are discussed in the section of this chapter dealing with *Attitudes to Privacy & Data Protection in Europe and Ireland.*

Telecommunications & Information

Longer established than the Internet, and even more widely used, the telephone is part of everyday living and business. In recent years, the mobile phone has become an almost indispensable lifestyle accessory, including (or especially) for the young. Modern technology now allows certain transactional details of calls made and received to be recorded. This is called *traffic data* and refers to the data that is created by your phone company (telco) or Internet service provider (ISP) when you make a phone call, go on the Internet or send an e-mail. At a routine administration level, it allows for the preparation of an itemised bill, which is of considerable benefit to the customer.

However, the data can also reveal considerable information about the phone user's private life. For land-line phone calls, it can reveal the number you dialled, together with the duration and time of the call. Additionally, for mobile phones, it includes a record of the *location* of the cell-phone in question as it moves about from cell to cell. For this reason, traffic data generated by mobile calls is more personal and revealing.

In relation to the Internet, traffic data would encompass the e-mail addresses on all correspondence to and from the subscriber, a record of date, time, and size of message, as well as other transmission details, but, hopefully, excluding message subject and content. It would also encompass a record of every login session, every web page visited and read, every search term entered, every file downloaded, every purchase made, and so forth – in short, virtually the entirety of one's online "session".

Understandably, people put an important privacy value on their phone communications and interception of calls for law enforcement

---

9   Section 2D (Fair Processing of Personal Data) deals primarily with the information to be provided by a data controller to a data subject to make processing fair.

agencies is strictly regulated under law,[10] and EU initiatives accompanied by national measures set rules on the use and retention of telecommunications data.[11]

The impact of these developments on personal health information management is uncertain. However, the greater use of text messaging, for example, to remind people of medical appointments is already happening and the potential of the Internet for interactive healthcare services and advice is very considerable.

Biometric Data

New technologies always bring new terminology and a term that is increasingly heard is *biometric data*. Biometric-based systems of identification are receiving substantial interest, at present. The term refers to the automatic identification of a person based on his or her physiological (or, less frequently, behavioural) characteristics. This method of identification is considered superior to other traditional methods involving passwords and PINs for various reasons, including that the person to be identified is required to be present at the point-of-identification and there is no need to remember passwords. Various types of biometric systems are being used for real-time identification: the most popular are based on face, iris and fingerprint matching. The major advantage of a biometric trait is that it is as unique as the individual from whom it was created. Unlike a password or PIN, a biometric trait cannot be lost or stolen and it should not be capable of duplication. This makes biometrics an obvious antidote to identity theft and, potentially, a crucial anti-fraud instrument.

There are two principal means by which a biometric can be employed: either a reader at a point verifies that a person's biometric (fingerprint, iris scan, face) matches that held on the card, a so-called authentication / verification system, or a reader at a point checks the person's biometric with a central database, a so-called identification system. It is the latter that raises major privacy issues, in particular as regards the potential uses and disclosures of the information held, especially if the information in the biometric databases is linked with other personal information systems.

---

[10]   This is discussed in **Chapter 2**.
[11]   This is discussed in **Chapter 3**.

Given the commercial, national security and anti-fraud benefits of biometrics, it seems inevitable that their use will increase over time. In that regard, it is worth noting that biometric data is personal information within the meaning of Irish data protection law and, therefore, is already subject to the same privacy rules as other types of personal information.

However, speaking at the EU Conference on Biometrics in Dublin in June 2004, the Data Protection Commissioner asked:

> "Will the use of biometrics add significantly to the accuracy or security of existing verification or identification systems, or is it a further means of intruding on our private lives in the guise of enhanced security?"[12]

eGovernment, eCommerce & the Information Society

The significant use of the Internet by individuals in Ireland is consistent with the Government's public commitment to developing the Information Society and delivering public services over the Internet – what is known as "eGovernment".

The Department of the Taoiseach's Information Society Policy Unit has overall responsibility for developing, co-ordinating and driving implementation of the Information Society agenda in Ireland. Its stated aim is to ensure that Ireland develops as a fully participative, competitive, knowledge-based Information Society, with all of the benefits that entails. To that end, considerable political attention and official resources are devoted to enhancing the use of information and communications technology (ICT) to deliver better public services. Some of these initiatives are described briefly below.

REACH – ePublic Services

REACH is a cross-Departmental agency of the Department of Social & Family Affairs, established by the Government in 2000 to develop a strategy for the integration of public services and to develop and

---

[12] Data Protection Commissioner (2005), *Appendix 5*. (An asterisked addition to the *Appendix* states that the Minister for Justice, Equality & Law Reform signalled the need to have a national debate on the issue of a National Identity Card. Such a card would be likely to have some biometric element.)

implement the framework for electronic government. It can be best characterised as an eGovernment response to the view that the public want to access public services, including health services, more easily.

REACH's mission is to:

> "… radically improve the quality of service to personal and business customers of Government and to develop and deploy the Public Services Broker (which will be known as "reachservices"[13]) to help agencies achieve that improvement".[14]

Information Society Commission

The Information Society Commission (ISC) is an independent advisory body to Government, reporting directly to the Taoiseach. It draws on representation from the business community, the social partners, and government itself. The Commission has a key role in shaping the evolving public policy framework for the Information Society in Ireland. It contributes to the policy formulation process, monitors progress and highlights issues that need to be prioritised. It has a dedicated eHealth steering group, which carried out a major study on eHealth in Ireland in 2004 (outlined later in this chapter).

eCommerce Legislation

As part of the eGovernment programme, the Electronic Commerce Act was introduced in 2001. The then Minister for Public Enterprises described the legislation as:

> "… a first step in adapting our Statute Book to take account of the realities of the Internet. It would be impossible and undesirable to introduce a new set of laws for eCommerce. There is no reason the laws that currently govern traditional commerce should not apply to eCommerce. Company law, consumer law and privacy law already lay down principles

---

13 "Reachservices" is an electronic model for service delivery that will provide a standard means of access to public services through the use of an integrated set of processes, systems and procedures, with the aim of providing integration across services and agencies, time and channels (phone, counter and Internet).

14 See http://www.reach.ie.

that apply equally off-line as on-line. What may be required, however, is that this legislation be amended to take account of this new way of doing business."[15]

Accordingly, the measure was not intended as a wide-ranging innovation but, instead, simply removed existing legal impediments and uncertainties that had arisen as a result of the onset and continuing growth of eCommerce. However, it was still important, in that its aim was to:

♦ Allow consumers and businesses the freedom to use electronic communications.

♦ Satisfy existing legal requirements.

♦ Ensure that privacy is preserved.

The Information Age & the Challenge for Privacy

In his 1997 *Annual Report*, the Data Protection Commissioner stated that data protection law:

"… is not an obstacle to progress, even if its prescriptions sometimes seem irksome to those enthused by what information technology can do. On the contrary, it exists to ensure that this technology is used properly and to create the climate of public confidence in which application of the technology can flourish."[16]

This theme was re-iterated in his *Annual Report* for 2003:

"Data Protection Law, by providing a framework for the use of personal data, can both reassure people that their data will only be used within their expectations, while at the same time allowing organisations to utilise modern technologies for commercial and practical advantage. This is crucial for the on-going and future success of eGovernment and eCommerce initiatives."[17]

---

[15] Electronic Commerce Bill 2000, Dáil Éireann, Second Stage, Vol.519, 23 May.

[16] Data Protection Commissioner (1998).

[17] Data Protection Commissioner (2004).

In between those *Annual Reports*, the Commissioner issued a press release, in which he outlined his belief that eGovernment and eCommerce initiatives must have full regard to privacy concerns. He asserted that:

> "Respect for the fundamental human right to privacy and data protection is the key enabler of eCommerce and eGovernment. These initiatives simply have to be built upon public credibility and assurance about the right to privacy. This assurance is exactly what data protection law provides."[18]

COMBATING PUBLIC SECTOR FRAUD, UNIQUE IDENTIFICATION & PRIVACY ISSUES

A universal issue for government is the potential of modern information technology to assist in combating public sector fraud. Understandably, this enjoys considerable public support. However, the issue has become inextricably intertwined with unique personal identification mechanisms, which are seen as controversial, in that they raise fundamental privacy concerns.

The PPSN

Almost a decade ago, in an effort to combat fraud and abuse of public services, the Social Welfare Act 1998 was passed, creating a "Public Service Card" with a unique Personal Public Service Number (commonly known as the PPSN).[19] This number replaced the Revenue & Social Insurance (RSI) number previously used for tax and social welfare purposes only.

---

[18] "Privacy Safeguards are Vital for e-Commerce", *Press Release*, Office of the Data Protection Commissioner, September 2001.

[19] The legislation now governing the use of the PPSN is contained in the Social Welfare (Consolidation) Act 1993, as amended by the Social Welfare Acts 1998, 1999, 2000, 2002 & 2003. The PPSN is managed by the Client Identity Services Section of the Department of Social & Family Affairs.

As a unique identifier, the PPSN is intended to facilitate speedy and accurate identification of individuals accessing public services. It is particularly useful where there may be a number of people with similar or identical names and / or addresses. The PPSN is seen as one of the main facilitators of eGovernment, but its use has attracted privacy criticisms.

The legislation regulating the use of the PPSN provides that it can be used by the public bodies named in the Social Welfare Acts or by any person or body authorised by these public bodies to act on their behalf – a listing is published on the Department of Social & Family Affairs website.[20] It also allows for the exchange of personal information between these bodies in certain specified circumstances.

The Department of Social & Family Affairs has issued a *Code of Practice on the Personal Public Sector Number*.[21] This *Code* aims to ensure that both individuals and agencies are aware of their rights and obligations regarding the use of the PPSN, including when it should be used, and when it cannot be used – for example, the PPSN cannot be used for private or commercial transactions.

Public Service Identity

The Social Welfare (Miscellaneous Provisions) Act 2002 took the process a step further by defining a person's Public Service Identity (PSI). A PSI consists of a person's PPSN, surname, forename, date of birth, place of birth, sex, all former surnames [if any], all former surnames [if any] of their mother, address, nationality, date of death in the case of a deceased person, and such other information as may be prescribed by the Minister for Social & Family Affairs.

Unique Identifiers & Privacy Concerns

The Data Protection Commissioner has always had concerns about the use of national identifiers. As far back as 1991, the first Commissioner stated that:

---

[20] http://www.welfare.ie/topics/ppsn/index.html.
[21] Department of Social & Family Affairs (2004).

> "... there is an inherent tension between administrative efficiency and fraud prevention, on the one hand, and the protection of individual privacy on the other".[22]

At present, the only privacy safeguard laid down by the PPSN legislation is a provision making it an offence for anyone other than a State agency (or person acting in an authorised manner on its behalf) to attempt to obtain an individual's PPSN. Not surprisingly, therefore, the Commissioner criticised the scheme while it was being debated, saying that:

> "... the proposed sharing of personal data, obtained and kept by legally separate entities, for such diverse purposes is fundamentally incompatible with ... the basic tenets of data protection law."[23]

There also has been ongoing debate about the PPSN's possible use as a wide-ranging and unique public identifier (including in the health sector). This will be considered in greater detail in **Chapter 11**.

THE IRISH HEALTHCARE SYSTEM

Not surprisingly, given the importance of the health system in terms of public expenditure, electoral considerations and general social well-being, it is inevitable that healthcare should feel the pressure to embrace the information revolution[24]. The Irish health system is an information-intensive sector. Daily, there are thousands of contacts between members of the public and health service professionals, with

---

[22] Data Protection Commissioner (1992), p.18. He was referring, in particular, to the commitment to introduce a universal identity number in the Programme for Government, as well as the intention of the then Department of Social Welfare to introduce a national ID card based on the RSI number.

[23] As above.

[24] For those interested in reading generally about the Irish healthcare system, the following books are suggested: Leahy, A.L. & Wiley, M.M. (1998). *The Irish Health System in the 21st Century*. Dublin: Oak Tree Press; Wren, M.-A. (2003). *Unhealthy State: Anatomy of a Sick Society*. Dublin: New Island; Robins, J. (1997). *Reflections on Health: Commemorating 50 years of the Department of Health, 1947 to 1997*. Dublin: Institute of Public Administration.

personal health information being collected in a variety of settings over the lifetime of an individual for a number of specific and general health-related purposes. These contacts invariably give rise to some record for clinical, management, insurance, legal or other purpose.[25] VHI, for example, handles approximately 500,000 claims *per annum*, all of which contain personal information and most of which include some details relating to health matters of the claimants or their families.[26]

Ultimately, every country's health system is different, shaped by historical, cultural, economic, social, political and even personal factors. Certainly, the Irish system has a unique mix of the public and private.[27] It is also complex and fragmented in terms of structures, processes and, most importantly, people. The availability and provision of healthcare services have become major public and political issues. Increasing levels of Government spending on health, rising public expectations, significant organisational reform, ongoing industrial relation conflicts and critical media examination have all contributed to a debate on the nature, direction and value of our health system. All of this has led – *via* a number of strategy papers and reports – to a recent major institutional reform programme.[28]

Prior to the current reform programme, the last major re-organisation of the Irish health system took place as a result of the Health Act 1970, which itself was based on a 1966 White Paper[29] and four reports (on general hospital services, mental illness, mental handicap and child health). The present reform agenda has concentrated principally on institutional change. It involves a new policy and oversight role for the Department of Health & Children.

---

25   McDougall (1998), which stated that: "consumer health information is the fastest growing area in health information world-wide".

26   Molony (2004).

27   Department of Health & Children (2001). In Ireland, public funding makes up approximately 78 per cent of all the money spent on healthcare. Private funding, through insurance arrangements, makes up approximately another 8.5 per cent of funding. The balance is what individuals pay in "out-of-pocket" expenses; for example, the fees non-medical cardholders pay for general practitioner (GP) and other therapy services.

28   Arguably, the two reports that have had the greatest impact on the reform programme are Prospectus Consultants (2003) and Brennan (2003).

29   Department of Health (1966).

The Health Boards and numerous other health agencies have been abolished as distinct individual agencies and replaced with the national Health Service Executive (HSE). Completing this picture is the new national health information standards body, the Health Information & Quality Authority (HIQA).[30]

These institutional reforms have left unchanged the mass of voluntary organisations that provide healthcare services at local, regional and national level. Further, the process has not impacted, as yet, on the organisation of healthcare providers in the primary care sector. For example, general practice, which is at the core of the Irish health system, is organised into about 1,600 individual centres that are effectively independent private sector business entities, a significant percentage of which are still single-handed. Most persons attending general practitioners do so as private patients. Where general practitioners provide services for public patients, they do so under a contract for services as independent contractors rather than as employees. Consequently, the extent to which the totality, nature and quality of patient information they obtain, use, keep and disclose can be determined solely by the Department of Health & Children, the HSE or HIQA is questionable.

Despite this, the expectation is that, over time, these and other organisational and service-related changes will lead to an integrated, quality-based and patient-centred health service, as set out in the most recent (2001) national health strategy – *Quality & Fairness.*[31] A more integrated approach to primary care services, with a consequential increase in information sharing, was also envisaged in the complementary primary care strategy – *Primary Care: A New Direction,*[32] also issued in 2001.

Common to all the new bodies –and the reform process generally – is the unequivocal recognition that better healthcare must be built on improved information systems and greater use of technology. *Quality & Fairness* highlighted this point:

---

[30] There is more detail on the role of the HIQA in **Chapter 10**. For information on the HSE, visit its website at http://www.hse.ie.

[31] Department of Health & Children (2001). Specifically, the goals of *Quality & Fairness* are: better health for everyone; fair access; responsive and appropriate care delivery; high performance.

[32] Department of Health & Children (2001a).

"To meet the objectives of the Health Strategy and to deliver the quality of health services that people require, information is needed which is appropriate, comprehensive, high-quality, available, accessible and timely. Good information systems based on fast, efficient flows of shared information are, therefore, essential to the success of the Strategy."[33]

The 2004 National Health Information Strategy – *Health Information: A National Strategy* – further emphasised the importance of information:

"The primary objective of the health service is to ensure that the highest levels of health and social well-being are achieved for individuals and the whole population. This strategy proposes to exploit information to the fullest in pursuit of this objective."[34]

As the Information Strategy acknowledged, the implications of this process for patient information will be very significant. Much of this book is concerned with further considering those implications.

EHEALTH

Already, advances in science and technology have impacted considerably on the Irish health system. This was recognised explicitly by the Medical Council in its 2004 *Guide to Ethical Conduct & Behaviour*:

"The pace of scientific and technological change in medicine is increasing rapidly and will require new ethical guidelines in the near future. This edition introduces new regulatory mechanisms for information and communications technology in medicine but does not deal in any depth with emerging biotechnology issues. Such issues will require the medical profession and the society in which it works to come together to explore ethical values, scientific information and the expectations and limitations which they establish."[35]

---

[33] Department of Health & Children (2001).
[34] Department of Health & Children (2004).
[35] Medical Council (2004), *Introduction* by Professor Gerard Bury, President.

More generally, *Quality & Fairness* outlined the connection between the health system and the rest of the eGovernment agenda:

> "There is now a considerable public policy commitment to eGovernment with the intention of promoting Ireland as a centre of eCommerce excellence. The widespread availability of low-cost, high-speed, Internet access will be a critical enabler of eHealth developments. The health system is working with the eGovernment programme, including REACH, which will ensure that the benefits from these developments are fully realised."[36]

The scope of eHealth

eHealth is popularly defined as "health services and information delivered through the Internet and related technologies".[37] In terms of scope, eHealth is broad, encompassing (but not limited to):

- Health information websites informing the public and healthcare professionals on the latest best practice.

- Electronic patient records providing complete, real-time and accurate information on an individual's medical history.

- Decision support systems assisting clinical assessments and enabling patients to monitor their own condition, where appropriate.

- Hospital and practice management systems automating manual procedures and providing key financial performance data.

- Remote access technologies connecting patients, students and professionals to specialists who would have otherwise been out of their reach.

- Health data networks supporting epidemiological studies.

Benefits of eHealth

eHealth is not an end in itself. There are a number of clear benefits to be had from the electronic enablement of the health service:

---

[36] Department of Health (2001), *Chapter 5*.

[37] Eysenbach (2001).

♦ Empowering individuals and their families to manage their own health and participation better – for example, through the provision of consumer health and disability support information and clear guidelines to consumers on why and what information is useful for them to retain or provide.

♦ Improving the co-ordination and integration of care delivery to individuals – for example, a general practitioner referring a patient for specialist care, or accessing critical information during emergency care.

♦ Allowing population health initiatives to occur in timely fashion – for example, mapping of notifiable diseases to contain disease outbreaks before they spread and better targeting of resources to high-need areas.

eHealth in Ireland Today

A major study on eHealth in Ireland[38] was published by the Information Society Commission in December 2004. The aim of the study was to provide a clear analysis of Ireland's progress against various eHealth targets, to identify the benefits associated with implementation and to provide a baseline for monitoring progress on an ongoing basis. The report found that Ireland currently spends less on ICT in healthcare than (i) investment levels internationally and (ii) accepted ICT investment levels in other economic sectors. It identified a number of successful examples of eHealth projects, especially websites as information resources.[39] It recommended a significant increase in Government spending on ICT in the healthcare sector, to deliver benefits and savings to all stakeholders in the healthcare system.

---

[38] Information Society Commission (2004). The report can be viewed at http://www.isc.ie.

[39] A similar view of the value of websites is found in the Medical Council's *Guidelines* (Medical Council, 2004, p. 20) where it states that "the Medical Council recognises that the Internet and practice websites can provide valuable services to patients". It adds that doctors must take responsibility for the content of their sites, which must be non-promotional, evidence-based, verifiable and compatible with Section 14 (which deals with media and advertising). In addition, it cautions that particular care must be exercised over links to other sites.

The year 2004 also saw Ireland host the Second EU eHealth Conference,[40] whose theme was "Supporting the European Citizen". At the conference, the Minister for Health & Children brought on-line health services a step closer, by showcasing an initiative to develop an Irish health services Web portal, called "Health Ireland".[41] This is a multi-phase, multi-year project that aims to provide access to a range of health information and services through an easy-to-use and trusted mechanism. Initially, the portal will be available *via* the Internet, but there are plans for the initiative to be rolled out across a range of channels, such as call centres, walk-in centres, television, PDA and mobile phone text messaging.

The conference came in the same week as an action plan[42] adopted by the European Commission, which shows how information and communication technologies can be used to deliver better quality healthcare Europe-wide. The "eHealth action plan" covers everything from electronic prescriptions and computerised health records to using new systems and services to cut waiting times and reduce errors. The proposals will contribute to better care at the same or lower cost. The action plan sets out the objective of a "European eHealth Area" and identifies practical steps to achieve goals, through work on electronic health records, patient identifiers and health cards, and the faster rollout of high-speed Internet access for health systems to allow the full potential of eHealth to be delivered.

HEALTH INFORMATION, PRIVACY & SOCIETY

The reform process, increasing emphasis on information management and eHealth initiatives are all likely to challenge long-established principles of patient privacy, common law traditions of confidentiality as well as longstanding professional and ethical codes on using and safeguarding personal health information.

---

[40] Cork, 5 and 6 May 2004.

[41] It will be called *Sláinte Éireann* in Irish.

[42] European Commission (2004).

This concern with the privacy, confidentiality and security of health information is not confined to Ireland. The Australian Federal Privacy Commissioner stated:

> "Most people consider health information to be highly personal and, therefore, need to be confident that their privacy will be protected whenever they use a health service … Clear and open communication between the health service provider and health consumer is integral to good privacy."[43]

In an address to the Canadian Medical Association on privacy and health information in November 2000, the Canadian Privacy Commissioner stated:

> "When we talk about confidentiality, we are talking about trust. When we take someone into our confidence and share something personal about ourselves, we do so in the belief that we can trust that person not to divulge the secret to anyone else. This concept of trust is at the very heart of the doctor-patient relationship. Even though we may not know our physicians especially well on a personal level, we know they have taken an oath to respect our privacy. We trust them to respect that oath. We tell our doctors things about ourselves we might not share even with our spouses. As with so many other aspects of our privacy, the security of this most personal of trust relationships is threatened. There is a powerful and steadily-increasing demand for our personal health information from any number of secondary users. Much of the time, we don't even know who they are."[44]

In the same speech, he referred to an observation of Dr. Hugh Scully, the former President of the Canadian Medical Association, who claimed:

---

[43] Federal Privacy Commissioner (2001). The Privacy Amendment (Private Sector) Act 2000 extended the operation of the Privacy Act 1988 to cover the private health sector throughout Australia.

[44] Radwanski (2001).

"The right of privacy and consent are essential to the trust and integrity of the patient / physician relationship. The right of privacy is worthy of protection not just for the good of society's individuals, but also for the good of society itself."

Even in the United States, the Consumer Bill of Rights & Responsibilities, which was published in November 1997 by the President's Quality Commission, underscored the importance of the confidentiality of identifiable health information when it affirmed:

"Consumers have the right to communicate with healthcare providers in confidence and to have the confidentiality of their individually identifiable healthcare information protected ..."[45]

In his *Annual Report* for 2001, the Data Protection Commissioner stated:

"... I believe that the handling of medical data within the health sector needs a major overhaul, to ensure that patient data can flow as medical treatment requires, while ensuring that medical confidentiality is accorded utmost priority. It is also important that medical practitioners at every level should have clear guidance on what is and what is not legally permissible."[46]

He strongly advocated the adoption of clear *Codes of Practice* for the health sector. In that regard, a guide to data protection in Irish General Practice was prepared for the National General Practice Information Technology Group (GPIT Group).[47] The *Guide* was circulated widely throughout the Irish health system, not just to GPs. It was a collaborative effort between the GPIT Group, the Irish College of General Practitioners and the Irish Medical Organisation, in association with the Office of the Data Protection Commissioner. In welcoming the guide, the Data Protection Commissioner said that it:

---

[45] President's Advisory Commission on Consumer Protection & Quality in the Healthcare Industry, see http://hcqualitycommission.gov.

[46] Data Protection Commissioner (2002).

[47] Lennon *et al.* (2003).

"… gives comprehensive advice on data protection in the [general practice] sector".[48]

Healthcare Professionals & Privacy Awareness

As we will see, the central challenge is in striking the appropriate balance between the needs of health service management to deliver more efficient and effective service provision and safeguarding the legitimate privacy concerns of the individual patient.

The implications of this are perhaps greatest for the multiplicity of healthcare professionals who provide patient services. There is increasing awareness among them regarding information management issues, but this has been paralleled by a growing sense of confusion as to the relevant rules regarding the use and disclosure of personal health information.

Three factors can be identified as most relevant:

♦ First, there is uncertainty about the nature and scope of the legal and ethical rules governing privacy, confidentiality and security of personal health information. This makes health service professionals more cautious about the collection, use, retention and disclosure of information.

♦ Second, at the same time, individuals in society have become more accustomed to, and aware of, their rights as citizens, consumers and patients. This has added to the concern among health professionals about their medico-legal liability. Uses and disclosures of data that previously seemed unexceptionable might now attract action for a breach of confidence. Accordingly, there is a need to clarify the relationships between traditional professional ethical codes (which tended to be rooted in confidentiality) and the information governance principles of data protection law. At the very least, ethical codes need to be redrafted to reflect the applicable data protection principles, so that the professional groups they cover have greater protection from potential legal action over the (unintended) unlawful use of patients' information.

---

[48] Data Protection Commissioner (2004).

♦ Third, the demands that are placed on the health system are greater and more varied than ever before. Healthcare always generated patient information, but there is an increasing push to have such information developed in a more integrated fashion, that not only benefits individual patient care, but also allows management to use the same information for better planning. The creation of a national system of electronic health records is likely to raise fresh questions about who is responsible for those records and who should be allowed access to them.

Accordingly, ensuring that the necessary information is properly collected, used, managed and disclosed to greatest effect poses a challenge that goes far beyond the administrative and technological structures in the Irish health system. It is important that the applicable responsibilities and rights in relation to personal health information should be clearly set out and their implications elaborated against the broader legal frameworks that shape them.

ATTITUDES TO PRIVACY & DATA PROTECTION IN EUROPE & IRELAND

Finally, in an introductory chapter, it is important to consider whether people see privacy and information protection as important. The EU has carried out a number of studies and while, as might be expected, there are varying attitudes to privacy and data protection in Member States, it is evident that privacy is important.

EU Studies

For example, a 2003 EU Eurobarometer[49] study on people's attitudes to data protection issues[50] threw up a number of interesting results. On average, in 2003, 60 per cent of all EU citizens were concerned, to a

---

[49] In 1974, the Commission of the European Communities launched the Eurobarometer series of surveys, designed to provide a regular monitoring of the social and political attitudes of the publics of the nine member-nations.

[50] EUROPA (2003). This study was a follow-up to earlier studies in 1991 and 1996. Details can be found at http://europa.eu.int/comm/public_opinion/ archives/ebs/ebs_196_data_protection.pdf.

greater or lesser degree, about the broad issue of the protection of their personal privacy. However, the study also showed that awareness of data protection rights tended to be quite low in most Member States. In Ireland, 71 per cent agreed that awareness of personal data protection was low and 73 per cent were worried about leaving any personal details on the Internet. Only 25 per cent of Irish people polled were aware of their data protection right to privacy, and only 6 per cent of that percentage had actually exercised it.

When it came to *medical services and doctors*, the survey found that, on average, 84 per cent of EU citizens trusted the medical profession with their information and, in Denmark and the Netherlands, more than nine out of 10 citizens polled held this sentiment. The country that had the lowest level of trust was Greece (73%). In Ireland, the percentage was 84 per cent, up from the 81 per cent recorded in 1991 but down from the 87 per cent recorded in 1996. Those in Ireland who did not trust medical services and doctors to treat their information correctly were 10 per cent, 7 per cent and 10 per cent respectively in 1991, 1996 and 2003.

As regards *insurance companies*, the EU percentage who do not trust insurance companies to use their personal information in an acceptable way fell from 51 per cent in 1996 to 48 per cent in 2003. This fall was not shared in Ireland, which saw the level of distrust rise from 42 per cent in 1991 to 35 per cent in 1996 before increasing substantially in 2003 to the EU average of 48 per cent. Levels of trust followed a similar pattern, with a major fall from 47 per cent in 1996 to 36 per cent in 2003.[51] Throughout the EU, women were found to generally have a less jaundiced view about insurance companies, with only 44 per cent of them holding a negative view, compared to 51 per cent of men.

Irish Surveys

According to a survey in 2000 of the top 500 Irish companies, conducted by Rits IT Consultants,[52] only 29 per cent undertook an audit on a regular basis to ensure compliance with the Data Protection

---

[51]   A similar fall in confidence in banks and other financial institutions was noted in Ireland, with the percentages of citizens trusting the way these bodies handled client information falling from 50 per cent to 44 per cent.

[52]   Rits Group (2000).

Act 1988. In addition, in 1999, an informal *Irish Times* survey of the top Irish websites,[53] including Government institutions and leading private companies, found that these sites routinely breached the terms of the Data Protection Act and the principles laid down in the (then unimplemented) EU Data Protection Directive. Of the 100 sites studied, it was found that almost none posted even the most basic privacy statement, explaining to the public what is done with personal information gathered on the site.

While the position in relation to the number and quality of privacy statements has improved in recent years, it appears that much remains to be done. During 2004, the Commissioner's Office conducted a survey of 242 public sector websites in respect of their use of privacy statements.[54] In all, the survey found that 53 sites had adequate privacy statements; 46 had inadequate content in their privacy statements; 8 had poorly-positioned privacy statements and 135 had no identifiable privacy statement. The Commissioner's Office is contacting those sites identified as having problems with their privacy statements and further assessing those sites with no statements. When that process is complete, consideration will be given to initiating enforcement proceedings against parties identified as non-compliant. It is proposed to carry out a similar survey, during 2005, on private sector websites.

Conscious of these issues, in particular, the crucial importance of public awareness, in 2002 the Data Protection Commissioner commissioned a face-to-face public awareness survey, designed to be representative (in terms of age, sex, social class, region and area) of the adult population aged 15 and over living in Ireland.[55] The key findings were that Irish people value their privacy highly, ranking it higher even than issues such as consumer protection, ethics in public office, and equality in the workplace. The survey also indicted that Irish people place a slightly higher privacy value on their personal financial records than on their medical records: 77 per cent of adults rated their "financial history" as "very important" (with a further 18 per cent

---

[53]   "Monitoring your electronic footprints: Irish websites are blatantly ignoring EU legislation on data protection", *The Irish Times*, 22 October 1999.

[54]   Data Protection Commissioner (2005), *Appendix 7: Absence of Privacy Statements on Websites.*

[55]   Data Protection Commissioner (2003), *Appendix 2.*

rating it as "important"), compared with a 72 per cent "very important" rating for "medical records" (with a further 21 per cent "important" rating). On the negative side, it found that people are growing increasingly concerned about the erosion of their personal privacy. In particular, intrusive business practices, fears about Internet privacy, and a lack of information about Government initiatives have contributed to a "trust deficit" that could undermine Ireland's progress towards eCommerce.

The survey results showed that opinion was polarised on the use of the PPSN by Government Departments and agencies to link and to transfer information, with 26 per cent of all adults in favour to at least some extent and a slightly higher 31 per cent opposed. However, there also appeared to be a degree of ambivalence and uncertainty, with 16 per cent claiming to be neither for nor against this development and more than one in four (27 per cent) unable to form an opinion. However, these figures on the PPSN should be viewed with some caution now, as a subsequent major publicity campaign in 2002 by the Department of Social & Family Affairs should have improved public appreciation of the nature and role of the PPSN.

Overall, in terms of awareness of the Data Protection Commissioner's Office and data protection rights, the study suggested that there was a large element of uncertainty among the general public both as to their rights as well as to the role of the Commissioner. Public knowledge of data protection is likely to have increased since 2002.

Scapegoating Data Protection

Finally, there is the matter of scapegoating data protection law and presenting it as a problem rather than as a solution. This has occurred especially in the United Kingdom – even in the healthcare area[56] – with the result that, in 2004, the Information Commissioner, who has responsibility for data protection, felt compelled to state:

> "I need to address – and dispel – some data protection myths. You will all have read in your newspapers about the Data Protection Act, this nightmarish piece of red tape that endangers public safety, prevents effective policing, stops

---

[56] "Data Law is a Killer", *The Times*, 15 May 2001. See **Chapter 10** for the background to this article.

medical research and is apparently responsible for most other social ills.

Here are a few examples of the sort of statement that we commonly encounter in the media and elsewhere. It is asserted that the Data Protection Act:

◊ stops you from videoing your child's school's nativity play;

◊ means colleges will have to ban students from using mobile phones which take pictures;

◊ prevents schools contacting parents when there is an outbreak of head lice;

◊ means you cannot voice concerns about a child's welfare to social services, and

◊ stops patient health records from being used for medical research.

No, no, no, no and no.

The Act does none of these things. Nor is the Act responsible for far worse ills."[57]

The analysis above holds good for Ireland. As this book will endeavour to show, data protection, particularly in the healthcare area, can be good – both for the individual citizen and for society as a whole.

---

[57] Thomas (2004). The "far worse ills" referred to concerned the Soham Murder investigations and the death of two pensioners whose household gas had been cut off.

2
PRIVACY CONCEPTS

INTRODUCTION

Of all the human rights, privacy is perhaps the most difficult to define and limit. The notion has its roots deep in history. The Bible has numerous references to it. Equally, it is recognised in other religions. There was also substantive protection of privacy in early Hebrew culture, classical Greece and ancient China. These protections mostly focused on the right to solitude and, throughout history, the accepted meaning of privacy has varied widely according to context, culture and environment. Invariably, ideas on privacy have always been tied up with the wider society and, in particular, the relationship between the State and collective interests, on the one hand, and the individual on the other. Not surprisingly, therefore, even though the actual law of privacy may vary from country to country, it is seen as an essential integral element of the genuinely democratic state.

In that regard, the *Preamble* to the Australian *Privacy Charter*[58] provides that:

> "A free and democratic society requires respect for the autonomy of individuals, and limits on the power of both state and private organisations to intrude on that autonomy ... Privacy is a key value which underpins human dignity and other key values such as freedom of association and freedom of speech. ... Privacy is a basic human right and the reasonable expectation of every person."

Interestingly, in the United States, the Bill of Rights protects many fundamental liberties that Americans take for granted, but it says nothing directly about a right to privacy *per se*. Many individual States

---

[58]   Australian Privacy Charter Group (1994).

have, however, placed a right to privacy in their State Constitutions. In addition, there is a long history of judicial pronouncements on privacy in the US. Most famously, in the 1890s, American lawyers Samuel Warren and Louis Brandeis wrote a seminal piece on the right to privacy as a tort action, and quoted with approval Judge Cooley's description of privacy as "the right to be left alone".[59] Brandeis argued that privacy was the most cherished of freedoms in a democracy, and he was concerned that it should be reflected in the Constitution.

In the UK, reflecting on the difficulty of trying to limit and define the scope of privacy, the Calcutt Committee said that:

> "… nowhere have we found a wholly satisfactory statutory definition of privacy".[60]

However, the Committee was satisfied that it would be possible to define it legally and adopted this definition in its first report:

> "The right of the individual to be protected against intrusion into his personal life or affairs, or those of his family, by direct physical means or by publication of information."

In Ireland, the Law Reform Commission[61] carried out a major study on privacy with particular emphasis on surveillance and interception of communications. Its *Report*, in 1998, concluded that:

> "… privacy as a concept includes a wide range of personal interests or claims which place limits on the right of society and of its members to acquire knowledge of, and to take action regarding, another person. At its core lies the desire of the individual to maintain control over information, possessions and conduct of a personal kind, and, as a corollary, to deny or control access thereto by others. As such, it is now universally recognised as a human right, and

---

[59] Brandeis & Warren (1890).

[60] Calcutt, D. (1990).

[61] The Law Reform Commission was established by section 3 of the Law Reform Commission Act 1975. It is an independent body with members appointed by the Government. The Commission's programme of law reform is prepared in consultation with the Attorney General and approved by the Government.

is to be distinguished from other interests such as secrecy and confidentiality."[62]

Privacy can therefore be viewed as a fundamental (though not an absolute) human right, deserving of legal recognition and protection.

In England, the law of privacy can be traced as far back as 1361, when the Justices of the Peace Act provided for the arrest of peeping toms and eavesdroppers. Various countries developed specific protections for privacy in the centuries that followed. In 1776, the Swedish Parliament enacted the first freedom of information legislation with the Access to Public Records Act, which required that all government-held information be used for legitimate purposes. In France, in 1789, the Declaration of the Rights of Man & the Citizen[63] declared that private property was inviolable and sacred. Later, in 1858, France prohibited the publication of private facts and set stiff fines for breaches.[64] These early national legal efforts came to be very much complemented and enhanced by a series of international developments in the 20th century.

INTERNATIONAL PRIVACY INSTRUMENTS

It is premature to assess fully the history and influence of the 20th century but, even now, it is possible to state that the century witnessed the first international efforts to highlight globally the value of privacy

---

[62] Law Reform Commission (1998).

[63] At the time that the Declaration was drafted by the Marquis de Lafayette, it was intended as part of a transition from an absolute to a constitutional monarchy. In the event, France soon became a Republic but this document remained fundamental. The principles set forth in the declaration come from the philosophical and political principles of the Age of Enlightenment, such as individualism, the social contract and the separation of powers. It may have also been based on the Virginia Declaration of Rights developed by George Mason, an American Revolutionary leader from Virginia, whose objections led to the drafting of the Bill of Rights.

[64] The "Rachel affaire": Judgment of June 16, 1858, Trib. pr. inst. de la Seine, 1858 D.P. III 62. See Hauch, J.M. (1994).

and the need for its protection. These efforts gave rise to a number of important instruments, declaration and agreements, most notably:

♦ Universal Declaration on Human Rights (1948).

♦ European Convention on Human Rights & Fundamental Freedoms (1950).

♦ International Covenant on Civil & Political Rights (1966).

♦ Charter of Fundamental Rights of the EU (2000).

♦ EU draft Constitution (2004).

The modern privacy benchmark at an international level can be found in the 1948 Universal Declaration of Human Rights, which specifically protected territorial and communications privacy. Article 12 states:

> "No-one should be subjected to arbitrary interference with his privacy, family, home or correspondence, nor to attacks on his honour or reputation. Everyone has the right to the protection of the law against such interferences or attacks."

The International Covenant on Civil & Political Rights (ICCPR)[65] and the UN Convention on the Rights of the Child[66] both adopt similar language.

At the European level, the 1950 Council of Europe Convention for the Protection of Human Rights & Fundamental Freedoms[67] states in Article 8 that:

> "(1) Everyone has the right to respect for his private and family life, his home and his correspondence.
>
> (2) There shall be no interference by a public authority with the exercise of this right except as in accordance with the law and is necessary in a democratic society in the interests of national security, public safety or the economic

---

[65] Opened for signature, ratification and accession by UN General Assembly resolution 2200A (XXI) of 16 December 1966 and entered into force 23 March 1976, in accordance with Article 49.

[66] UN General Assembly Doc A/RES/44/25 (12 December 1989), Annex, Article 16.

[67] Convention for the Protection of Human Rights & Fundamental Freedoms, Rome, 4 November 1950.

well-being of the country, for the prevention of disorder or crime, for the protection of health or morals, or for the protection of the rights and freedoms of others."

The Convention created the European Commission on Human Rights and the European Court of Human Rights to oversee enforcement. Both have consistently viewed Article 8's protections expansively and its restrictions narrowly.

The Court has reviewed Member States' laws and imposed sanctions on several countries for failing to regulate wiretapping by governments and private individuals.[68] It has also reviewed cases of individual's access to their personal information in government files, to ensure that adequate procedures were implemented.[69] It has also expanded the protections of Article 8 beyond government actions to those of private persons, where it appears that the government should have prohibited those actions.[70] Presumably, under these combined analyses, the Court could have ordered the imposition of data protection principles, if information was improperly processed to the detriment of the individuals concerned.[71]

The Article 8 privacy right is balanced by Article 10, which allows for freedom of expression. It is the tension between these very often competing rights that is at the core of modern debates about press freedom, defamation and the protection of privacy. It is most logical to view Articles 8 and 10 as complementary and not contradictory but, in practice, the exercise of one of these rights can sometimes be restricted by the exercise of the other. For this reason, the European Commission and the European Court of Human Rights have defined in case law the limits to the exercise of each of these rights and, in particular, the extent to which public authorities are able to interfere. Nevertheless, in the years following the adoption of the European Convention on Human Rights, it became apparent (especially with advances in

---

[68] European Court of Human Rights, *Klass & Others v. Federal Republic of Germany*: Judgement of 6 September 1978, Series A No. 28 (1979). *Malone v. Commissioner of Police*, 2 All E.R. 620 (1979). See also Burke, K.C. (1981).

[69] European Court of Human Rights, *Leander v. Sweden*: Judgement of 26 March 1987, 9248/87.

[70] Judgement of 26 March 1987 (*Leander* Case) at 848, 849.

[71] Ryssdal, R. (1992).

information technology) that efficient legal protection of personal privacy required more specific and systematic development and this led directly to the Data Protection Convention in 1981.

CATEGORIES OF PRIVACY

Looking at the applicable international instruments, it is possible to discern that notions of privacy can be subdivided into key categories, each giving rise to its own particular issues. This classification was best formulated by a 1970s Government-backed Canadian Task Force, which identified three categories of claims to privacy:

- ♦ **Territorial privacy:** A claim to privacy advanced in a territorial or property sense based on the existence of a physical domain within which a claim to be left in solitude and tranquillity is recognised.

- ♦ **Privacy of the person:** The notion that each person has a "personal space" bounded not by physical walls and fences but by legal norms and social values that protect him or her from physical harassment and guarantee the individual freedom of movement and expression, freedom from physical assault and freedom from unwarranted search and seizure of the person).

- ♦ **Privacy in the information context:** A human right, based on the assumption that all information about a person is in a fundamental way his or her own, for him or her to communicate or retain as he or she sees fit, subject only to exceptions created by overriding social values that may require him or her to disclose information about himself or herself to the authorities in certain defined circumstances. [72, 73]

From the perspective of this book, it is "privacy in the information context" that is most relevant.

---

[72] Department of Communications and Department of Justice (Canada) (1972).
[73] This concept also encompasses "the interest in freedom from surveillance and the interception of one's communications", which was identified by the Australian Law Reform Commission in its research on privacy. Privacy LRC 22 (1983).

THE IMPORTANCE OF THE LEGAL PROTECTION OF PRIVACY

At national level, privacy law in many countries has lagged behind international aspirations. The subject continues to attract significant attention and public debate, especially in the aftermath of the 11 September 2001 attacks in the United States and the proposed and actual counter-terrorism response adopted by numerous governments. In its 1998 *Privacy Study*, the Law Reform Commission considered why privacy was deserving of legal protection. It concluded that:

> "... privacy is not merely instrumental to the achievement of other goals but is a basic human right that applies to all persons in virtue of their status as human beings."[74]

It noted a growing public concern in many countries at the lack of comprehensive or effective legal protection in this area and observed that numerous countries, including Ireland, have a web of laws that protect isolated aspects of privacy, with only a few countries, mainly European, having tailor-made privacy laws. Drawing on a wide range of international conventions and expert commentaries, the Commission asserted that "it is not possible to overstate just how fundamental privacy is in a developed and civilised legal system". It then outlined some of the many important overlapping values that are served by privacy:

+ Privacy is closely connected to notions of inherent human dignity.

+ Privacy is closely related to human freedom, autonomy and self-determination.

+ Privacy provides vital space for personal growth and development and for the exercise of freedom.

+ Privacy is much more than a tool for protecting the seclusion of the individual. It is an organising principle of civil society.

+ Privacy is closely connected to the democratic life of the polity.[75]

---

[74] Law Reform Commission (1998).

[75] Law Reform Commission (1998).

PRIVACY LAW IN IRELAND

As stated above, there is no single privacy law in Ireland. Instead, a variety of legal sources, from the Constitution down, create a patchwork of privacy rights and responsibilities. More specifically, in relation to information protection, the Law Reform Commission observed that there is "no overall protection of private information under Irish law at present".[76]

Nonetheless, current Irish law does offer some protection for personal information. This chiefly occurs in:

♦ Rights of anonymity in certain criminal proceedings.

♦ Family matters.

♦ Matters connected with personal taxation.

♦ The legal or equitable doctrine of confidence.

♦ Data protection law.

♦ Freedom of information legislation.

Application of European Convention on Human Rights in Ireland

Ireland has signed and ratified the European Convention for the Protection of Human Rights & Fundamental Freedoms. It was signed by the then Minister for External Affairs on 4 November 1950. Its provisions were later formally ratified on 25 February 1953, and the Convention entered into force for Ireland on 3 September of that year.[77] However, it was only in 2003 that the Oireachtas (Irish Parliament) enacted the European Convention on Human Rights Act.[78]

---

[76] Law Reform Commission (1998).

[77] Note that, while the convention has been binding on Ireland as an international treaty since 1953, its provisions are not actually applicable directly in Ireland, because Article 15.2.1 of the Irish Constitution reserves the sole and exclusive power of making laws to the Oireachtas alone, and Article 29.5.6 provides that no international agreement shall be part of the law of the State, save as may be determined by the Oireachtas.

[78] No.20 of 2003.

In terms of domestic enactment, two options were possible and, apparently, both were considered by the Government.[79] The first was simply to provide that the Convention should have the force of law in the State. This formula has already been followed in the case of other international Conventions, such as the Lugano Convention and the Hague Convention on Child Abduction. The other option – and the one adopted – was to avoid, as far as possible, any risk of possible interference with the legislative supremacy of the Oireachtas or the judicial supremacy of the Courts and to provide that, subject to the Constitution, statute law and rules of common law should be interpreted in a manner consistent with the State's obligations under the Convention. Consequently, the provisions of the Act are designed to ensure there will be two complementary systems in place in Ireland for the protection of human rights and fundamental freedoms. The superior rules under the Constitution will take precedence, in keeping with the State's dual doctrine on giving effect to international obligations and the primary role of the Oireachtas in that regard.

The Irish Constitution & Privacy

Although there is not an express reference to a right to privacy in the Irish Constitution, the Supreme Court has ruled that an individual may invoke the personal rights provision in Article 40.3.1 to establish an implied right to privacy. This article provides that:

> "... the State guarantees in its laws to respect, and, as far as practicable, by its laws to defend and vindicate the personal rights of the citizens."[80]

It was first used to establish an implied constitutional right in the case of *McGee v. Attorney General*,[81] which recognised the right to marital privacy. This case was followed by others, such as *Norris v. Attorney General*[82] and *Kennedy v. Ireland*.[83] In the latter case, the Supreme Court

---

[79] As per the Minister for Justice, Equality & Law Reform in the Second Stage debate on the European Convention on Human Rights Bill 2001, Dáil Éireann, 14 June 2001.

[80] Government of Ireland (1937).

[81] *McGee v. Attorney-General* [1974] I.R. 284.

[82] *Norris v. Attorney General* [1984] I.R. 36.

ruled that the illegal wiretapping of two journalists was a violation of the Constitution, stating:

> "... the right to privacy is one of the fundamental personal rights of the citizen which flow from the Christian and democratic nature of the State ... The nature of the right to privacy is such that it must ensure the dignity and freedom of the individual in a democratic society. This can not be insured if his private communications, whether written or telephonic, are deliberately and unjustifiably interfered with."

In the same case, the then High Court judge (later Chief Justice), Mr Justice Liam Hamilton, added:

> "... the right of privacy ... is not an unqualified right. Its exercise may be restricted by the constitutional rights of others, by the requirements of the common good and it is subject to the requirements of public order and morality ... The nature of the right to privacy must be such as to ensure the dignity and freedom of an individual in the type of society envisaged by the Constitution, namely a sovereign, independent and democratic society."

Having considered the above, the Law Reform Commission (in its 1998 Report) concluded that Irish Constitutional law on privacy could be summed up as deriving from two general anchorage points.

The first turns on the implication of a right of privacy from a variety of rights already protected explicitly in the text of the Constitution, including:

♦ Rights dealing with the family (Article 41), and the family in the context of education (Article 42).

♦ The inviolability of the dwelling (Article 40.5).

♦ The right of private property (Articles 43 and 40.3).

♦ The freedom to form associations and unions, to assemble peaceably and without arms (Article 40.6).

---

83   *Kennedy v. Ireland* [1987] I.R. 587.

♦ The freedom of conscience and the free expression and practice of religion, etc. (Article 44).

♦ The guarantee of privacy in voting under Article 16.1.4°.

The second anchorage point for privacy in the Constitution turns on a consideration of human personhood – on what it means to be a human being and the need for some islands of withdrawal in which the person may flourish. This second point rests on a view of the person detached from any particular social relationships or property, etc., he or she may have. It is encapsulated in the views quoted above of Mr. Justice Hamilton in *Kennedy v. Ireland*, in which privacy is seen to spring from the person as a fundamental human right related to the individual's dignity. This view finds strong echoes in the jurisprudence of the European Court of Human Rights, which bases the Article 8 conception of privacy on the "physical and moral integrity of the person".

As a final observation on the Constitution and the right to privacy, as interpreted by the Supreme Court, the content and boundaries of that right remain unclear and, without legislation, will remain so. At a policy level, in a Parliamentary democracy, it is arguable that leaving the development of a privacy framework to the courts simply cannot meet the need for a clear statement of public policy.[84] As we shall see, the enactment of data protection law provides a valuable precedent for legislation dealing with other privacy issues, such as surveillance.

Common Law Duty of Confidence & Privacy

The common law is derived from judicial decisions, rather than the Constitution, statute law or international treaties. Precedents established in prior court decisions are used to determine the development of legal principles. England, and former English colonies including the United States, Canada, Australia and Ireland, use the common law. Subject to consistency with the Constitution, Article 50.1 of *Bunreacht na hÉireann* provides that the common law – and other law – that existed prior to the introduction of the Constitution continue to have full effect until such time as they are amended or repealed by legislation. Despite increasing recourse to statute law to regulate areas

---

[84] For very recent developments in this area, see the final section in this Chapter.

of social and commercial activity, the common law remains very relevant to important fields of Irish law such as the law of contract and the law of torts. One advantage of common law is that the courts can modify it to meet the changing needs and demands of society.

The amalgam of common law doctrines that constitute a privacy shield (that is trespass, nuisance, defamation, negligence and confidence) was constructed to protect privacy in the context of property and in the enjoyment of property. It is clear that, on their own, they do not meet the present-day need for protection of privacy from modern Information Age technology. Inevitably, there are many areas which have not been litigated. As a result, it is impossible to state with any certainty whether a duty of confidence exists in these areas and, therefore, that the consent of individuals is required for the processing of their data. Even where there is case law, it may be difficult to extrapolate general principles from the particular circumstances of any one case. Further, there is no certainty that a decision made many years ago by a court on a specific matter would be unchanged in a decision made today in the context of modern society. Notwithstanding that, with the common law, the past is unquestionably the best guide to the present.

The three basic requirements for the application of the equitable doctrine of breach of confidence are that:

♦ The information is itself of a private nature.

♦ It is imparted in circumstances giving rise to a duty of confidentiality.

♦ Its dissemination was unauthorised.

There has been a loosening of the second requirement over the past few years, which has seen courts effectively impose a duty of confidentiality in some circumstances in the absence of a specific relationship of confidentiality (indeed, any relationship at all) between the parties.

As will become clear, the duty of confidence is especially relevant to personal health information. This is founded on the ethical duty of medical confidentiality, which derives from the Hippocratic Oath and which has been affirmed in most codes of healthcare professional conduct worldwide.

Legislation & Privacy

Legislation, or statute law, is law enacted by the Oireachtas (Parliament), which consists of the Dáil, Seanad and President.[85] Legislation begins its public life as a Bill that is introduced into either the Seanad (Upper House) or Dáil (Lower House). It is debated in both Houses and, if successfully passed, it becomes law when signed by the President and comes into operation on that day, unless a contrary intention appears.[86] For example, there may be provision, in the statute, for its commencement (in whole or in part) by way of Ministerial order.

All legislation must be constitutional and, if the President is uncertain as to the constitutional validity of any statute, she or he can send it to the Supreme Court for consideration.[87] Recently, legislation in relation to nursing home charges was so referred and found to be unconstitutional.[88]

In Ireland, most Bills are sponsored by Government Ministers with responsibility for the area in question – for example, proposed health legislation is sponsored by the Minister for Health & Children, finance legislation by the Minister for Finance, etc. Given that the Government invariably has a majority of seats in both Houses, this means that most Government-sponsored Bills are enacted. However, the Bill as initiated, and the Bill as passed, may differ significantly. This is because amendments may be made to a Bill as it progresses through the Oireachtas[89] – several important amendments were made to the Data Protection Acts in the course of their enactment.

---

[85] Government of Ireland (1937). Article 15 also provides that "the sole and exclusive power of making laws for the State is vested in the Oireachtas".

[86] Government of Ireland (1937), Article 25.4.1.

[87] Government of Ireland (1937), Article 26.

[88] Health (Amendment) (No.2) Bill 2004, referred to the Supreme Court in December 2004.

[89] The Dáil, rather than the Seanad, is the main legislative chamber and most amendments to Bills are likely to take place at Committee and Report Stages. First Stage of a Bill is essentially its publication. Second Stage sees a general debate on the Bill's nature, purpose and provisions. Committee Stage involves a section-by-section examination of its terms. Report is similar to Committee Stage, but only matters raised at Committee may be considered on Report. Fifth Stage is simply a formal acknowledgement that the Bill has passed all Stages in

Finally, legislation may be described as primary or secondary. Primary legislation is a statute enacted in the manner described above. Secondary legislation refers to law created by statutory regulations, which are provided for in primary legislation and are intended to allow mainly for administrative and other procedural issues arising from the implementation of the statute. Statutes normally provide that the Minister with responsibility for the Act can make these regulations without the need to come back to the Oireachtas for approval. However, the statute may specify that the Minister must consult with other appropriate Ministers[90] or obtain the consent of the Minister for Finance (if there is a financial issue involved) before he or she can make them[91].

In recent years, legislation has been enacted to deal with specific areas of privacy concern as well as general information protection related issues. Wiretapping and electronic surveillance is regulated under the Interception of Postal Packets and Telecommunications Messages (Regulation) Act. The Act followed a 1987 decision of the Supreme Court ruling that wiretaps of journalists violated the constitution.[92] The issue of employee monitoring is also causing growing concern, and there have been calls for national and EU legislation to limit the use of electronic surveillance in the workplace.

However, the enactment of freedom of information (1997 and 2003) and data protection (1998 and 2003) legislation represent the most significant statutory interventions into the area of protecting personal information, including health information. Freedom of information is mainly about holding the State and its institutions to account through greater transparency. Data protection law is focussed on the individual and his or her relationship with all persons (not just the State) keeping personal information. While data protection is the principal subject of

---

the relevant House. A guide to the legislative process can be found on the Oireachtas website (www.oireachtas.ie).

90 This is the case with the Data Protection Acts, where the Minister for Justice, Equality & Law Reform has to consult with the Minister for Health & Children, before making subject access regulations for personal health information.

91 In making regulations for registration fees under the Data Protection Acts, the Minister for Justice, Equality & Law Reform is required to obtain the consent of the Minister for Finance.

92 *Kennedy v. Ireland* [1987].

the remainder of this book, **Chapter 13** is dedicated to elaborating the relationships between these two significant legislative initiatives. In addition, certain concepts explicitly introduced into the Data Protection Act 2003, such as the public interest and information provided in confidence, have already been considered in much greater detail under Irish freedom of information law. Accordingly, reference will be made, as appropriate, to their FOI interpretations as they arise for consideration in later chapters.

Developments in Irish Privacy Law in 2005

In a speech to the Seanad on 9 February 2005, dealing with privacy and defamation, the Minister for Justice, Equality & Law Reform took the opportunity to consider whether the Government should introduce privacy legislation to replace the existing tort of invasion of privacy. He set out his views as follows:

> "The question is whether any developments in that area should be left to the courts or whether the State, through its legislative institutions – particularly the Oireachtas – has a duty to act pre-emptively by forging ahead with a privacy tort law reform. I believe that, in the area of tort, our courts have amply demonstrated their capacity over the years to develop principles of law and redress on a case-by-case basis as necessary. This is one of the areas of our common law that has remained largely untouched by legislation. It seems, with few exceptions, the better for it … if one leaves it to an organic, case-by-case build-up of jurisprudence, the Legislature is in a position to correct trends with which it does not agree rather than unleash forces that it never had in mind."[93]

In that regard, he found it "interesting" that the British government had declined to follow the recommendations contained in a Parliamentary Commission report of 2003, which recommended the introduction of a privacy law in the United Kingdom, thus indicating their inclination to rely on the traditional route of development of the law by the courts rather than introduce a law on privacy.

---

[93]   Privacy & Defamation Statements, Seanad Éireann. Vol.179, 9 February 2005.

A few months later, in a speech to the Irish Society for European Law on *The European Convention on Human Rights & the Media*, the Minister developed this view further with a challenge:

> "... to those who would advocate the introduction of new Irish privacy legislation, I usually respond with an invitation as to whether anyone, including those here present, could draw up a new tort of invasion of privacy without, a few years later, being surprised at how the judges were interpreting it in a way they never intended."[94]

However, in a report in *The Irish Times* on 16 June 2005,[95] it was stated that the Cabinet agreed to set up a working group to consider the need for privacy legislation (in particular, to restrict press intrusion into private lives) to accompany the long-anticipated reform of the defamation laws. The latest position (at end June 2005) on the introduction of privacy legislation is that the Minister for Justice, Equality & Law Reform, stated in response to a Parliamentary Question that:

> "... drawing an exact line between what is and what is not permissible is difficult [but the Government believed] we should not shy away from the issue just because it is difficult if we can come up with a law which is a help and protects privacy."[96]

---

[94]　McDowell (2005).

[95]　"Working group to consider privacy law", *The Irish Times*, 16 June 2005.

[96]　As reported in *The Irish Times* on 24 June 2005, "Minister promises Defamation Bill for Autumn", Marie O'Halloran.

3

THE EVOLUTION OF DATA PROTECTION LAW

INTRODUCTION

The previous chapter outlined the nature and scope of privacy and found that a key element related to information privacy. Interest in this particular aspect of privacy increased in the 1960s and 1970s with the advent of information technology. The surveillance and information processing potential of powerful computer systems prompted demands in a number of European countries for specific rules governing the collection, keeping, use and disclosure of personal information. The concept quickly came to be known as "data protection". Since then, it has given rise to its own distinct series of international instruments that have influenced national laws in Europe and beyond.

The first data protection law was enacted in the Land of Hesse in Germany in 1970, followed by Sweden, Germany (1977) and France (1978). Although Britain did not introduce a data protection law until 1984, the 1970s saw the publication of the *Younger Report on Privacy* (1972)[97] and the *Lindop Report on Data Protection* (1978).[98] Both reports examined the risks to privacy posed by the growth in the use of computers to process personal information.

In Ireland, the Data Protection Act 1988[99] was introduced to allow ratification of a Council of Europe Convention on Data Protection,[100] but

---

97 Younger (1972).

98 Lindop (1978).

99 Data Protection Act 1988 (No.25 of 1988).

100 The Act's long title states that its intention is "to give effect to the [Council of Europe] Convention for the Protection of Individuals with regard to the Automatic Processing of Personal Data" and a copy of the Convention is attached as a Schedule to the Act.

the timing had much to do with facilitating the development of the country as an international financial services centre. The Data Protection (Amendment) Act 2003 was also concerned with giving effect to an international obligation – this time, a European Union Directive that was an important element of completing the Internal Market.

As this chapter will show, data protection in Ireland and abroad has been shaped consistently not just by information privacy concerns but, almost equally, by the twin desires of facilitating international trade and avoiding the imposition of undue burdens on business.

INTERNATIONAL INITIATIVES

The two major – and broadly similar – international data protection instruments are:

♦ The Organisation for Economic Co-operation & Development's 1980 *Guidelines Governing the Protection of Privacy & Transborder Flows of Personal Data.*[101]

♦ The Council of Europe's 1981 Convention for the Protection of Individuals with regard to the Automatic Processing of Personal Data.[102]

OECD *Guidelines*

The *Preface* to the OECD *Guidelines* states:

"The development of automatic data processing, which enables vast quantities of data to be transmitted within seconds across national frontiers, and indeed across continents, has made it necessary to consider privacy protection in relation to personal data."

It goes on to say that:

"… although national laws and policies may differ, member countries have a common interest in protecting privacy and

---

[101] OECD(1980). Adopted on 23 September 1980.
[102] The Convention is open to signature by any country, including countries that are not members of the Council of Europe.

individual liberties, and in reconciling fundamental but competing values such as privacy and the free flow of information."

In some ways, the *Guidelines* were ahead of their time – for example, in the conclusion that limiting the relevant rules solely to the automatic processing of personal data would have considerable drawbacks.

Council of Europe Convention

The Convention's object and purpose is simply stated, namely:

> "... to secure in the territory of each party for each individual, whatever his nationality or residence, respect for his rights and fundamental freedoms, and in particular his right to privacy, with regard to automatic processing of personal data relating to him ('data protection')."

As stated in **Chapter 2**, the Data Protection Convention derived directly from the European Convention on Human Rights and Fundamental Freedoms, especially the rights in Article 8.

Subsequently, in order to adapt the general principles set out in the 1981 Convention to the specific requirements of various sectors of activity in society, a number of (non-binding) Recommendations have been adopted by the Council of Europe. Recommendations have the advantage that they are easier to draw up, to adopt and to implement. Instead of signature and ratification by each of the Council of Europe Member States, they only require unanimous adoption by the Committee of Ministers. It is therefore simpler to adapt them to changing circumstances than to amend Conventions; and, above all, although they are not legally binding, they contain standards of reference. Essentially:

> "... a recommendation constitutes, therefore, a request to consider in good faith the possibility of elaborating and implementing domestic law in conformity with

internationally agreed interpretation of the principles laid down in the Convention."[103]

Council of Europe Recommendations on Medical Information

There are Recommendations on medical databanks[104] and the protection of medical and genetic data.[105] The former has not had a major impact, and even the concept of "databanks" now seem antiquated. Importantly, however, it introduced the notion that subject access to personal health information might be handled through a physician rather than directly by the patient. It also developed the idea that erroneous patient information might still be retained in the record held, even after the correct information came to light, and would be retained because the incorrect information might have had some bearing on treatment received, etc. The erroneous nature of such information, and the reason for its retention, would, however, have to be clearly marked within the record.

The 1997 Recommendation updated the 1981 Recommendation in the light of current trends and of the increasing use of genetic data. It called on governments to:

> "… take steps to ensure that the principles contained in … this Recommendation are reflected in their law and practice … [and] ensure wide circulation of the principles ... amongst persons professionally involved in the collection and processing of medical data."

The 1997 Recommendation sets out requirements for the fair and lawful processing of personal medical data and for specific issues relating to unborn children and genetic information. In brief, it deals with:

♦ Consent to processing of personal medical data.

♦ Requirements for the disclosure of such data.

♦ Requirements for disclosures for the purpose of scientific research; rights of data subjects.

---

[103] For this and other information on the Council of Europe's role in data protection, see http://www.coe.int/dataprotection/.

[104] Council of Europe Recommendation, R(81)1, on *Automated Medical Databanks.*

[105] Council of Europe Recommendation, R(97)5, on the *Protection of Medical Data.*

♦ Long-term retention of personal medical data.

♦ Security of information kept.[106]

♦ Trans-border data flows.

Like its predecessor, for whatever reason, the 1997 Recommendation is not widely known or explicitly followed. Perhaps, inevitably, it was overshadowed by the 1995 EU Directive on Data Protection (see below), which Member States were required to transpose into national law.

Impact of the OECD *Guidelines* & Council of Europe Convention

Before considering the Directive, it is worth emphasising that the principles contained in the OECD *Guidelines* and the Council of Europe Convention continue to form the core of the data protection laws of dozens of countries.

These two instruments have had a profound effect around the world; over 20 countries have adopted the Council of Europe Convention and several others have signed it, but have not yet adopted it into law. The OECD *Guidelines* have also been very influential in national legislation, especially in countries in the Asia-Pacific region where Australia has led the way in promoting them. However, in recent years, in Europe, the OECD *Guidelines* have tended to be increasingly overlooked, as the EU Commission has taken a growing interest in data protection. It would be unhelpful if this process was to lead to a split, or even dispute, among countries in different parts of the world, between those who choose to follow the European model of data protection and those who adopt an alternative approach. However, this split is a possibility, given the stance taken by Australia (discussed later in this **Chapter**).

---

[106] Interestingly, cost is not one of the considerations, unlike in the EU Directive and Irish data protection law.

EUROPEAN UNION INFLUENCES

EU Directive on Data Protection (95/46/EC)

In 1996, *The Economist* magazine posed an important (rhetorical) question:

> "Is there a method of regulation that would allow the economic benefits of copious information to be enjoyed, while still defending privacy for those who value it?" [107]

before answering:

> "A promising approach is to require the information-gatherer to gain permission for subsequent use. This idea informs a recent European Union directive on data protection. Under the directive, which governments must act upon by 1998, consumers have to be notified in advance of how a company would like to use their names and of the information that is attached to them. They can say no to such use; if they say yes, they have the right to know where their data have gone."

The EU Data Protection Directive was developed in the context of creating the infrastructure necessary for the completion of the Internal Market. It set a baseline common level of privacy in EU Member States. This not only re-inforced existing data protection law, but extended it to establish a range of new rights for individuals (data subjects), with additional obligations for those keeping personal information (data controllers). These included improved protection over the processing of sensitive personal data by generally requiring the "explicit and unambiguous" consent of the individual(s) concerned. The Directive also emphasised "enforceability", effectively meaning that data subjects have rights enshrined in explicit rules with a national supervisory authority that can act on their behalf.

As a Directive, it had to be transposed (or enacted) into national law in each individual EU country. The deadline for this to happen was October 1998, but Ireland did not comply until the passing of the

---

[107] *Economist* (1996).

Data Protection Act 2003. Explaining the delay, the Minister of State at the Department of Justice, Equality & Law Reform stated that it was:

"... due to a combination of factors, including the need to consult widely, pressure of other work and, not least, the complexities arising in this particular context".[108]

The Directive (as an instrument of EU law) must confine itself to the processing of personal data in areas falling within the scope of the European Union. Accordingly, it specifically excludes matters covered by *Title V (Provisions on a Common Foreign & Security Policy)* and *Title VI (Provisions on Co-operation & in the fields of Justice & Home Affairs)*. It also lists the following processing activities as excluded, even in cases where such activities do come under EU law: namely, public security, defence, State security and the activities of the State in areas of criminal law. In addition, Recital 16 states that the Directive's scope does not include sound data and visual images, if processed for any of those purposes. This would mean, for example, that video surveillance for the processing of road traffic offences would be excluded. Notwithstanding these exceptions, Member States had the discretion to apply the principles in the Directives to any area of information processing that they wished.

EU Data Protection & Telecommunications

In 1997, the European Union supplemented the 1995 Directive by introducing the Telecommunications Privacy Directive,[109] which complemented and particularised the general Data Protection Directive. It imposed wide-ranging obligations on carriers and service providers to ensure the privacy of users' communications, including Internet-related activities. It regulated areas that, until then, had been covered uncertainly in national data protection laws.

---

[108] Data Protection (Amendment) Bill 2002, Dáil Éireann, Second Stage, Vol.555, 22 October 2002.

[109] Directive 97/66/EC of the European Parliament and of the Council of 15 December 1997 concerning the processing of personal data and the protection of privacy in the telecommunications sector. This was transposed into Irish law by the European Communities (Data Protection & Privacy in Telecommunications) Regulations 2002 (S.I. No.192 of 2002).

The 1997 Directive was replaced by Directive 2002/58/EC, which was intended to adapt and update the existing provisions to meet new and foreseeable developments in electronic communications services and technologies. This Directive was transposed into Irish law by the European Communities (Electronic Communications Networks & Services) (Data Protection & Privacy) Regulations 2003.[110] According to *Guidance Notes* issued by the Department of Communications, Marine & Natural Resources,[111] the objective of the Regulations is to create the necessary legal framework in this country to ensure consumers and users receive the same level of protection of personal data and privacy, regardless of the technology by which a particular service is delivered. The Regulations would also assist in providing a similar level of protection for citizens of the EC, regardless of which Member State they are in, and thereby would enhance confidence in the protection of personal data and privacy when transacting business by electronic means anywhere within the Community.

Regulating the Retention & Use of Telecommunications Traffic & Location Data

In recent years, there has been a major debate in this area on the relative merits of the privacy considerations of such information *versus* the crime and security dimensions.

In 2004, the Data Protection Commissioner expressed concern that traffic data needed to be regulated securely in order to prevent its use:

- As a source of great assistance to marketers, including telcos and ISPs.

- As a way of profiling people's habits.

- To monitor a person's movements by reference to the location of a call as an information source and / or to snoop on them, if necessary.

- To make wrong assumptions about an individual's personal behaviour.

---

[110] S.I. No.535 of 2003 (which revoked S.I. No.192 of 2002).

[111] Department of Communications, Marine & Natural Resources (2003).

- ◆ To blackmail a person, perhaps if the communication service provider did not have adequate data security to provide against the potential for unlawful access by hackers and others.

- ◆ As a means of surveillance on every citizen, just in case they offend.

That explains why, in 2001, the Commissioner had required telcos and ISPs to register with his Office. During the registration process, he discovered that all traffic data for telcos was being retained routinely for a period of six years. The Commissioner was dissatisfied with this retention period and pressed instead for a six-month period as the norm. However, the Department of Justice, Equality & Law Reform had concerns regarding access for security and crime investigations and indicated that a retention period of three years was necessary for security and crime prevention purposes. While the Commissioner disagreed, the Government decided in March 2002 that the Minister for Public Enterprises should issue (confidential) Directions under s.110(1) of the Postal & Telecommunications Services Act 1983, requiring telcos to retain detailed non-anonymous traffic data for a three-year period for the purpose of facilitating requests from the Gardaí and the Defence Forces.[112]

That measure was intended to be temporary, pending the introduction of substantive legislation to this effect. This was provided for in Part 7 of the Criminal Justice (Terrorist Offences) Act 2005. The relevant provisions of the legislation require telecommunication service providers (both fixed line and mobile operators) to retain telecommunications data (traffic and location) for a period of up to three years following an appropriate request from the Garda Commissioner. The provisions in Part 7 can be invoked for the purposes of the prevention, detection, investigation or prosecution of crime (including terrorist offences) or the safeguarding of the security of the State. It should be pointed out that the legislation also introduced safeguards against misuse of the retained data, by extending the duties of the designated judge and complaints referee

---

[112] These requests could be made under sections 98A and 98B of the 1983 Act, as inserted by s.13 of the Interception of Postal Packets & Telecommunications Messages (Regulation) Act 1993.

under the Interception of Postal Packets & Telecommunications Messages (Regulation) Act 1993 to the data retention provisions of Part 7. Most importantly of all, the provisions do not relate to ISPs or the actual content of the communication.[113]

Other EU Data Protection Measures

As well as the above, there are a number of other EU measures in the data protection area, including:

- Regulation (EC) 45/2001 of the European Parliament and of the Council of 18 December 2000, on the protection of individuals with regard to the processing of personal data by the Community institutions and bodies and on the free movement of such data.

- Treaty on the European Union: Title 1, Article F:

  "The Union shall respect the national identities of its Member States, whose systems of government are founded on the principles of democracy.

  The Union shall respect fundamental rights, as guaranteed by the European Convention for the Protection of Human Rights & Fundamental Freedoms signed in Rome on 4 November 1950 and as they result from the constitutional traditions common to the Member States, as general principles of Community law."

- EU Charter of Fundamental Rights of 7 December 2000: Article 8:[114] Data protection in the EU has an enhanced basis after the promulgation of the *Charter of Fundamental Rights of the European Union* by the December 2000 European Council of Nice. Article 8 of the *Charter* enshrines data protection as a fundamental right of the Union and requires the existence of fully independent data

---

[113] See s.62 of the 2005 Act, which provides that Part 7 applies to data relating to communications transmitted by means of a fixed line or mobile telephone and does not apply to the content of such communications.

[114] The Article 29 Working Group, in *Recommendation 4/99: On the Inclusion of the Fundamental Right to Data Protection in the European Catalogue of Fundamental Rights,* had specifically argued that "inclusion of data protection among the fundamental rights of Europe would make such protection a legal requirement throughout the Union and reflect its increasing importance in the information society". (7 September 1999).

protection authorities to monitor compliance as an integral part of that right. The specific terms of Article 8 are as follows:

1. Everyone has the right to the protection of personal data concerning him or her.

2. Such data must be processed fairly for specified purposes and on the basis of the consent of the person concerned or some other legitimate basis laid down by law. Everyone has the right of access to data which has been collected concerning him or her, and the right to have it rectified.

3. Compliance with these rules shall be subject to control by an independent authority.[115]

♦ (Draft) EU Constitution 2004: Article 51 of the Draft Treaty that aims to establish a Constitution for Europe, agreed in June 2004, further enhances the basis of data protection by recognising that everyone has the right to the protection of personal data concerning him or her. It also provides that compliance with data protection rules shall be subject to the control of a fully-independent authority.[116]

European Charter on Patients' Rights

Apart from governmental and international bodies, citizens' groups have been active in promoting information privacy. At a European level, in the health sector, patients' rights groups have prepared the *European Charter of Patients' Rights*,[117] which provides 14 rights including: the right to access information, consent, free choice, privacy and confidentiality. While it does not have official status in Ireland, in April 2005, the Minister for Health & Children launched the report of an academic review of the *Charter* in Ireland by a multidisciplinary research team from the School of Nursing and the School of Law &

---

[115] The Charter has no binding legal force at present.

[116] Currently (June 2005), the future of the EU Constitution looks very uncertain, after unsuccessful referenda on its adoption in France and the Netherlands.

[117] Cotturri, G., Inglese, S.A., Moro, G., Roffiaen, C. & Scattolon, C. (2002). A first draft was produced in July 2002 and final version in November 2002, which was followed by an international seminar, where Ireland was represented by the Irish Patients Association, on whose website the Charter can be found – http://www.irishpatients.ie.

Government at Dublin City University.[118] The review found that the *Charter* had strengths and weaknesses and noted that it emphasised the need for patients and society to recognise that rights also imply responsibilities.

The key information-related rights in the *Charter* are:

3: Right to Information

Every individual has the right to access to all kind of information regarding their state of health, the health services and how to use them, and all that scientific research and technological innovation makes available. This includes a patient having a right of direct access to his or her clinical file and medical records, to photocopy them, to ask questions about their contents and to obtain the correction of any errors they might contain.

4: Right to Consent

Every individual has the right of access to all information that might enable him or her to actively participate in the decisions regarding his or her health; this information is a prerequisite for any procedure and treatment, including the participation in scientific research.

6: Right to Privacy & Confidentiality

Every individual has the right to the confidentiality of personal information, including information regarding his or her state of health and potential diagnostic or therapeutic procedures, as well as the protection of his or her privacy during the performance of diagnostic exams, specialist visits, and medical / surgical treatments in general. This principle envisages that all the information relative to an individual's state of health, and to the medical/surgical treatments to which he or she is subjected, must be considered private, and as such, adequately protected.

---

[118]   O'Mathúna *et al.* (2005).

THE ECONOMICS, TRADE & BUSINESS DIMENSIONS OF DATA PROTECTION LAW

While data protection is clearly grounded in the notion of human rights, it is also driven by economic motivations. Reference was made earlier to the EU Directive and the Internal Market. The Directive is a key element of the harmonisation strategy to achieve the economic benefits of a "Europe without frontiers". Much earlier, but similarly, the 1980 OECD *Guidelines* explicitly recognised that, although countries have a common interest in protecting privacy, there is a real risk that unco-ordinated domestic rules may hinder trans-border data flows that can contribute to global economic development. In fact, the OECD only became involved in privacy issues because of the economic imperatives to have a compatible framework amongst member countries, whereby privacy was effectively protected without unnecessarily interfering with, what would today be called, electronic commerce. (However, having embarked upon the task for economic reasons, the OECD produced a rational, effective and well-expressed privacy framework document, which does not subordinate privacy to economic considerations.)

In the Council of Europe Convention, the economic imperative is less marked. The Convention presents itself unapologetically as a human rights treaty. However, the *Preamble* does state briefly that it recognises that it:

> "… is necessary to reconcile the fundamental values of the respect for privacy and the free flow of information between peoples".

It is not surprising, therefore, that the 1988 Data Protection Act, introduced to allow Ireland to ratify the Convention, should have an expressly-stated business and economic rationale, which the then Minister for Justice set out as follows:

> "The maintenance of unrestricted data flows is particularly important for our economy, especially in view of the establishment of the international financial services centre on the Custom House Docks site. This is because several European countries have legislation restricting the export of

data for processing to countries which have less strict data protection laws or perhaps none at all. The absence of data protection legislation here could thus be a factor that international companies would take into account when deciding whether or not to establish a business here, particularly in the area of data processing. For this reason it is desirable that the Bill should be enacted and the [Council of Europe] Convention ratified as soon as possible." [119]

The need to have regard to business considerations was further evidenced in the consultation paper on implementing the EU Directive issued by the Department of Justice, Equality & Law Reform in 1997,[120] which outlined the following three substantive policy considerations:

♦ The need to have a law, under which data subjects and data controllers alike will be clear on their respective rights and duties, while at the same time being sufficiently flexible to embrace ever-changing new information and communications technologies.

♦ The need to ensure that no additional burden or bureaucracy is placed on business or data controllers generally, which is not required for compliance with the Directive.

♦ The need to minimise the burden on business, etc. of adapting to a new data protection regime, by keeping intact as much of the Data Protection Act 1988 as appropriate.

The 1995 EU Directive is clearly motivated by economic considerations, particularly the need to harmonise data privacy laws within the Union, although it also stresses the importance of fundamental human rights. The Directive's general philosophy is not unlike the other instruments and can be conveniently summarised from Article 1:

"1. In accordance with this Directive, member states shall protect the fundamental rights and freedoms of natural

---

[119] Data Protection Bill, 1987: Second Stage. Minister for Justice (Gerard Collins), Dáil Éireann, Volume 375, 17 November 1987.

[120] Department of Justice, Equality & Law Reform (1997).

persons, and in particular their right to privacy with respect to the processing of personal data.

2. Member states shall neither restrict nor prohibit the free flow of personal data between member states for reasons connected with the protection afforded under paragraph 1."

Both the Council of Europe Convention and the OECD *Guidelines* have now had reviews to ensure their continued relevance: the *Guidelines* were reaffirmed by a 1998 Ministerial declaration; the Convention received an updating protocol in 2001. Further, the European Commission has reviewed the Directive's transposition.

INTERNATIONAL DEVELOPMENTS IN DATA PROTECTION LAW

As stated above, a fundamental economic objective of the EU Data Protection Directive was to enhance the free flow of data within the European Union by removing barriers caused by internal borders. However, for countries outside the EU, the principal effect is frequently seen as the creation of an economic barrier at what might be called the EU's external border. This is because one very important aspect of the Directive is that it imposed an obligation on Member States to ensure that the personal information relating to European citizens is covered by acceptable information protection law whenever it is exported to, and processed in, countries outside Europe. The result is growing economic pressure outside Europe for privacy laws that mirror the European approach. The consequence for countries that refuse to adopt requisite standards is that they may find themselves unable to engage in certain types of information flows with EU Member States, particularly if sensitive personal information is involved. Canada, for example, introduced the Personal Information Protection & Electronic Documents Act (PIPEDA) in 2000 in response to the European Directive on Data Protection – it was accepted as meeting the requisite standard by the EU Commission on 14 January

2002.[121] Other countries, in particular Australia, have been less impressed by the EU model.

Even without the trans-border data flow requirement, it is understandable that the EU Directive would have a significant impact on data protection thinking and actions in many countries outside of Europe, especially those seeking closer ties with the EU. However, it is important to stress that many democratic countries already have their own highly-regarded data protection or information privacy regimes in place. While these national laws were heavily influenced by the same international instruments as affected European countries (namely the OECD *Guidelines* and Council of Europe Convention), they were also shaped by each country's own cultural and legal frameworks. In some cases, these countries consider their data protection laws to be superior to Europe's and it is informative and insightful to have some knowledge of them.

New Zealand

The Privacy Act 1993[122] is based on the principles of the OECD's *Guidelines.*[123] The supervisory authority is the Privacy Commissioner, whose key function is to oversee the operation of the 1993 Act. At the heart of the Privacy Act are 12 principles or rules, covering:

♦ Rule 1: Purpose of collection of personal information.

♦ Rule 2: Source of personal information.

♦ Rule 3: Collection of personal information from individual.

♦ Rule 4: Manner of collection of personal information.

♦ Rule 5: Storage and security of personal information.

---

[121] This will allow certain personal data to flow freely from the EU to recipients in Canada subject to the Canadian Act, without additional safeguards being needed to meet the requirements of the EU Data Protection Directive. The decision fulfils an undertaking made in 1999 by Canada and the EU in their *Joint Statement on Electronic Commerce in the Global Information Society*, in which both parties promised to work together to build confidence in cross-border electronic commerce and to ensure the free flow of personal data on the basis of high data protection standards.

[122] The 1993 Act has been amended twice since its inception, in 1993 and 1994, but these were minor amendments.

[123] OECD (1980).

- Rule 6: Access to personal information.

- Rule 7: Correction of personal information.

- Rule 8: Accuracy, etc. of personal information to be checked before use.

- Rule 9: Retention of personal information.

- Rule 10: Limits on use of personal information.

- Rule 11: Limits on disclosure of personal information.

- Rule 12: Unique identifiers.

The Privacy Commissioner may issue codes of practice that modify the Information Privacy Principles set out in the Privacy Act, to take into account the special characteristics of specific industries, agencies or types of personal information. The provisions in a code may be more or less stringent than the principles. In July 1993, the Privacy Commissioner issued the first code of practice under the Privacy Act, aimed at the health sector. That temporary code was replaced by the Health Information Privacy Code 1994, which commenced on 30 July 1994. The code was issued with particular characteristics of the health sector and health information in mind, including the fact that much health information is collected in a situation of confidence and trust. It was reviewed in 1999, but the review found no need for change.

On 12 December 2000, the Statutes Amendment Bill was introduced into Parliament to amend the Privacy Act 1993 in order to secure a finding from the European Commission that New Zealand's law provides an "adequate level of protection" for the purposes of Article 25 of EU Data Protection Directive. This was necessary because the Privacy Act had no equivalent to the data export controls that are a common feature of European data protection laws. The effect of the amendment is to empower the Privacy Commissioner to issue transfer prohibition notices to prevent the transfer of personal information from New Zealand to another State if satisfied that certain privacy protection measures are not in place in the country concerned.

Australia

The Privacy Act 1988 (as amended by the Privacy Amendment (Private Sector) Act 2000) provides the statutory basis for data protection law in Australia. It was the 2000 Act that extended the operation of the 1988 statute to cover the private sector (including the private health sector) throughout Australia. In the health sector, the legislation, through its 10 National Privacy Principles, promotes greater openness between service providers and consumers regarding the handling of health information. It introduced, for instance, a general right of access for consumers to their own health records, and requires healthcare data controllers to have available documentation that clearly sets out their policies for the management of personal information. In November 2001, the Federal Privacy Commissioner issued detailed *Guidelines on Privacy in the Private Health Sector*, which elaborated further the existing statutory principles.[124]

The *Guidelines*[125] were published on the basis of the co-regulatory approach offered by the Privacy Amendment (Private Sector) Act 2000. The legislation allows for flexibility in how organisations (including healthcare service providers) deal with their privacy obligations. In fact, the Act recognised the particularly sensitive nature of health information, and placed extra protections around its handling, including enforcement mechanisms to deal with breaches of the privacy standards. The *Guidelines* acknowledge that the healthcare service provider's principal concern is the healthcare of the patient and, accordingly, their aim is to assist healthcare service providers to meet their obligations under the National Privacy Principles, while providing treatment and care.

On 26 January 2001, EU Data Protection Commissioners[126] adopted an opinion on the level of protection provided for by the Australian Privacy Amendment (Private Sector) Act 2000. In the Working Party's opinion, the Australian legislation could be regarded as adequate for the purpose of exporting personal data from the EU to Australia, only if appropriate safeguards were introduced to meet a number of specific concerns – for example, through voluntary codes of conduct approved by the Australian Privacy Commissioner or by a change in the law. In the meantime, EU operators were advised to put into place contractual safeguards before exporting data to Australia, especially when the

---

124 Federal Privacy Commissioner (Australia) (2001).
125 Federal Privacy Commissioner (Australia) (2001).
126 Meeting as the EU Directive Article 29 Data Protection Working Party.

transfer concerned human resources data. This opinion was not well-received in Australia. The then Attorney-General responded that:

> "Many of the EC Committee's comments display an ignorance about Australia's law and practice and do not go to the substance of whether our law is fundamentally 'adequate' from a trading point of view. It seems that the prescriptive approach taken in many EU Member States is assumed to be the only acceptable way to go in many areas of privacy protection." [127]

He added:

> "Obviously officials from Australia and the EC will continue to talk in order to address these concerns to everyone's satisfaction. However, Australia will only look at options that do not impose unnecessary burdens on business."

By 2003, the Australian position appeared to have hardened, the Attorney-General concluding that his country had taken the view that the EU's privacy protection model was not suitable as the basis for an international standard on privacy. In his view:

> "... it is prescriptive, it gives significant powers to a bureaucracy and it does not allow for innovative developments".[128]

Canada

Canadian data protection policy is based on an explicit recognition of the need for a multiplicity of solutions, involving Federal data protection legislation (covering banking, telecommunications and transportation sectors) and Provincial legislation (covering all other sectors), together with the adoption of the Canadian Standards Association's *Model Code for the Protection of Personal Information*.[129] This model has created its own set of challenges, centred around

---

[127] "European Data Protection Commissioners' Opinion of Australia's Privacy Law", *Media Release*, Office of the Attorney-General, 26 March 2001.

[128] Attorney-General (Australia) (2003).

[129] Canadian Standards Association (1996).

harmonising and defining the interplay between Federal and Provincial law and practice, clarifying the function and status of sectoral codes of practice and teasing out the relationship of the legislation to the Canadian Standards Association's privacy standard.

Canada has two Federal information privacy laws: the Privacy Act 1980 and the Personal Information Protection & Electronic Documents Act 2000. The former imposes obligations on most Federal government departments and agencies to respect privacy rights by limiting the collection, use and disclosure of personal information and gives individuals the right to access and request correction of personal information about themselves held by these Federal Government bodies. As regards information in the private sector, individuals are protected by PIPEDA in much the same way.[130]

The Federal Privacy Commissioner is the supervisory authority under both statutes. The Provinces and Territories have their own data protection statutes, which, in most cases, are framed also to include freedom of information principles. Interestingly, several Provinces and Territories – Alberta, Saskatchewan, Manitoba and Ontario – have passed legislation to deal specifically with the collection, use and disclosure of personal health information by healthcare providers and other healthcare organisations. Each Province and Territory has its own enforcement body.

There is also, at national level, the 1998 *Health Information Privacy Code* prepared by the Canadian Medical Association[131] and based on the Canadian Standards Association's *Model Code for the Protection of Personal Information*.[132] The *Health Information Privacy Code* articulates principles for protecting the privacy of patients, the confidentiality and security of their health information and the trust and integrity of the therapeutic relationship.

---

[130] Initially, PIPEDA applied only to personal information about customers or employees that was collected, used or disclosed in the course of commercial activities by the Federally-regulated private sector. The Act now applies to personal information collected, used or disclosed by the retail sector, publishing companies, the service industry, manufacturers and other provincially-regulated organisations. The Act does not apply to the personal information of employees of these Provincially-regulated organisations.

[131] Canadian Medical Association (1998).

[132] Canadian Standards Association (1996).

The Code has 10 Principles that:

♦ Recognise the patient's right to privacy.

♦ Acknowledge the special nature of health information.

♦ Limit the collection, use, disclosure and access to this information.

♦ Give patients information on the non-therapeutic use of their health information.

♦ Recognise the patients' right to consent to the use of their health information.

♦ Reinforce a patient's right to access their health information.

♦ Emphasise the need for accurate recording of a patient's health information.

♦ Address security safeguards.

♦ Stress that accountability is owed first and foremost to the patient.

♦ Provide that policies, procedures and practices relating to health information must be transparent so that patients can clearly understand the extent and circumstances of health information collection, use, disclosure and access.

United States

The US traditionally has had a different approach to privacy protection than European and Commonwealth countries. Legislation, at Federal and State level, tends to be more fragmented, more specific to data categories, and less uniform than in other countries. This is due mainly to the First Amendment to the Constitution, which imposes limits on the government's ability to regulate the flow of information, including personal data. However, the information management and privacy protection ethics of American healthcare professionals spring from the same primary source as in other Western countries – namely, Hippocrates.

The *Code of Ethics* of the American Medical Association specifies in its *Core Principles* that physicians "shall safeguard patient confidences within the constraints of the law."[133] The Code's *Opinion* affirms that:

---

[133] American Medical Association (2004), 2004/2005 edition. See http://www.ama-assn.org, where the *Code* can be downloaded.

> "... the information disclosed to a physician during the course of the relationship between physician and patient is confidential to the greatest possible degree ... The physician should not reveal confidential communications or information without the express consent of the patient, unless required to do so by law."

It also states that: "The utmost effort and care must be taken to protect the confidentiality of all medical records, including computerised records". In that regard, it lays out a series of safeguards, designed to secure medical confidentiality in a computerised environment.

The Privacy Act 1974 covers personally identifiable data held by the Federal Government, no matter what their source or subject, that are stored in "systems of records" from which data are retrieved by personal identifiers. It provides *inter alia* that individuals must be allowed upon request to see information about themselves. In addition, it prohibits disclosure of personal data without the consent of the data subject, except in some special circumstances set out in the Act. However, under the Privacy Act, Federal agencies are allowed wide discretion in making disclosures pursuant to their mandates.

State laws vary greatly in the ways and extents to which they protect privacy of health information. Most recognise some form of patient–physician privilege (the patient's right to defend against forced court disclosure of his or her record), but the scope of protection varies greatly.

Against the above background, the Health Insurance Portability and Accountability Act 1996 (HIPAA) Privacy Rule – effective from April 2003 – is the first wide-ranging Federal protection for the privacy of personal health information.

United Kingdom

Finally, for the sake of better understanding many of the references and points that will occur in later chapters, it is opportune to outline briefly the data protection system in the UK.

In 1984, the UK introduced the Data Protection Act, which applied to computerised personal information of living identifiable individuals. While it had universal registration for all data controllers and data processors, nonetheless it was a fairly minimal piece of legislation in terms of obligations and rights. Initially, there was a Data Protection Registrar to oversee and enforce the legislation. The UK gave effect to the EU Directive through the Data Protection (Amendment) Act 1998. With the introduction of the Freedom of Information Act 2000, a new supervisory authority (essentially the Data Protection Registrar with extended powers) assumed responsibility for both data protection and freedom of information under a new title of Information Commissioner.[134]

There is a need (which will become apparent shortly) for terminological clarification regarding the constituent elements of the UK so as to avoid confusion and to ensure consistency in this book.[135] In short, "Britain" may be taken to mean England & Wales, "Great Britain" refers to England, Wales & Scotland and the "UK" refers to Great Britain and Northern Ireland.

The Data Protection Acts cover the UK, while the Freedom of Information Act 2000 excludes Scotland, which has its own Freedom of Information (Scotland) Act 2002. The Information Commissioner has responsibility for data protection throughout the UK, but his remit on FOI does not include Scotland. To confuse matters further, the National Health Service in each constituent political element has varying degrees of autonomy, which means that their actual implementation of the UK-wide data protection law differs, in some areas considerably.

---

[134] http://www.informationcommissioner.gov.uk.

[135] The UK consists of four constituent national entities: namely England, Wales, Scotland and Northern Ireland. In a historical and political sense, Britain may be understood to mean England & Wales, which have been formally unified since 1536. Great Britain was created by an Act of Union in 1707. The legislative union of Great Britain & Ireland was implemented in 1801 and the current name of the country, the United Kingdom of Great Britain & Northern Ireland, was adopted in 1927. In recent years, devolution has seen the creation of a Northern Ireland Assembly, a Welsh Assembly and a Scottish Parliament.

GENERALLY ACCEPTED DATA PROTECTION CONCEPTS & PRINCIPLES

Whatever the national differences, both in Europe and beyond, data protection law is now recognised as revolving around a series of principles relating to the collection, use, retention, safeguarding and disclosure of personal information.

The expression of data protection principles in various international declarations and national laws varies therefore only by degrees. All require that personal information must be:

- Obtained, kept, used, disclosed and transferred fairly and lawfully.
- Kept only for specified and legitimate purposes and not used or disclosed in any manner incompatible with those purposes.
- Adequate, relevant and not excessive in relation to the purposes for which it is kept.
- Accurate and up-to-date.
- Kept securely and destroyed (or wholly anonymised) after its purpose is completed.

They also require identifiable accountability in relation to such information and some effective mechanism for ensuring the enforcement of the principles, in particular meaningful rights for individuals to establish whether information is being kept on them, to access such information and to rectify or erase it (where appropriate). These principles will be discussed in considerable detail in the following chapters, especially as they relate to personal health information. There is also a widespread distinction drawn between information that is regarded as sensitive (for example, health information) and therefore requiring higher standards of protection and other less sensitive information.

Privacy, Confidentiality & Security

Finally, the terms security, confidentiality and privacy are used frequently in a data protection context, sometimes almost interchangeably. But they have distinct meanings and roles that should be understood. The Canadian Federal Privacy Commissioner teased out the difference and relationships between them:

> "I often wish the terms 'security', 'confidentiality', and 'privacy' were not so readily bundled. The problem with always talking about them this way, as a bundle, is that they tend to get used interchangeably. People think that they are talking about privacy, when what they are really talking about is security or confidentiality. That, I want to emphasize, is a mistake. They're entirely separate issues. Privacy is our right to control information about ourselves — including the collection, use, and disclosure of that information. Confidentiality is your obligation to protect someone else's personal information in your care, to maintain its secrecy and not misuse or wrongfully disclose it. And security is the process of assessing and countering the threats and risks to information.
>
> It's privacy that drives the duty of confidentiality and the responsibility for security. If privacy is not respected, ensuring confidentiality and security is not enough. If you collect, use, or disclose information about someone, without their consent, you've violated their privacy. That fact doesn't change just because you ensure confidentiality and security of the information." [136]

In a real sense, data protection encapsulates all these elements into one unified human rights notion, which is perhaps why the Data Protection Commissioner described the Irish data protection legislation in the following way:

> "At the heart of the legislation is an awareness of privacy as a basic human right. A human being is not merely a collection of items of information in a form which can be processed – as the Act defines data. He or she is a unique individual entitled to be valued as such."[137]

---

[136] Radwanski, G. (2001).
[137] Data Protection Commissioner (1998).

4

THE SCOPE OF THE DATA
PROTECTION ACTS 1988 TO 2003

INTRODUCTION

In previous chapters, we explored, nationally and internationally, concepts of, and laws on, privacy. We highlighted how, in recent decades, the notion of data protection has come to the fore in the privacy area, as the information age created new challenges for individuals in terms of exercising control over their personal information.

In that context, we have seen how international privacy and economic considerations have shaped data protection principles globally and how European influences, in particular, have been at the forefront of this process. In particular, the 1981 Council of Europe Convention and the 1995 EU Directive have been significant forces in determining the shape of Irish data protection legislation. Accordingly, to be appreciated properly, the Data Protection Acts 1988 to 2003 must be understood against this global backdrop, which has ensured a broad consistency of data protection law in many countries.

However, the Irish Acts also have uniquely domestic features, too. This chapter sets out the scope of the two statutes. Subsequent chapters then look at specific issues such as obtaining, keeping, securing, using and disclosing personal information, with particular reference to personal health information.

THE LIMITED SCOPE OF THE 1988 ACT

The Data Protection Act 1988 was intended to allow Ireland to ratify the 1981 Council of Europe Data Protection Convention and to facilitate the development of the International Financial Services Centre in Dublin. The goal of ratification still allowed the Government considerable discretion in terms of the scope of its data protection law. Most importantly, the matter of having the data protection principles cover manual, as well as computerised, information was an option. Ultimately, in many ways, the 1988 Act was a minimalist piece of legislation, designed to introduce a floor of rights in relation to computerised personal information only, rather than a wider measure aimed at information privacy generally. This is evident from the comments below, beginning with the opening speech of the Minister for Justice in introducing the Data Protection Bill 1987:

> "In the early seventies large information systems had become computerised to such an extent that fears began to be expressed on an increasing scale about the threat to privacy that they could pose. The fears were not based primarily on the amount of the information stored in the systems. The real basis for the concern was the ease and speed with which computerised information could be collected, re-arranged, transferred and retrieved, and the fact that this information could include sensitive personal information and could be used for all kinds of purposes without the knowledge of the individuals to whom it related. Moreover, the ability to link computerised information systems gave rise to apprehension that the State would be in a position to have virtually instant access to all the information it held separately on each individual and, through file matching, to build up a comprehensive profile on every member of society. There were fears, too, that computerised personal information could more easily be stolen or copied or otherwise obtained improperly by those to whom it should not be disclosed." [138]

---

[138] Dáil Éireann, Second Stage, Vol.375, 17 November 1987.

These concerns about computerised systems were repeated by the Data Protection Commissioner in his initial *Annual Report*. However, he went on to consider the issue of manual processing of personal data and opined that:

> "This threat to individual privacy can also exist where the data are processed manually but to a much lesser extent. In either case, the recorded information may suffer from inaccuracy, irrelevancy, inadequacy and obsolescence. It can be used for a purpose totally foreign to that for which it was collected … and it can be so unprotected as to be accessible to all and sundry… These dangers are multiplied when the personal information is automated …"[139]

The limited nature of the 1988 Act was again referred to by the first Commissioner when he stated:

> "The Act is heavily weighted in favour of data controllers, whether in the public sector or the private sector. This is probably due to the fact that it provides the very minimum standard of data protection that is consistent with ratification of the Convention." [140]

His successor as Commissioner commented that the 1988 Act arose more from a perceived need to ratify the Convention:

> "… than from a strong public demand for data protection legislation prompted by informed debate on the question of computers and privacy".[141]

All of this led McMahon & Binchy, in *Irish Law of Torts*, to comment on the first data protection statute:

> "The introduction of this legislation was attributable to economic and practical considerations rather than the protection of privacy." [142]

---

[139] Data Protection Commissioner (1990), p.3.

[140] Data Protection Commissioner (1993), p.17. He was particularly concerned at the number of exceptions, which he described as "inordinate".

[141] Data Protection Commissioner (1995), p.5.

Clearly the fact that the 1988 Act was limited to electronic information only, and had a considerable number of exclusions and exemptions, meant that the amending statute required to implement the EU Directive would be a significant piece of legislation, rather than a mere add-on to the original Act.

Consultation on the Implementation of the EU Directive

Prior to the introduction of the Bill to give effect to the EU Directive, there was a formal consultation process. Most legislation is the subject of some consultation with interested parties, with the degree of consultation varying depending on the nature of the measure and the sponsoring Department's attitude to the value of public input. In the case of the Directive, the Department of Justice, Equality & Law Reform issued a formal consultation paper on the transposition of the Directive into Irish law. The purpose of the consultation paper was:

> "... to seek views on how best to implement those particular provisions where the Directive gives to Member States flexibility or discretion in their implementation".[143]

THE DATA PROTECTION ACT 2003

The primary purpose of the Data Protection Act 2003 was:

> "... to give effect to the provisions of Directive 95/46/EC of the European Parliament and the Council on the protection of individuals with regard to the processing of personal data and on the free movement of such data".[144]

More specifically, the Minister of State at the Department of Justice, Equality & Law Reform advised the Seanad that the measure was:

> "... designed to bring our domestic data protection law into line with the requirements of the EU directive and to make

---

[142] McMahon & Binchy (1990), p.698.

[143] Department of Justice, Equality & Law Reform (1997), p.6.

[144] Data Protection (Amendment) Bill 2002, Second Stage, Dáil Éireann, Vol.555, 22 October 2002.

certain improvements to existing arrangements in the light of experience gained since 1988. In doing so, it seeks to establish an appropriate balance between the protection of the privacy of data subjects, the public interest and the need to facilitate the international flows of data that are an essential feature of today's information society. Providing protection for personal data in this way will encourage greater support for and participation in efforts to reap the full benefits of the information society, whether by way of e-commerce or e-government." [145]

In brief, the 2003 Act strengthens the privacy rights of individuals, adds to the obligations on data controllers to fairly process personal information, and gives new powers to the Data Protection Commissioner. The single most important change is that it extends the data protection principles to manual files.

The Consultation Paper stated that the reasons for excluding manual information from the scope of the Data Protection Act 1988 were two-fold. First, such information was not regarded as posing a privacy threat comparable to computerised information systems. Second, it was believed that the inclusion of manual information would place a heavy burden on industry and entail very high costs.[146]

Most of the Act's provisions came into effect on 1 July 2003, with the exception of those relating to enforced subject access and new requirements for registration.[147] The full effects of the extension to manual records will not take effect until October 2007. Manual data already held in filing systems need not be brought into conformity with sections 2, 2A and 2B of the Act until 24 October 2007. However,

---

[145] Seanad Éireann, Second Stage, Minister of State at the Department of Justice, Equality & Law Reform.

[146] Department of Justice, Equality & Law Reform (1997), p.9.

[147] Data Protection (Amendment) Act 2003 (Commencement) Order 2003 (S.I. No.207 of 2003) brought the Data Protection (Amendment) Act 2003 into operation with effect from 1 July 2003, except section 5(d), insofar as it inserts subsection (13) of section 4 of the Data Protection Act 1988 (which relates to enforced access in connection with employment), section 16 and section 22 insofar as it repeals the Third Schedule to the Data Protection Act 1988 (which relates to registration of data controllers and data processors).

the right of rectification, erasure or blocking of data that is incomplete, inaccurate or stored in a way that is incompatible with the legitimate purposes pursued by the data controller will apply progressively to such manual data during that period, in particular when a person makes an access request under s.4 of the Act.[148]

Some Key Definitions

In his Review of the first 10 years of data protection legislation in Ireland, the Commissioner stated:

> "The 1988 Act was drafted in general terms, rather than being couched in terms specific to the technology of the time, and this explains how robustly the Act has retained its relevance even as the applications of computer technology have advanced at a remarkable pace." [149]

While this is true, the Act is also a highly technical piece of legislation, with a range of key inter-related definitions determining its scope and application. Many of those definitions remained unchanged with the 2003 statute, although others had to be amended significantly because of the extension of the legislation to manual information systems. All the relevant definitions are set out in section 1 of the Data Protection Acts but the key ones are discussed below, slightly simplified:[150]

Information

In the 1988 Act, "data" meant information in a form in which it could be processed [in an automated fashion]. The 2003 Act defines "data" to mean automated data and manual data. In the case of manual data, it must be recorded in a systematic manner. Further, under s.1(2), for the purposes of the Data Protection Acts, information is inaccurate if it is misleading or incorrect as to any matter of fact.

---

[148] S.36(4) of the Data Protection Acts 1998 to 2003.

[149] Data Protection Commissioner (1999).

[150] Since the definitions are so crucial, there is little to be gained by attempting overly simplistic summaries of them.

Manual Information

Specifically, for manual information to be within the scope of the Act, it must be "recorded as part of a relevant filing system or with the intention that it should form part of a relevant filing system". It must meet *all* of the following four criteria:

♦ The information should be part of a set.

♦ The set should be structured.

♦ The structure should refer to individuals or to criteria relating to individuals.

♦ Specific information relating to a particular individual should be readily accessible.   **GÁLWAY COUNTY LIBRARIES**

The Office of the Data Protection Commissioner has formulated the following recommended tests or guidance to help in determining whether manual data is part of a relevant filing system and therefore subject to the Data Protection Acts 1988 & 2003:

♦ **The personal data must be part of a set** – that is, a regular filing system within a particular organisation, which the organisation maintains for conducting its business. If the organisation maintains different departments in different locations, the data subject should specify the subject matter and the department / office where he or she believes the file / data is located.

♦ **The set must be structured by reference to individuals** – if a file exists with a person's name or ID number on it, this meets the criterion. If the file does not have a name on it, but has sub-divisions with a name or ID, and the file title indicates that it contains personal data – for example, records of sick absences – then this would also meet the criterion.

♦ **The data must be readily accessible** – if files are archived and are not used for decision-making as part of the day-to-day operations of the organisation, and retrieval involves disproportionate effort (or perhaps even substantial cost, where a storage company is used), then the data could be said to be not readily accessible. In such a circumstance, the data subject would need to be able to identify particular data by file reference or date so that, on a reasonable view of things, the data could be said to be readily accessible.

♦ **Such access cannot be simply random but must be according to specific criteria** – the data cannot be located in miscellaneous files. At the same time, the search criteria do not have to meet the standards inherent in a computer system.[151] The more readily accessible the particular information is, the clearer it is that it is, in fact, part of a relevant filing system.

Personal Information

Personal information means any information (including an opinion or comment) about a living individual who is capable of being identified, either from that information or from that information in conjunction with any other information currently in the possession of or likely to come into the possession of the data controller.

Personal Information & Deceased Persons

The definition of personal information does not apply to deceased individuals, but there is no reason why it could not. The EU Directive did not expressly confine itself to living persons.[152] The matter of including deceased individuals within Irish data protection coverage was considered during the course of preparing the Data Protection Act 2003, but apparently there was not significant public interest in doing so.[153] The implications for deceased persons, in terms of their health information, are discussed later in this chapter.

Personal Information & Legal Persons

Personal information relates to a natural person. A "natural person" is a human being, as opposed to an entity recognised by the law as a "legal person", such as a company.[154]

There is no prohibition on giving legal persons the same rights under data protection law as enjoyed by natural persons. However,

---

[151] See note on the *Durant* case at the end of this Chapter.

[152] Article 2(a).

[153] Data Protection Bill 1987, Dáil Éireann, Second Stage, Vol.375, 17 November 1987.

[154] See Interpretation Act 1937 (No.38 of 1937), s.11.

most countries have opted not to extend the scope of their data protection legislation in this way. In 1987, the then Minister for Justice stated:

> "As regards the question of extending possible protection to legal persons ... , it seems to me that there is an essential difference between the privacy interests of natural persons and those of an artificial entity such as a corporation, though I appreciate that corporations too have trade secrecy and confidentiality interests that can be damaged. The exclusion of companies or other bodies is not to be taken as exempting them from the provisions relating to data controllers or processors if they qualify as such." [155]

Disclosure

This means the release of information (by whatever means) to any third party, but does not encompass a communication made directly or indirectly by a data controller or a data processor to an employee or agent for the purposes of enabling that person to carry out their duties. Importantly, where the identification of a data subject depends partly on the information released, and also on other information in the possession of the data controller, the information shall not be regarded as disclosed unless the other information is also released. The provision covers a simultaneous disclosure of the other information and its advance or subsequent disclosure.[156]

Processing

The 1988 Act had defined processing in terms of the performance automatically of logical and or arithmetical operations, which terminology was consistent with the limited coverage of the statute to electronic information systems. However, the EU Directive defined processing in a very broad functional sense, rather than according to technological notions.[157] This broader approach was adopted in the

---

[155] Data Protection Bill 1987, Dáil Éireann, Second Stage, Vol.375, 17 November 1987.

[156] This point was clarified by the Minister for Justice at Committee Stage of the Data Protection Bill 1987, Dáil Éireann, Vol.382, 29 June 1988.

[157] Article 2(b).

2003 Act, which defines "processing" to encompass any of the following:

- Obtaining, recording or keeping the information.
- Collecting, recording, organising, storing, altering or adapting the information.
- Retrieving, consulting or using the information.
- Disclosing the information by transmitting, disseminating or otherwise making it available.
- Aligning, combining, blocking, erasing or destroying the information.

CATEGORIES OF SENSITIVE PERSONAL INFORMATION

In line with the Council of Europe Convention and the EU Directive, Irish data protection legislation recognises that certain categories of personal information require higher standards of protection from those who seek to obtain, hold, use or disclose them. These are the so-called categories of sensitive information. The 1988 Act provided, in section 2(6), that the Minister for Justice, after consultation with any other Minister concerned, could make Regulations for:

> "... the purpose of providing additional safeguards in relation to personal data as to racial origin, political opinions, religious or other beliefs, physical or mental health, sexual life or criminal convictions".[158]

The section 2(6) provision was put into the Data Protection Act 1988, not because it was considered necessary to actually provide a higher standard of protection for sensitive personal information, but rather as a precautionary move against other countries refusing to allow their sensitive information to be sent here. The Minister for Justice explained that it was:

---

[158] Section 2(6). These specified categories matched Article 6 (Special Categories of Data) of the Council of Europe Convention.

> "... prudent to provide for the possibility that additional safeguards could prove to be necessary in regard to those particular kinds of data. It might be, for example, that one of the other parties to the Convention might impose severe restrictions on processing a particular category of health data and might be reluctant to allow the export to this country of that type of data for processing here unless similar safeguards existed in this country ... Accordingly, it seems desirable to provide the authorities here with a reasonable degree of flexibility in reacting to any situations of that kind that might come about in the future, and that is what the amendment sets out to do." [159]

No Regulations were made under that provision, but persons keeping such information are required to register with the Commissioner (see **Chapter 5**).

"Sensitive personal data" is defined in the 2003 Act, similarly to the Directive, to mean personal data as to:

- ◆ The racial or ethnic origin, the political opinions or the religious or philosophical beliefs of the data subject
- ◆ Whether the data subject is a member of a trade-union.[160]
- ◆ The physical or mental health or condition or sexual life of the data subject
- ◆ The commission or alleged commission of any offence by the data subject.
- ◆ Any proceedings for an offence committed or alleged to have been committed by the data subject, the disposal of such proceedings or the sentence of any court in such proceedings.

Sensitive Information & Health

The Data Protection Commissioner has expressed his view on the sensitive nature of personal health information:

---

[159] Data Protection Bill 1987, Dáil Éireann, Committee Stage, Vol.382, 29 June 1988.
[160] Trade union membership data was not specified as sensitive data in the 1988 Act.

"Personal medical data are considered to be highly sensitive, not only for the medical information they may contain, but also because they relate especially to sensitive areas of one's private life."[161]

It should be further recognised that, while all personal health information is sensitive, some is likely to be especially so – for example, information on sexual health – and where such information is held, additional protective safeguards should be put in place, not just as regards security, but also in terms of use and disclosures that stray from what the patient might reasonably expect.

Although personal health information was explicitly identified as sensitive in the 1988 Act, in reality the effect of that Act on the Irish health sector was not overly significant, as at the time of its introduction most medical records were still kept manually. Increasing computerisation across the Irish health system, the extension to manual records introduced by the 2003 Act, together with its additional rights for data subjects and new obligations on data controllers, all ensure that data protection will have a major impact on the management of personal health information in the future.

Personal Health Information

There is no definition of personal health information in the Data Protection Acts. However, a survey of other jurisdictions[162] indicates that it is likely to encompass recorded information (including opinions, assessments and intentions) about a living identifiable individual relating to:

♦ Any aspect of the physical or mental health of the individual, as well as any genetic data or human tissue data that could be predictive of the health of the individual, or his or her relatives or descendants.

---

[161] Data Protection Commissioner (2002), p.41.

[162] Several jurisdictions have data protection legislation dealing solely with health information or the health sector, and they tend to have definitions of personal health information – for example, Personal Health Information Protection Act 2004 (Ontario).

- ◆ The actual, required or intended provision of healthcare to the individual.

- ◆ The individual's express wishes about the future provision of health services to him or her.

- ◆ Payment for healthcare provided to the individual and medical insurance details.

- ◆ Any identification number, symbol or other reference assigned to the individual, intended to assist the provision of healthcare services to the individual or generally.

- ◆ Any other identifying information about the individual that is collected in the course of, or is incidental to, the provision of healthcare, even though (on its own) it may not be obviously health information – this would include such basic information as name, age, sex and other personal information, such as employment and social circumstances.

If health information is kept in such a way that it cannot directly or indirectly be associated with an identifiable individual, it is no longer "personal health information" and the privacy concerns are therefore less significant. However, anonymisation of personal health information is more than simply removing the patient's name.

It is worth pointing out that much personal information has an economic value and that structured personal health information can be extremely valuable, not just to healthcare providers and health agencies but also to a range of businesses, such as pharmaceutical and insurance companies, for marketing and other commercial purposes.

Personal Health Information & Deceased Individuals

While the definition of personal health information applies only to information relating to living and identifiable individuals, that is not to say that lower standards should apply to information held on identifiable deceased persons. In that regard, the Medical Council has stated that:

"... the medical records of a deceased person remain confidential and death does not absolve a doctor from the obligation of confidentiality".[163]

In fact, best practice requires that the same principles of good information management be applied to records of deceased persons as to living individuals.

In Canada, there is an interesting provision in their data protection law, reflecting the particular sensitivity of health information. Section 2(1) of PIPEDA states that "personal health information" is information about "living or deceased" individuals, whilst "personal information" is information about an identifiable individual. Section 3(m) of the Canadian Privacy Act 1980 states that "personal information" does not include information about an individual who has been dead for more than 20 years.

In the USA, the HIPAA privacy regulation protects personal health information of the deceased in the same manner as living individuals, although there are a number of exceptions, including for research.

DATA CONTROLLERS & DATA PROCESSORS

The Data Protection Acts create a framework whereby obligations are imposed on data controllers and data processors and rights are given to data subjects. Therefore, it is essential to be able to identify data controllers and data processors and to distinguish between them.

Data Controllers

The most important question that anyone keeping personal information has to ask is whether they are a data controller within the meaning of the Data Protection Acts. This may involve consulting a legal advisor or, more obviously, seeking the advice of the Data Protection Commissioner. However, in every case, the answer is determined by the application of law and fact. Issues of ownership of information are avoided in Irish data protection law by concentrating

---

[163] Medical Council (2004), p.30.

instead on who *controls* the information. A data controller is defined as a person who, either alone or with others, controls the contents and use of personal information. Consequently, a data controller is:

♦ The **individual** (for example, a GP or other independent healthcare professional) who, or

♦ The **organisation** which

decides, either alone or with others, what personal information is to be collected, kept, used, retained, disclosed or transferred. It is crucial to emphasise that a data controller must have a legal personality. This is particularly relevant in the health service, as a project or service programme cannot be a data controller, unless it has been established with a legal identity of its own. Related to this, the concept of data controller encompasses the organisational entity, for example, it is not the Chief Executive of a health agency or Managing Director of an insurance company who is the data controller but the agency or company itself.

All data controllers must comply with the obligations set out in the Acts on how they collect and use personal information. In addition, some data controllers must register with the Data Protection Commissioner, in order to make their information handling practices more transparent (see **Chapter 5**).

Data Controllers & Appropriate Authority

The Data Protection Acts contain a rather unique provision designed to protect Government Ministers from being affected directly by the requirements and responsibilities of the legislation. Section 1(3) enables the Government, Ministers and any other "appropriate authority"[164] to delegate to a civil servant or civil servants their functions as data controllers or data processors. In addition, it deems civil servants, members of the Defence Forces and members of the Garda Síochána to be employees of their Minister or the civil servant he or she has designated or the Garda Commissioner, as the case may be, for the purposes of the Data Protection Acts. Where a Minister designates a particular civil servant, that civil servant becomes the

---

[164] "Appropriate authority" has the meaning assigned to it by the Civil Service Regulations Acts 1956 to 1958.

(registerable) data controller (or data processor, as applicable) with all the applicable obligations. The justification for this provision was set out by the Minister for Justice as follows:

> "There is no loophole here and no diminution in the liability of the State and Ministers for the wrongful acts of their civil servants. The Bill recognises the reality of the situation and puts responsibility, including liability for criminal proceedings for breaches of various provisions of the Bill, where it should lie, on those who are responsible for running the data systems of Departments. Everyone knows that Ministers have nothing to do with the day-to-day operation of the system. The Bill does that, without taking in any way from the liability of Ministers and the State for the wrongful acts of their civil servants." [165]

It must be admitted that the above extract reveals a misunderstanding of the aims and nature of Irish data protection law, even the limited version introduced by the 1988 Act. It indicates strongly that the Act is primarily about maintaining and running computer systems rather than regulating the fair collection, use, disclosure, etc. of personal information held in an automated format.

In his final *Annual Report*, the first Data Protection Commissioner concluded that the provision allowing for civil servants to be designated as data controllers:

> "… can work only so long as the individuals designated are in fact data controllers (i.e. they actually control the contents and use of the personal data concerned). Since there is a danger that this may not always be the case in reality, the procedure should be looked at again".[166]

It should be pointed out that the effect of designation in no way diminishes the right of any individual under the law of tort, as extended by section 7 of the Data Protection Acts, to relief for any damage he or she may suffer as a result of non-compliance with the data protection

---

[165] Data Protection Bill 1987, Dáil Éireann, Committee Stage, Vol.382, 29 June 1988.
[166] Data Protection Commissioner (1993), p.16.

principles by a designated civil servant or any of his or her subordinate civil servants. This is because the State is liable for wrongs committed by civil servants in the course of their duty, and that still applies to any wrong committed by a designated civil servant because his or her relationship to the Minister is not changed in any way.

DATA CONTROLLERS & PERSONAL HEALTH INFORMATION

Given its wide-ranging nature, personal health information is collected, recorded and used in a variety of situations and by numerous types of data controllers. A health agency may collect it from applicants to establish eligibility or suitability for particular services. Hospitals obtain and keep information on admissions, treatments, discharges and so forth. Similarly, healthcare professionals, like GPs, opticians, dentists, etc., also keep relevant client health records. For risk assessment reasons, an insurance company may require that an applicant for a policy undertake a medical examination. For other reasons, a school or college legitimately may record certain health information on its students.

In practice, most organisations invariably keep some health information on their employees. It was recognition of that fact that led in the 1988 Act to the exemption from registration (imposed on data controllers keeping sensitive personal information) for data controllers holding personal health information, where such information was held for normal personnel purposes only and not released for any other purpose.

For the most part, an individual or other entity (keeping personal information) will recognise and accept that he, she or it is the data controller in relation to any such information. In other cases, this may not be so straightforward because of genuine confusion over who really controls the contents and use of the information. Further, in a small number of instances, an organisation may be arguing against accepting responsibility because it suits its business interests to do so. Given the issues involved, it is worthwhile teasing out a range of possibilities that have particular relevance to keepers of health information.

Some Scenarios

If an individual makes an appointment with a private psychologist operating from his or her own premises, then the psychologist is very clearly the data controller in terms of the information recorded on the patient. Alternatively, if the individual is in hospital and is seen by a psychologist who is an employee of the hospital, then it is the hospital who is the data controller. Similarly, where a person is admitted to hospital for an operation, then the hospital is the data controller in relation to any information it chooses to record on him or her. If that person is a private hospital patient, then his or her medical consultant will be the data controller in relation to the information that he or she keeps on the patient. If the patient is a public one, then the hospital rather than the medical consultant will be the data controller in relation to any information recorded by the consultant on the patient, because the hospital (as employer), rather than the consultant (as employee), will determine formally the use to which the information may be put. However, if the hospital allows the consultant to use that information for any purpose not connected with the consultant's employment with the hospital, then the consultant, in addition to the hospital, will be a relevant data controller in relation to that information. Moreover, if a consultant who is employed by the hospital uses a hospital's computer system for recording information on his or her private patients, then the hospital will be a data processor in respect of that information (since it is providing data processing facilities for a person who is not, in that context, acting in the course of his or her employee duties).

In the primary care field, if a person attends a single-handed general practice or dental practice, then the doctor or dentist is the data controller, irrespective of whether the patient visits in a private or public capacity. Where the person attends a multi-disciplinary primary care centre, or visits a GP practice, then it is likely to be the centre or the practice that is the data controller providing (a) that it has some distinct legal existence and (b) that the practice or centre is actually organised in a way that its activities are managed as a collective entity. Otherwise, each of the persons in the primary care centre or the partnership practice who is not an employee will be individually and collectively responsible as data controllers. (See later for data controller and partnerships.)

For business and other organisations, where medical reports, etc. on potential or actual employees or clients are kept separately by a medical practitioner on behalf of a company and not made available to the latter for processing, then the company cannot be the data controller in relation to such records as it does not control them. However, once the medical practitioner releases any information to the organisation and the latter records it, then the organisation becomes a data controller in relation to such information. Moreover, if the organisation (without actually physically holding the information) can materially direct the medical practitioner to keep, use, disclose or secure such information then it becomes a data controller, *in addition* to the medical practitioner, in terms of that information. Taking this a step further, if the organisation makes *all* the decisions in relation to the information concerned, the medical practitioner will be a data processor, since they have no control over the information. However, it would be a rare situation where a healthcare professional had absolutely no control over the contents and use of information in his or her possession.

Insurance Companies

In another scenario, an insurance company might request an individual to undergo a medical examination, prior to acceptance for a policy, or where the individual has made a claim on foot of a policy. The examination is carried out by a clinician on behalf of the company. If the clinician releases the entire report or a summary of findings to the company and it records them, then the insurance company becomes a data controller for that information. If the clinician retains a copy for his or her medico-legal or other purposes, he or she is also a data controller. Where the amount of information kept by the clinician, as well as any uses to which it may be put, is determined solely by the insurance company, then the clinician is simply a data processor for that information (on the basis that he or she does not exercise control over contents and use).

Public Patients

In one of the examples above, the point was made that the GP was the data controller, irrespective of whether the patient was attending in a private or public capacity. About 30% of people in Ireland are covered by medical cards under the General Medical Services Scheme, previously operated by Health Boards but now by the Health Service Executive. This entitles them, among other benefits, to free GP services. The GPs providing the services are independent contractors, operating under contracts for services rather than contracts of employment. Under freedom of information law (see **Chapter 13**), the medical records of public patients are considered to fall within the scope of FOI. This is because section 6(9) of the Freedom of Information Acts 1997 to 2003, which deals with rights of access to public records, specifically provides:

> (9) A record in the possession of a person who is or was providing a service for a public body under a contract for services shall, if and in so far as it relates to the service, be deemed for the purposes of this Act to be held by the body, and there shall be deemed to be included in the contract a provision that the person shall, if so requested for the purposes of this Act, give the record to the body for retention by it for such period as is reasonable in the particular circumstances.

Without the subsection, such records would not have been covered. No equivalent provision is found in the Data Protection Acts. Consequently, the issue of who is the data controller for the personal health information of public patients is resolved simply by establishing who controls the contents and use of such information. In taking this approach, it is critical to grasp a fundamental differentiation between determinations made by the HSE on the nature and scope of the healthcare services to be provided by healthcare professionals and individual decisions taken by a practising GP on what information he or she believes should be collected, kept, used and disclosed for the proper care of his or her patients.

Under the GMS Scheme contract, doctors are required to keep adequate clinical records but this is not elaborated in any way.[167] If the

---

[167] For the most part, the contract deals with attendance records and what should happen to patient records in the event of a doctor dying, retiring or leaving the GMS Scheme or a patient deciding to transfer to another doctor. (See the Department of Health-issued Circular 13 of 1972, which introduced the GMS

HSE was in a position, under the contract or otherwise, to actually require GPs to process (as defined in the Data Protection Acts) information, then it (the HSE) would be the data controller (as well, perhaps, as the GP). That is not the position, so the HSE is not the data controller. Moreover, even if the HSE could direct GPs (or any other healthcare professionals), *under the contract,* in such a manner, there would still remain the legal principle of confidentiality between the healthcare professional and the patient which the contract could not override. This would make it effectively impossible for the HSE to be a data controller in relation to such information (unless, of course, legislation provided otherwise).

Some of the above may appear at variance with the position outlined in Case Study 4 of the 2003 *Annual Report* of the Data Protection Commissioner where it is stated that the case:

> "... highlights the important distinction between a data controller in respect of public patients (which is the Health Board or hospital or health centre as the case may be) and private patients (where it is the relevant health professional)".[168]

However, the central issue in that case appears to relate to the position surrounding the transfer of patient records when a doctor is replaced and the issue of obtaining the actual rather than copy records.

Clinical Records Provisions under the GMS Scheme

For completeness, the relevant paragraphs on clinical records in the 1989 GMS Scheme contract are set out below:

CLINICAL RECORDS

22. The medical practitioner shall keep adequate clinical records and shall in relation to such records observe article 5

Scheme fee per item contract, in particular, paragraphs 13 of the agreement and paragraphs 18 and 19 of the appended contract. The 1989 capitation contract, as introduced, is set out in Circular 1 of 1989 and the relevant paragraphs are 9 of the agreement and 22 and 24 of the schedule to the agreement.)

[168] Data Protection Commissioner (2004).

of the Health Services Regulations 1971 (S.I. 105 of 1971) as if they were records kept in accordance with those regulations.

23. When a person on the medical practitioner's list is transferred to the list of another medical practitioner providing services under Section 58 of the Health Act 1970, the former medical practitioner shall, subject to the written consent of the person (or in the case of a child, his parent) give to the second medical practitioner a summary of the medical history and condition of the patient.

On the death of a participating medical practitioner, the health board should arrange through the Director of Community Care and Medical Officer of Health for the transfer of the records of his GMS patients to the doctor providing services for these patients. Where it is necessary to take custody of the records this should be done by the appropriate Director of Community Care and Medical Officer of Health. Where a participating medical practitioner retires or resigns from the GMS scheme, the health board should inform each patient, when notifying him of the name of the new doctor, that the records are being transferred to this doctor. The patient should be notified that if he does not agree to the transfer of his records he should indicate this to the health board within 14 days of the notification. Records deposited with the Director of Community Care and Medical Officer of Health may be destroyed after a reasonable time.

One final note: at any time that the HSE or other health agency or person takes custody or possession of any medical records (for example, in the situations envisaged in paragraph 23 above), it becomes a data controller for those records.

Data Controllers & Partnerships

Irish healthcare service providers come in various legal forms. For example, in the general practice sector, many GPs are organised into partnerships. Accordingly, the matter of partnerships within the definition of data controllers is important. It was specifically addressed in the Dáil debates on the then Data Protection Bill 1987. The Minister for Justice stated that:

> "... any partner who controls personal data either alone or with other partners will be a data controller. That will be a matter of fact in each case. So far as partners who may have to register are concerned, there is provision under section 20 for regulations to prescribe such matters and procedure as the particulars to be included in entries in the register, and also any other matters that may be necessary or expedient for the purposes of enabling the registration provisions to have full effect. This will give an appreciable degree of flexibility which will deal with any difficulty in relation to the registration of partnerships. I would envisage that a partnership would in effect be registered as such in the sense that partners who had control over the personal data concerned would be registered as data controllers. In virtually all cases that would have to include all the partners." [169]

Therefore, in terms of a GP partnership or group practice or a multi-disciplinary primary care centre, the registerable data controller would be the practice or the centre where the practice or centre operates as a single functional unit for the purposes of patient care and practice management. The practice or centre should have a single privacy policy and one nominated person within the practice who is responsible for overseeing the implementation and effective operation of the privacy policy. General practitioners (and other independent healthcare providers) who work within practices that do not meet these criteria might have to register individually.

Data Protection, the Media & Personal Health Information

In line with the EU Directive, Irish data protection legislation provides exemptions from its provisions where the processing of personal data is carried out solely for journalistic purposes or for the purpose of artistic or literary expression. However, this exemption only applies

---

[169]   Data Protection Bill 1987, Dáil Éireann, Vol.382, 29 June 1988.

when the public interest in freedom of expression is considered to outweigh the right to privacy, to the extent that publication would be considered to be in the public interest. Data protection law therefore recognises the important role of the media, but the public interest test requires the media to act responsibly when considering publication. Clearly, this is relevant when the media is reporting health details of pregnant celebrities, hospitalised politicians or even members of the public who may have been injured in an attack, etc. The area is likely to be especially problematic where the individuals concerned or their families do not want the information to be released publicly.

Recognising the sensitive nature of this area, in his *Annual Report* for 2003, the Data Protection Commissioner stated that he would consider:

> "... over the next 18 months whether a specific data protection code of practice – to have legal effect – is needed [in this area]. Such a code would only come about after consultation not alone with media interests but with the general public so as to ensure that it is both balanced and proportionate."[170]

DATA PROCESSORS

Identifying a Data Processor

If a person keeps or otherwise processes personal information on behalf of someone else, and does not exercise responsibility for, or control over, the information, then such a person is a "data processor", while the other person is the data controller. A data processor is distinct from the data controller for whom they are processing the personal data. An employee of a data controller, or a section or unit within a hospital, pharmacy, etc., which is processing personal data for the entity as a whole, is not a "data processor". However, someone who is not employed by the data controller, but is contracted to provide a particular data processing service (such as payroll) would be a data processor.

---

[170] Data Protection Commissioner (2004).

Unlike data controllers, data processors have a very limited set of responsibilities under the Data Protection Acts. These responsibilities concern the necessity to keep personal data secure from unauthorised access, disclosure, destruction or accidental loss. In addition, under section 16(1) of the Data Protection Act 1988, all data processors "whose business consists wholly or partly in processing personal data on behalf of data controllers" are required to register with the Data Protection Commissioner.

Reading the Oireachtas debates on the Data Protection Bill 1987, it is clear that the term "data processor" was intended to catch professional computer bureaux. For example, in the Seanad, the Minister for Justice said "data processors – these are people who are in the business of processing data on behalf of data controllers".[171] Given that intention, it is interesting to reflect on whether the new – and much wider – definition of processing in the 2003 Act might have unconsidered implications for persons handling personal information for another party.

Data Processing & Electronic Communications

The National Healthlink Project[172] is the biggest General Practice to Hospital Electronic Messaging Project in the State. It allows for the secure transfer of clinical patient information (such as laboratory and radiology results) *via* the Internet, and is available for use by health agencies, hospitals and GPs. As the project deals with the transfer of confidential patient data, Healthlink sought the advice of the Data Protection Commissioner as to how best to meet its obligations. The result was the preparation of a legally binding agreement between the participating data controllers (GPs) and the data processor (Healthlink). In terms of ensuring information security, Healthlink uses a secure infrastructure to safeguard the delivery of electronic clinical patient information. Regular security audits are also carried out.

---

[171] Data Protection Bill 1987, Seanad Éireann, Second Stage, Vol.120, 6 July 1988. See also Dáil Éireann, Second Stage, Vol.375, 17 November 1987.

[172] http://www.healthlink.ie.

Data Controllers & Data Processors: Duty of Care

Section 7 of the Data Protection Acts impose on data controllers and data processors a duty of care to individuals in respect of whom they process personal data, that is, to the extent that the law of torts does not already impose such a duty (for example, where it may not have been possible to establish a sufficient relationship between a data processor and the individual concerned so as to give rise to a duty of care). As a result of section 7, any damage resulting from a breach of the relevant provisions of the Acts could make the controller or processor liable in negligence, breach of confidence, defamation or breach of contract.

More than one data controller & data processor

It should be clear from all of the above that, in relation to any set of information, there may be more than one data controller. Equally, in relation to particular sets of personal information, it is possible for a person to be both a data controller and a data processor. This is determined by the person's relationship with other parties in respect of such information and the person's own level of control over the content and use of the information.

GENETIC DATA

Advances in medical technologies have given rise to new data protection concerns in relation to the significance and impact of genetic tests and the processing of genetic data. The protection of genetic data can be considered nowadays to be a prerequisite in order to ensure respect for the equality principle, as well as to make the right to health a reality. Most recently-published international instruments actually prohibit any discrimination based on genetic data. Under Article 21 of the Charter of Fundamental Rights of the EU, "any discrimination based (...) on genetic features" shall be prohibited. This prohibition can also be found in the Council of Europe's Convention on Human Rights & Bio-Medicine (Article 11) and UNESCO's Universal Declaration on Human Genome & Human Rights (Article 6). The effectiveness of these provisions is directly related to the existence of strict rules limiting the opportunities for using genetic data. Indeed, the protection of the right to health is conditional upon the assurance that no genetic data may be known to third parties, who might use it to discriminate against and / or stigmatise the data subject.

Definitions and Characteristics of Genetic Data

National and international definitions of genetic data include:

♦ All data of whatever type concerning the hereditary characteristics of an individual or concerning the pattern of inheritance of such characteristics within a related group of individuals. (*Council of Europe Recommendation N°R(97)5*).

♦ Any data concerning the hereditary characteristics of an individual or group of related individuals. (*Article 2 (g) of the 2 August 2002 law of Luxembourg on the protection of persons with regard to the processing of personal data*).

♦ Non-obvious information about heritable characteristics of individuals obtained by analysis of nucleic acids or by other scientific analysis. (*International Declaration on Human Genetic Data, UNESCO*).

Genetics & Privacy

The matter of genetic testing has received some attention in Ireland. The relevant provisions of the recently-enacted Disability Act 2005 are discussed later in this Chapter, while medical research-related reports are considered in **Chapter 10**. On the non-medical purpose front, the Law Reform Commission issued, in March 20004, a Consultation Paper on the Establishment of a National DNA Database. The Commission had been asked to consider the matter with particular regard to the complex Constitutional and human rights issues involved. It recommended that any such database that might be established should be used, subject to various safeguards, only for crime investigation purposes and the identification of deceased and severely-injured persons.

European Union

The independent advisory Working Party set up under Article 29 of the EU Data Protection Directive produced a *Working Document on*

Genetic Data,[173] which outlines the privacy issues and implications arising from genetic testing and the processing of genetic data.

The Working Party also considered the extent to which genetic data is protected by the EU Data Protection Directive and felt that there was no doubt that genetic data is personal data under Article 2[174] of the Directive, and also falls within Article 8 dealing with sensitive data, as they may reveal information on the health status or ethnic origins of the individual or individuals concerned. Further, under Article 6, personal data must be collected for specified, explicit and legitimate purposes, and not further processed in a way incompatible with those purposes (the "finality principle"). In addition, personal data must be adequate, relevant and not excessive in relation to the purposes for which they are collected and further processed (the "proportionality principle"). Considering the complexity and the sensitivity of genetic information, there is a great risk of misuse and / or re-use for various purposes by the data controller or third parties. Genetic data may only be used if adequate, relevant and not excessive. This implies a strict assessment of the necessity and proportionality of the processed data.[175]

Further, under Article 10 of the Directive, the data subject has a right to receive information from the data controller (or his or her representative) when the data is collected directly from him or her. Under Article 11, the data subject also has a right to receive information from the controller (or his or her representative) when the data has not been obtained from him or her.

Given the sensitivity of genetic data, the right to information is particularly relevant in the context of the processing of such data. In

---

[173] Article 29 Working Party (2004).

[174] Article 2(a) defines personal data as meaning "any information relating to an identifiable natural person (data subject); an identifiable person is one who can be identified, directly or indirectly, in particular by reference to an identification number or to one or more factors specific to his physical, physiological, mental, economic, cultural or social identity".

[175] For example, the Spanish Data Protection Authority deemed that the creation of a file of genetic samples to identify newborns through DNA testing was not in order. The aim of such files would be to prevent mother-infant mismatches. The Spanish DPA took the view that the creation of a genetic file would contravene the principle of proportionality, since the same result could be reliably obtained with other means.

cases where the exemption provided for under Article 8.3[176] is applicable, the health professional might be confronted with the following dilemma: on the one hand, he or she could be bound by the obligation of secrecy, while, on the other hand, he could be obliged under Article 11 to provide information to the data subject (for example, where information is extracted from genetic material received from relatives).

All the data protection commissioners in the European Union have adopted the *Working Document on Genetic Data,* which sets out their collective view on how an individual's genetic privacy should be enhanced. The Working Party states that genetic data should be classified as an item of sensitive personal data, so that it gains additional privacy protection under the European Union's Data Protection Directive. This status is only achieved under current data protection law when genetic personal data is processed in a health- or criminal-related context.

USA

The EU Working Group refers to the USA, where there have been many cases in which individuals have decided not to undergo genetic tests – although they were necessary to protect their health – because they feared that the findings might come to be known by their employers and insurance companies. The resulting lively public debate led to the Genetic Information Non-discrimination Act 2005, section 2 (5) of which stressed that:

> "Federal legislation establishing a national and uniform basic standard is necessary to fully protect the public from discrimination and allay their concerns about the potential for discrimination, thereby allowing individuals to take advantage of genetic testing technology, research, and new therapies."

---

[176] The Article 8(3) exemption relates to processing of personal information for medical purposes by medical professionals (or equivalent persons) and is found in section 2B(1)(b)(viii) of the Data Protection Acts 1988 to 2003.

Based on this assumption, the Act lays down very strict rules under which genetic information may *not* be used by either employers or insurance companies.

Australia

In Australia, the Australian Government established a joint inquiry by the Australian Law Reform Commission and the Australian Health Ethics Committee, to look into the protection of genetic information and samples. The terms of reference required these bodies to examine what regulation may be needed to protect the privacy of human genetic samples and information. In addition to looking at the strict regulatory position, the inquiry also took into account the ethical considerations involved in the collection and uses of human genetic samples and information. The joint inquiry reported[177] in May 2003, making 144 recommendations, which it stated reflected the complex nature of genetic privacy.

Among other things, the report recommended that the concept of personal information and records in the Privacy Act be extended to include bodily samples. It was further recommended that individuals be given right of access to their own samples and to those of their first degree genetic relatives. Another key recommendation was that "health information" under the Privacy Act should include information about an individual who has been dead for 30 years or less – at present, the Privacy Act applies only to the living.

Iceland

In Iceland, in 2000, the government granted an exclusive license to a private commercial company to create and manage a central database of the entire country's medical records, so researchers could cross-reference that data with genetic and genealogical information.[178] The matter, particularly its commercial dimension, generated considerable

---

[177] The Australian Government is in the process of developing its response to the report, which is available on the Australian Law Reform Commission's website.

[178] The company concerned, deCode Genetics, was registered in the USA and based in Iceland. In 2000, it was granted the licence to construct the Icelandic Health Science Database, following approval of the Health Sector Database Act by the Icelandic Parliament on 17 December 1998.

controversy in Iceland and attracted international attention. In April 1999, the World Medical Association supported the Icelandic Medical Association's opposition to the database on privacy and related grounds[179] and adopted in 2002 a *Declaration on Health Databases* that protects patients' interests with regard to the creation of central health databases. At their annual meeting, in September 1998, the European Data Protection Commissioners recommended that the Icelandic authorities reconsider the project in light of the fundamental principles laid down in the European Convention for the Protection of Human Rights & Fundamental Freedoms, the Council of Europe Convention for the Protection of Individuals with Regard to Automatic Processing of Personal Data and its Recommendation (97)5 on Medical Data, and the EU Data Protection Directive.[180] In 2003, the Icelandic Supreme Court ruled that the law creating the database did not comply with the country's privacy protections.[181] (The Court cited Article 71 of the Icelandic Constitution: "Everyone shall enjoy the privacy of his or her life, home and family.").

Council of Europe

To date, the only legally-binding international instrument is the Convention on Human Rights & Biomedicine, adopted in 1997 in Oviedo.[182] The Convention bans all forms of discrimination based on the grounds of a person's genetic profile and allows the carrying out of predictive genetic tests only for medical purposes. To date, Ireland is not a signatory to the Convention.

Disability Act 2005 & Genetic Testing

An EU survey of Member States' national legislation and activities in the field of genetic testing was published in May 2005.[183] In replying

---

[179] "World Medical Association Opposes Icelandic Gene Database", *EBMJ*, April 24, 1999.

[180] International Conference of Privacy & Data Protection Commissioners (Spain) (1998).

[181] Ragnhildur Gudmundsdottir v. Iceland Supreme Court, 27 November 2003.

[182] The Convention is available at http://conventions.coe.int/Treaty/EN/Treaties/html/164.htm.

[183] Matthiessen-Guyader (2005).

on behalf of Ireland, the Irish Council for Bioethics[184] acknowledged that:

> "There has not been a wide-ranging public debate on genetic testing in Ireland as yet. The Council have talked about this issue, on occasions, in relation to genetic testing and insurance and employment in interviews with the print media and also on radio. However, this has been in the context of raising awareness of bioethical issues in the general sense."

In several respects, the situation had already moved on significantly from the time the survey was undertaken a few months earlier. This will be evident in **Chapter 10**, where recent studies published by the Health Research Board and the Irish Council for Bioethics are considered.

In addition, on the legislative front, the Disability Act 2005, in Part 4, has introduced a series of provisions dealing with genetic data and testing. The legislation establishes safeguards for the use of genetic data, generally, and set out specific provisions for its use in relation to employment and insurance purposes.

Section 41 of the Act defines "genetic data" and "genetic testing" as follows:

- ♦ "Genetic data" means data relating to a living person derived from genetic testing of the person;

- ♦ "Genetic testing" means the examination of samples taken from a living person for the purpose of analysing the person's deoxyribonucleic or ribonucleic acid by means of chromosomal analysis or by any other means for the purpose of:

  - ◊ confirming the identity or nature of an existing symptomatic disease.

---

[184] The Irish Council for Bioethics was established in 2002 as an independent, autonomous body to consider the ethical issues raised by recent developments in science and medicine. The Council is funded by a grant from Ireland's National Policy & Advisory Board for Enterprise, Trade, Science, Technology & Innovation (Forfás).

◊ ascertaining whether the person has a genetic predisposition or susceptibility to a disease

◊ identifying the carrier of a disease.

Section 42 provides that genetic testing shall not be carried out on an individual unless:

♦ The testing is not prohibited by law.

♦ The consent of the person to the processing of any genetic data to be derived from the testing has been obtained in accordance with the Data Protection Acts.

A person is prohibited from engaging in the processing[185] of genetic data in relation to:

♦ The employment of a person, except in accordance with the provisions of section 12A (Prior Checking of Processing by Commissioner) of the Data Protection Acts.

♦ A policy of insurance or life assurance.

♦ A policy of health insurance or health-related insurance.

♦ An occupational pension, a retirement annuity contract or any other pension arrangement.

♦ The mortgaging of property.

It is further provided that a person must not process genetic data, unless all reasonable steps have been taken to provide the data subject with all appropriate information concerning:

♦ The purpose and possible outcomes of the proposed processing.

♦ Any potential implications for the health of the data subject that may become known as a result of the processing.

It is an offence under section 31 of the Data Protection Acts to contravene either of the above two provisions.

Section 43 provides that, as regards family histories, information about the family history of an applicant for insurance shall be processed in accordance with statutory regulations (if any) as may be

---

[185] "Processing" has the meaning assigned to it by the Data Protection Acts.

made by the Minister for Justice, Equality & Law Reform under section 2B(1)(b)(xi) of the Data Protection Acts.[186] Before making such regulations, the Minister is required to consult with specified relevant persons, including the Data Protection Commissioner, and may consult with any other party he or she considers appropriate.

Section 44 obliges the Minister to initiate, not later than 1 January 2014, a review of the operation of Part 4 of the Disability Act, while section 45 makes it clear that nothing in that Part of the Act shall be construed as:

♦ Authorising the processing of personal data contrary to the provisions of the Data Protection Acts.

♦ Prohibiting the taking and using, in accordance with law, of bodily samples for the purpose of forensic testing or analysis in connection with the investigation of an offence, or for any other purpose not prohibited by law, by or on behalf of the Gardaí or the processing by them of genetic data (if any) derived from such testing or analysis.

THE *DURANT* CASE

In England & Wales, in the case of *Durant v Financial Services Authority*,[187] the Court of Appeal considered a number of points of law concerning the right of access to personal information under their Data Protection Acts (which, like ours, give effect to the EU Data Protection Directive). Two of the more important issues related to:

♦ What makes "data" "personal" within the meaning of "personal data"?

♦ What is meant by a "relevant filing system"?

---

[186] Section 2B sets out the conditions associated with the processing of sensitive personal information. Subsection (1)(b)(xi) allows the Minister for Justice, Equality & Law Reform to make regulations authorising processing of such information for reasons of substantial public interest.

[187] *Michael John Durant v Financial Services Authority* [2003] EWCA Civ.1746, Court of Appeal (Civil Division) decision of Lord Justices Auld, Mummery and Buxton dated 8 December 2003. A full text of the judgment is available from the Court Service website at www.courtservice.gov.uk.

What is personal data?

The Court of Appeal concluded that data will relate to an individual if it:

> "... is information that affects [an individual's] privacy, whether in his personal or family life, business or professional capacity".

This suggests that, in cases where it is not clear whether information relates to an individual, it is necessary to consider whether the information in question is capable of having an adverse impact on the individual concerned.

The Court then identified two notions that may assist in determining whether information "is information that affects [an individual's] privacy" and, therefore, "relates to" an individual. The first is whether the information is biographical in a significant sense: that is, going beyond the recording of the individual's involvement in a matter or an event that has no personal connotations. The second is that the information should have the individual as its focus rather than some other person or persons with whom he or she may have been involved or some transaction or event in which he or she may have figured or have had an interest.

To date, this issue of "relates to" has not arisen for judicial consideration under Irish data protection law. However, it has been considered by the High Court under the Freedom of Information Act 1997 in the case of *EH v The Information Commissioner*.[188]

What is meant by a "relevant filing system"?

On manual files encompassed by their Data Protection Acts, the Court of Appeal in *Durant* restrictively interpreted the meaning of "relevant filing system". It held that whether personal information in a manual filing system falls within the scope of the Acts depends not upon:

> "... whether the information could be obtained or even whether the information could be obtained easily. The question ... is whether it is structured in such a way that

---

[188] High Court, 21 December 2001. See also **Chapter 13**.

specific information relating to a particular individual is readily accessible."

In coming to this finding, the Court apparently was concerned about the burden of the data protection regime for business. In short, it would seem that data protection rules would apply to manual records only if they are of sufficient sophistication to provide the same or similar ready accessibility as a computerised filing system. That requires a filing system so referenced or indexed that a person looking for personal information is able:

> "... to identify at the outset of his or her search with reasonable certainty and speed the file or files in which the specific data relating to the person requesting the information is located and to locate the relevant information about him or her within the file or files, without having to make a manual search of them."[189]

Given that restrictive interpretation, it will be interesting to see whether the Irish Courts go the same way if the matter comes up for judicial determination.

---

[189] *per* Auld L.J. transcript, p.21.

5
REGISTRATION & ENFORCEMENT

INTRODUCTION

Introducing legislation conferring rights on individuals and imposing obligations on others is laudable in itself but unlikely to work, unless there is some mechanism that can give tangible effect to the rights and, at the same time, require compliance with the obligations. This was certainly the view of the Irish Government. In the Dáil, in 1987, the then Minister for Justice explained:

> "... as a practical matter, it is difficult to see how any legislation can be fully effective unless there is some form of supervisory authority with power to see that its provisions are complied with and, where they are not, to take remedial action. In most of the countries concerned, the supervising authority is independent of both the public and the private sector."[190]

Consequently, the 1988 Act set up the Office of the Data Protection Commissioner.[191] While such a body was not specifically required by the 1981 Council of Europe Convention, it pre-empted the EU Directive on Data Protection, which expressly requires a supervisory authority. As well as enforcement powers, the Commissioner's Office maintains a public register of certain data controllers and data processors. The registration system is important, not just in terms of openness but because it also creates a series of offences.

---

[190] Data Protection Bill, 1987, Dáil Éireann, Second Stage, Vol.555, 17 November 1987.

[191] Sections 9 to 15 of the Data Protection Acts deal with the establishment of the Office and the powers of the Commissioner.

REGISTRATION

When the Irish Government introduced the Data Protection Bill 1987, it had the advantage of being able to consider data protection laws already in force in other European countries. In particular, it was anxious to ensure that the system of control over data controllers and data processors should not be unduly onerous, especially as regards the need to register with the Data Protection Commissioner.[192] Accordingly, the approach adopted in Ireland in 1988 was two-tier, requiring only certain categories of data controllers (and all professional data processors) to register.[193]

Purpose of Registration

In his first *Annual Report*, the Data Protection Commissioner stated:

> "The essence of data protection is transparency. Those who keep personal data have to be open about it. They must be ready to acknowledge the fact that they keep such data, to state the nature of the data, and the purpose or purposes for which they keep them. One of the best ways of displaying openness is by means of a public register of those who keep and process personal data." [194]

---

[192] The first countries to introduce legislation – for example, Sweden and Norway – had required a licence from the controlling authority before anyone could establish a personal data register or file. In other countries (for example, the United Kingdom), universal registration was the norm, with a simplified version for small businesses or other activities that did not constitute any serious danger to individual privacy. By 1987, an even less rigid approach was emerging: the trend was towards a two-tier system, characterised by a requirement of registration for large-scale controllers and processors and others whose activities are more likely to give rise to concern and a simpler system of a self-regulatory kind for those whose keeping and use of personal data is limited in scope and poses no threat.

[193] The 1988 Act did not exclude the possibility of extending substantially the categories of data controllers required to register or, indeed, even the possibility of having universal registration but, in the event, this did not happen.

[194] Data Protection Commissioner (1990), p.2. He also described the Act as a "second generation" data protection law, because it combined a system of selective registration and self-regulation.

However, in his *Annual Report* for 1994, the Commissioner stated that he was "disappointed by the limited use of [the Register] made by the public".[195] One of the inevitable challenges that a registration system faces is achieving a meaningful balance between being a useful information resource to the public, on the one hand, and not being unduly bureaucratic for data controllers, on the other.[196]

Registration & the 2003 Act

The Data Protection Act 2003 essentially reversed the previous selective registration system by requiring almost every data controller to register, unless exempted under Regulations made by the Minister.[197] It seemed to envisage that Regulations would be drafted that would exclude as many "low risk" data controllers as possible – for example, small corner shops, small businesses that keep only payroll data about their staff – while ensuring that all significant data controllers became subject to the new registration requirement.

The rationale for these changes was outlined, in the Dáil, by the Minister for State at the Department of Justice, Equality & Law Reform:

> "This Bill proposes to replace [the existing registration categories] by providing for the registration of all data controllers and processors except those specifically excluded. Some of the excluded categories are already specified but there is also provision for the exclusion of prescribed categories. Prescribed in this context means prescribed by regulations made by the Commissioner with the consent of the Minister.
>
> As the directive contains some flexibility regarding registration, and since registration could be seen as involving an additional burden on small scale data controllers and processors, where there is no obvious risk to fundamental rights and freedoms, I intend to seek the views of interested

---

[195] Data Protection Commissioner (1995), p.17.

[196] See Data Protection Commissioner (1997), where he reflects on reform of the registration process.

[197] Section 16(1) of the Data Protection Acts 1988 to 2003. The new section 16(1) introduced by the Data Protection Act 2003 is not yet in operation.

and relevant parties regarding future registration obligations. I propose, therefore, that the registration requirements will be specified in regulations made by the Minister after consultation with the Commissioner rather than by the Commissioner with the consent of the Minister. The proposed change is largely one of form rather than substance but it is a recognition that registration is a policy issue and not just a technical matter."[198]

Another change in the 2003 Act is that data controllers, who hold personal data for two or more unrelated purposes, will have to make separate applications for registration for each such purpose.[199] Previously, data controllers had the option of listing many purposes on a single registration application.

The Data Protection Acts provide that a considerable amount of the detail relating to the registration process can be set out in Regulations. This avoids the primary legislation becoming overly detailed, as well as allowing greater flexibility in terms of changing the registration requirements as the need arises.

Registerable Persons

Subject to the commencement of the new section 16(1), the categories of data controllers and data processors required to register are:

- ♦ Data controllers who are:
  - ◊ Public authorities and certain other public bodies.[200]
  - ◊ Financial institutions.
  - ◊ Insurance companies.
- ♦ Data controllers whose business consists wholly or mainly in direct marketing, providing credit references or collecting debts.
- ♦ Data controllers who keep personal data belonging to any of the sensitive categories.[201] However, persons keeping information

---

[198] Data Protection (Amendment) Bill 2002, Select Committee on Justice, Equality, Defence & Women's Rights, 12 February 2003.

[199] Section 17(1)(c) of the Data Protection Acts 1988 to 2003.

[200] These bodies are set out in detail in Third Schedule to the Act.

[201] Outlined in **Chapter 4**.

relating to physical or mental health are not required to register, where such information is reasonably kept and used only for ordinary personnel administration purposes. This proviso was in recognition of the fact that businesses employ staff and therefore are likely to hold some health information on their employees, for example, sick leave or maternity records. Without the proviso, almost all data controllers would have been brought unintentionally within the registration requirements.

♦ Data controllers who are prescribed by regulations made under the Act by the Data Protection Commissioner with the consent of the Minister for Justice, Equality & Law Reform:[202]

◊ Internet access providers, that is, persons who are wholly or partly in the business of providing individuals with a connection to the Internet, and who keep personal data about such individuals.

◊ Telecommunications service providers, that is those persons who hold a licence under section 111 of the Postal & Telecommunications Services Act 1983, and who keep personal data about individuals to whom services are provided under that licence.

♦ Data processors whose business consists wholly or partly in processing personal data on behalf of data controllers.

In a press release issued at the time (January 2001), the Data Protection Commissioner stated his reasoning for adding Internet access providers and telecommunications companies to the registration list:

> "… given the extensive databases which telecommunications companies and IAPs hold and the sensitive and personal nature of much of the data which they hold, all such companies should be registered." [203]

---

[202] These data controllers were added to the registration list in January 2001 by virtue of the Data Protection (Registration) Regulations 2001.

[203] "Data Protection Commissioner Requires Telecommunications Industry & Internet Access Providers to Register", *Media Release*, Office of the Data Protection Commissioner, 9 January 2001.

Registration as a Data Controller or Data Processor

Depending on their particular circumstances, persons may be required to register as a data controller, as a data processor or as a data controller and data processor.

The Office of the Data Protection Commissioner has made every effort to make the actual registration procedure as straightforward as possible. The requisite registration forms (and all relevant details) are available from the Office or *via* its website.

Registerable data controllers and data processors must provide their name and address. Specifically, in the case of:

♦ **A partnership:** The partnership name must be provided together with the name of each partner.

♦ **A company:** The address of the registered office.

♦ **Any other business:** The address of the principal place of business.

Data controllers must identify the person within the organisation to whom subject access requests can be sent. They must also provide details in relation to the purposes for which the information is kept, a description of the kinds of personal information kept, the persons to whom it is envisaged that the information may be disclosed and any countries to which it is intended to transfer it.

For data processors, registration is even simpler and requires only the identity of any countries outside of the State where it intended to transfer personal information for processing.

The annual process of renewing registration gives data controllers and data processors an opportunity to update their registration details. However, if the details provided become outdated during the year, there is an obligation to apply to amend them. An amendment fee (currently €63.49) is payable and the amendment does not affect the one-year registration period. Renewal is still due at the same time as previously.

Registration & Sensitive Information

A registerable data controller keeping personal information relating to (a) racial origin, (b) political opinions, (c) religious or (d) other beliefs, (e) physical or mental health (other than any such data reasonably kept by the data controller in relation to the physical or mental health of employees and not used or disclosed for any other purpose), (f) sexual life or (g) criminal convictions is also additionally required to specify:

♦ Which of these kinds of personal information are kept.

♦ The applications for which each of these kinds of information is kept.

♦ Both the physical and technical safeguards in operation for the protection of the privacy of the data subjects concerned.

The requirements set out above apply to any registerable data controller keeping the types of sensitive information referred to, and not just those data controllers required to register as a result of keeping it.

Registration & Personal Health Information

It is clear that any data controller keeping personal health information must register with the Data Protection Commissioner (other than the aforementioned limited exception for routine personnel purposes). In its guide to practice computerisation, the Irish College of General Practitioners spells out the situation unequivocally:

> "Before any patient information can be entered and stored on your computer, you must register with the Data Protection Agency. It is a criminal offence not to do so."[204]

Effects of Registration

Section 19 of the Data Protection Acts spells out the effects of registration. It is an offence for registerable persons either to process personal information without being registered or to act contrary to the intentions expressed by them when applying for registration. For example, they may not keep personal information of a description other than that specified in the entry in the register, or keep or use such information for a purpose other than the purpose or purposes so described. If the source from which the data is obtained is described in the entry, they may not obtain the information from any other source.

---

[204] Favier & Boland (undated).

Finally, they may not transfer data to a place outside the State, other than a place named or described in the entry.

Information in the Public Register

The information to be included in an entry in the Register in relation to a data controller is set out in the Data Protection (Registration) Regulations 1988 (S.I. No.351 of 1988), namely:

- ◆ Name and address.
- ◆ Purpose or purposes for which he keeps or uses personal data.
- ◆ Description of the data.
- ◆ Persons or categories of persons (other than persons to whom data are disclosed pursuant to section 8 of the Act) to whom the data may be disclosed.
- ◆ Countries or territories to which the data may be directly or indirectly transferred.
- ◆ If required by the Commissioner, the persons or categories of persons from whom the data and information are obtained.
- ◆ If the data controller is not the person to whom requests for information under section 4 (1) (a) of the Act should be addressed, the name or job status and address of that person.
- ◆ Date on which the entry was made or, as the case may be, from which the relevant registration was continued.
- ◆ A reference to any other entry in the register relating to the data controller.

Accepting Applications

Under the 1988 Data Protection Act, the Commissioner was required to accept applications for registration, unless he or she was of the view that the information provided was insufficient or that the applicants were likely to contravene the provisions.[205] However, where the application was made by a person required to register by virtue of holding sensitive data, the Commissioner was required to *refuse* the application, unless he or she was satisfied that appropriate safeguards

---

[205] Section 17 (2).

(such as password protection of sensitive files) were being provided and would continue to be provided by the applicant.[206] This latter provision was redrafted in the 2003 Act, and now applies to anyone who keeps sensitive data – practically every data controller, since invariably they keep personal health information on their employees.

Prior Checking

The prior checking provision was introduced by the 2003 Act.[207] The Commissioner must consider each application for registration (from both data controllers and data processors) to see whether especially risky or dangerous types of processing (as prescribed in Regulations[208]) are involved. If so, he must establish whether the processing is likely to comply with the Act. Any negative findings by the Commissioner may be appealed to court.

Non-registerable data controllers can also request that such "prior checking" be carried out by the Data Protection Commissioner.

Registration & Fair Processing

Registration is intended to ensure greater transparency. However, in the next chapter, we see that it does not meet the requirements of fair processing when it comes to obtaining consent on an informed basis. In short, simply specifying in a registration entry that it is intended to disclose personal information to a particular disclosee does not, in and of itself, meet the overriding requirement of fair processing.

Registration Periods & Fees

The Acts provide for the making of Regulations setting out the period of registration[209] and for a range of other procedural matters relating to registration.[210]

---

[206] Section 17 (3).

[207] Section 12 A.

[208] No Regulations have been made, as yet. Such processing must appear to the Commissioner to be particularly likely (a) to cause substantial damage or substantial distress to data subjects or (b) otherwise significantly to prejudice the rights and freedoms of data subjects.

[209] Section 18.

[210] Section 20.

The Data Protection (Fees) Regulations 1988[211] prescribed the initial levels of registration fee, which were the same for all registerable data controllers. This was changed in 1990[212] to a two-tier system, based on employment numbers employed by the data controller. It was altered again in 1996[213] to a three-tier fee structure, still based on employment numbers. The stated object was to encourage greater registration of sole traders and professional persons, including doctors.

The Data Protection (Registration) Period Regulations 1988[214] provide that the period of registration is one year. The Data Protection Registration Regulations 1988[215] set out the procedures to be followed for registration, including details of the information to be provided.

ENFORCEMENT & COMPLIANCE

There are currently several major models for privacy protection. The regulatory model adopted by European countries (including Ireland), Australia, Hong Kong, New Zealand, and Canada is that of a public official who enforces a comprehensive data protection law. This supervisory official, known variously as a Commissioner, Ombudsman or Registrar, monitors compliance with the law and conducts investigations into alleged breaches. In some cases, the official can find against an offender and impose penalties. The official is also responsible for public education and international liaison in data protection and data transfer. In addition, in most of these jurisdictions, the supervisory official also fosters sectoral codes of practice (either voluntary or statutory), which are designed to complement the legislation by providing more detailed protection for certain categories of information, such as police files, consumer credit records and personal health information. This is the model favoured by the EU to ensure compliance with its data protection regime.

Some countries, such as the United States, have avoided general data protection rules in favour of specific sectoral laws governing, for

---

[211] S.I. No.347 of 1988.
[212] Data Protection (Fees) Regulations 1990 (S.I. No.80 of 1990).
[213] Data Protection (Fees) Regulations 1996 (S.I. No.105 of 1996).
[214] S.I. No.350 of 1988.
[215] S.I. No.351 of 1988.

example, video rental records, financial privacy and the health sector. In such cases, enforcement is achieved through a range of mechanisms. The problem with this approach is that it requires new regulations to be introduced with each new technology, so that protection frequently lags behind.

Finally, data protection compliance can also be achieved – in theory, at least – through various forms of self-regulation, in which industry bodies establish voluntary codes of practice in the absence of, or as a means of deterring, legislation. However, the record of these efforts has been disappointing, with little or no evidence that the aims of the codes are fulfilled. Adequacy and enforcement are the major problem with these approaches.

Accordingly, industry codes of practice work best when part of a wider legislative framework (such as under our Data Protection Acts), which ensures that they meet minimum acceptable standards and are subject to independent oversight. In that regard, the Australians regard their Privacy Amendment (Private Sector) Act 2000 as "world-leading co-regulatory legislation", allowing "businesses to tailor their privacy codes to their industry, provided they meet the minimum standards in the Act".[216] However enthusiastic such claims are, they must always be assessed on their objective merits.

The Data Protection Commissioner

In Ireland, the Office of the Data Protection Commissioner is responsible for upholding the rights of individuals set out in the Data Protection Acts and for enforcing the obligations imposed upon data controllers, data processors and any other person contravening the data protection principles created by the legislation. The Commissioner is appointed by Government, but is independent in the exercise of his or her functions.

The Mission Statement of the Office is:

"… to protect the individual's right to privacy by enabling people to know, and to exercise control over, how their

---

[216] European Data Commissioners' Opinion of Australia's Privacy Law, Darryl Williams, Attorney General for Australia, 26 March 2001 (see http://www.ag.gov.au).

personal information is used, in accordance with the Data Protection Acts, 1988 & 2003." [217]

The Office's Strategy Statement and Business Plan for the years 2004/2007 specified the following high level goals:

♦ To maximise people's ability to exercise their data protection rights.

♦ To maximise levels of compliance with data protection obligations among those keeping personal information.

♦ To provide practical and easily understood advice to people and organisations, which will support Information Society developments, while protecting Data Protection rights.

Functions & Powers of the Commissioner

The functions and powers of the Commissioner were originally set out in the 1988 Act, and amended and enlarged by the 2003 statute.

Complaints & Investigations

Under section 10 of the Data Protection Acts 1988, the Commissioner must investigate any complaints he receives from individuals who feel that personal information about them is not being treated in accordance with the Act, unless he or she is of the opinion that such complaints are "frivolous or vexatious".[218] The Commissioner must notify the complainant in writing of his decision regarding the complaint, and his decisions can be appealed to the Circuit Court.

The 2003 Act provides a formal basis for the amicable resolution of disputes between parties. This was viewed as bringing the legislation into line with actual established practice.[219]

The Commissioner may also launch investigations on his or her own initiative, where he or she is of the opinion that there might be a breach of the Act, or he or she considers it appropriate in order to ensure compliance with the Acts.

---

[217] See http://www.dataprivacy.ie.

[218] Section 10(1)(b)(i).

[219] Per Minister of State, Data Protection (Amendment) Bill 2002, Dáil Éireann, Second Stage, Vol.169, 24 April 2003.

Enforcing Compliance

Under section 10 of the Data Protection Acts, the Commissioner may require a data controller or data processor to take whatever steps the Commissioner considers appropriate to comply with the terms of the legislation. Such steps could include correcting the data, blocking the data from use for certain purposes, supplementing the data with a statement approved by the Commissioner, or erasing the data altogether.

The Commissioner exercises this power by providing a written notice, called an "enforcement notice", to the data controller or data processor. A person who receives an enforcement notice has the right to appeal it to the Circuit Court. It is an offence to fail or refuse to comply with an enforcement notice without reasonable excuse.

Prohibiting Overseas Transfer of Personal Data

Under section 11 of the Data Protection Acts, the Commissioner may prohibit the transfer of personal data from the State to a place outside the State. The Commissioner exercises this power by providing a written notice, called a "prohibition notice", to the data controller or data processor.

A prohibition notice may be absolute, or may prohibit the transfer of personal data until the person concerned takes certain steps to protect the interests of the individuals affected. A person who receives an enforcement notice has the right to appeal it to the Circuit Court. It is an offence to fail or refuse to comply with a prohibition specified in a prohibition notice without reasonable excuse.

The original provisions in the 1988 Act were repealed and replaced by a much stricter regime, as required by the EU Data Protection Directive. **Appendix 1** details the rules in relation to the transfer of personal information abroad.

Power to Obtain Information

Under section 12 of the Data Protection Acts, the Commissioner may require any person to provide him or her with whatever information he or she needs to carry out his or her functions, such as to pursue an investigation. The Commissioner exercises this power by providing a written notice, called an "information notice", to the person concerned.

Any person who receives an information notice has the right to appeal it to the Circuit Court.

Failure to comply with an information notice without reasonable excuse is a criminal offence. Further, knowingly to provide false information, or information that is misleading in a material respect, in response to an information notice is also an offence.

The only exceptions to compliance with an information notice are:

♦ Where the information in question is or was, in the opinion of the Minister for Justice, Equality & Law Reform, or in the opinion of the Minister for Defence, kept for the purpose of safeguarding the security of the State.

♦ Where the information is privileged from disclosure in proceedings in any court.

Powers of "Authorised Officers" to Enter & Examine Premises

Under section 24 of the Data Protection Acts, the Data Protection Commissioner may appoint an "authorised officer" to enter and examine the premises of a data controller or data processor, to enable the Commissioner to carry out his functions, such as to pursue an investigation.

The authorised officer, upon production of his or her written authorisation from the Commissioner, has the power to:

♦ Enter the premises and inspect any data equipment thereon.

♦ Require the data controller, data processor or staff to assist in obtaining access to data, and to provide any related information.

♦ Inspect and copy any information.

♦ Require the data controller, data processor or staff to provide information about procedures on complying with the Act, sources of data, purposes for which personal data are kept, persons to whom data are disclosed, and data equipment on the premises.

It is an offence to:

♦ Obstruct or impede an authorised officer

♦ Fail to comply with any of the requirements set out above

♦ Knowingly to give false or misleading information to an authorised officer.

Appeals to the Courts against the Decision of the Commissioner

Under section 26 of the Data Protection Acts, appeals can be made to the Circuit Court against:

- ◆ A requirement specified in an information notice.

- ◆ A requirement specified in an enforcement notice.

- ◆ A prohibition specified in a prohibition notice.

- ◆ A refusal by the Data Protection Commissioner to accept an application for registration, or for renewal of registration, or for an amendment of registration details.

- ◆ A decision of the Data Protection Commissioner in relation to a complaint by an individual.

Appeals to the court normally must be made within 21 days from the service of the notice, or from the data of receipt of the refusal or decision. The decision of the court is final, although an appeal against the Court's decision may be brought to the High Court on a point of law.

Education & Awareness

There is a statutory duty on the Commissioner to make available information and advice to the public, so that awareness of data protection can be increased.

The Commissioner's website[220] is clearly a major instrument in providing widely-accessible information on rights, responsibilities and topical issues. The Commissioner's *Annual Reports* demonstrate the range of promotional activities undertaken by the Office to heighten awareness – for example, presentations and media interviews including local radio, and a nationwide advertising campaign on trains and buses together with an educational video / DVD. Contacts are also maintained with Citizens' Information Centres throughout the country.

---

[220] http://www.dataprivacy.ie.

Privacy Audits

Under the 2003 Act,[221] the Commissioner now has the power to carry out privacy audits, as he or she sees fit, in order to ensure compliance with the Act and to identify possible breaches.

The previous Commissioner indicated that he intended to use this power to conduct "privacy audits" upon data controllers at random and on a targeted sectoral basis.

The data controller receives advance notice and the aim of the audits is to assist in improving data protection practices. It is only in the event of serious breaches being discovered, or failure of the data controller to implement recommendations, that further sanctions would be considered.

Codes of Good Practice

The promotion of sectoral or industry codes of practice is found in both the 1988 and 2003 Acts.[222]

The 1988 statute contained a provision for the Commissioner to approve codes of practice drawn up by trade associations. Under the 2003 Act, the Commissioner has an additional complementary power to prepare and publish "codes of practice" for guidance in applying data protection law to particular areas. Both types of code – whether drawn up by the Commissioner or by trade associations – may be put before the Oireachtas to have statutory effect. (These may be especially relevant to the health sector.)

European & International Role

The Commissioner is now the supervisory authority for the purposes of the EU Directive, and is responsible for the dissemination of information on EU findings relating to the adequacy of data protection rules in countries and territories outside the European Economic Area.

The Commissioner is also required to perform functions in relation to data protection that the Minister may confer on him or her, as well as those that would enable the Government to give effect to international obligations of the State. Specifically at the European and

---

[221] Section 10(1A) of the Data Protection Acts 1988 to 2003.
[222] Section 13 of the Data Protection Acts 1988 to 2003.

international level, the Commissioner has the following responsibilities:

- **Article 29 Working Party:** The Commissioner is a member of the Working Party on data protection, established under Article 29 of EU Data Protection Directive 95/46/EC. This Working Party brings together the Data Protection Commissioners of the EU, the European Data Protection Supervisor and the EU Commission. It discusses matters of common interest, and agrees common positions on the application of the Directive.

- **European Databases and Data Protection Supervision:** The Commissioner is designated under the Europol Act 1997 as the "national supervisory body" for Ireland for the purposes of the Europol Convention. This function involves monitoring the data protection activities of An Garda Síochána in liaising with Europol Headquarters in The Netherlands.

- **Customs & Excise:** The Commissioner is designated under the Customs & Excise (Mutual Assistance) Act 2001 as the "national supervisory body" for Ireland for the purpose of the Customs Information System Convention.

- **Eurojust:** The Commissioner is also a member of the Joint Supervisory Body for Eurojust (co-operation by judicial and prosecution authorities) and an observer on the Schengen Joint Supervisory Authority, pending Ireland's implementation of the Schengen Information System.

- **Eurodac:** The Commissioner is the supervisory authority in the State for the purposes of the Eurodac system, established under Council Regulation 2725/2000, as a means of Member States sharing fingerprint data in relation to asylum seekers.

Prosecution of Offences under the Data Protection Acts & the European Communities (Electronic Communications Networks & Services)(Data Protection & Privacy) Regulations 2003[223]

Section 30 of the Data Protection Acts provides that the Commissioner may bring summary proceedings for an offence under the Acts. The

---

[223] S.I. No.535 of 2003.

Commissioner also has the power to prosecute offences in relation to unsolicited marketing under the Electronic Communications Regulations.[224] The Regulations created a range of offences in relation to direct marketing, including sending unsolicited marketing messages to individuals who are not customers by fax, SMS, e-mail or automated dialling machine; making an unsolicited telephone call for the purpose of direct marketing, if the sender is notified of an objection to such communications or an objection is recorded in the National Directory Database for that phone line.

Annual Report

The *Annual Report* of the Data Protection Commissioner provides the incumbent Commissioner with a yearly opportunity to reflect publicly developments in data protection both nationally and internationally, to review cases and complaints and to outline his or her view on matters of data protection and the public interest.

Health issues have featured in *Annual Reports* in all of the aforementioned categories. Cases reviewed have included chemists and the disclosure of sensitive prescription information and infectious diseases,[225] an investigation into a medical consultant's practice and the issue of patient consent, access to medical records on a change of general practitioner, and the forwarding of a medical consultant's clinical notes by a Health Board to a risk management group.[226] *Annual Reports* have also focused on the issues surrounding a unique identifier for the health sector,[227] and an outline of data protection challenges for the health sector generally.[228]

Promoting Changes to Data Protection Law

While the Irish Data Protection Commissioner does not have an express statutory function to review the operation of data protection

---

[224] The *Annual Report* of the Data Protection Commissioner for 2004 reported (p.5) that "successful prosecutions were taken by my Office – the first ever by the Office since its establishment in 1988".

[225] Data Protection Commissioner (2003), p.36.

[226] Data Protection Commissioner (2004), pp. 28, 33, 38 respectively.

[227] Data Protection Commissioner (2004), p.50.

[228] Data Protection Commissioner (2002), p. 41.

legislation,[229] in practice, he or she would be consulted on any proposals to change data privacy law, as for example, when the 1988 Act was revised to comply with the EU Directive.

OFFENCES, PENALTIES & COURT PROCEEDINGS

The Data Protection Acts create a number of offences, set out below.

1. Registration-related Offences:

- **Failure of a data controller or a data processor to register:** Data controllers who continue to keep personal data, and data processors who process personal data, without meeting their requirement to register are liable to be prosecuted. However, if a data controller or data processor has a registration application pending in the Commissioner's Office, then there is no offence.

- **Failure to adhere to the particulars contained in the register entry:** A registered data controller specifies, in its registration application, what types of personal data will be kept, for what purpose, to whom the personal data will be disclosed, and to what places outside the State the data will be transferred. A registered data controller who knowingly treats personal data in a way not covered by the particulars included in the register entry is guilty of an offence, under section 19(6). The same rule applies to employees or agents of the data controller, other than data processors, who are subject to the same restrictions as the data controller in respect of the handling of the personal data. Data controllers, and their employees and agents, should ensure therefore that the particulars included in the register entry describe adequately the scope of the data controller's dealings with the personal data. If a data controller wishes to treat personal data in a way not covered by the register entry, then the data controller should amend the register entry accordingly.

- **Failure to notify the Data Protection Commissioner of a change of address:** Under section 19(6), it is an offence for a data

---

[229] Unlike the New Zealand Privacy Commissioner, for example, who is required to do so every five years and to recommend amendments.

controller or data processor, in respect of whom there is a register entry, to fail to notify the Commissioner of any change of address.

♦ **Provision of false or misleading information when applying for registration:** It is an offence under section 20(2) knowingly to furnish the Commissioner with false or misleading information when applying for registration.

2. Failure to Comply with Notices Issued by the Commissioner:

♦ **Failure to comply with an enforcement notice:** Under Section 10(9), it is an offence for any data controller or data processor, without reasonable excuse, to fail or refuse to comply with a requirement specified in an enforcement notice. There is a right of appeal against requirements specified in such notices.

♦ **Failure to comply with a prohibition notice:** Under Section 11(15), it is an offence for any person, without reasonable excuse, to fail or refuse to comply with a prohibition specified in a prohibition notice.

♦ **Failure to comply with an information notice:** Under Section 12(5), it is an offence for any person, without reasonable excuse, to fail or refuse to comply with a requirement specified in an information notice. In addition, knowingly to provide false information, or information that is misleading in a material respect, in response to an information notice is also an offence.

3. Other Offences:

♦ **Unauthorised disclosure of personal data by a data processor:** Under Section 21(2), it is an offence for a data processor (or employee or agent) knowingly to disclose personal data without the prior authority of the data controller on whose behalf the information was processed.

♦ **Disclosure of personal data which was obtained without authority:** Section 22 of the Data Protection Acts deals with the threat to privacy posed by persons who are not data controllers or data processors (or their employees and agents) and who, having obtained unauthorised access to personal information, then disclose it to others. Section 22(1) makes such conduct an offence. Unauthorised access can occur by "hacking" into a computer system, by someone gaining access to a data controller's equipment when the staff are not present, or by someone stealing a diskette, tape or manual file on which information is recorded. Whichever way the unauthorised access takes place, it will be an offence only where the person concerned proceeds to disclose to another person the information he or she has accessed.

♦ **Obstruction of, or failure to cooperate with, an authorised officer:** Section 24 confers certain powers upon an "authorised officer", that is, a person authorised by the Data Protection Commissioner to exercise powers of entry and inspection. It is an offence for any person to obstruct or impede an authorised officer in the exercise of a power; to fail to comply with any of the section 24 requirements to cooperate with the authorised officer; or knowingly to give false or misleading information to an authorised officer, in purported compliance with such requirements.

♦ **Offences by directors, managers, officers etc. of bodies corporate:** Data controllers and data processors that are bodies corporate are bound by the Data Protection Acts in the same way as individuals. Section 29 provides that directors, managers, secretaries or other officers of a body corporate that has committed an offence under the Act are also guilty of that offence, if it is proved to have been committed with their consent or connivance or to be attributable to any neglect on their part. If there is no officer of a body corporate who can be shown to bear personal responsibility for the offence, only the body corporate commits the offence. If there is, both the officer and the body corporate can be prosecuted. This principle is extended to bodies corporate that are managed by their members. Any member who is personally responsible for the offence can be prosecuted as if he or she were a director or manager of the body corporate concerned.

Penalties for Offences under the Data Protection Act

Penalties for the above offences include:

♦ **Criminal sanctions:** As provided in section 30, summary proceedings for an offence under the Data Protection Acts may be brought and prosecuted by the Data Protection Commissioner. Under section 31, the maximum fine on summary conviction for such an offence is €3,000. For conviction on indictment, the maximum penalty is a fine of €100,000. If the commission of an offence under the Data Protection Acts also involves violence – for example, if an authorised officer is assaulted in trying to gain access to premises – then the offender can be proceeded against for assault and be liable to imprisonment.

♦ **Civil sanctions:** Where a person suffers damage as a result of a failure by a data controller or data processor to meet their data protection obligations, then the data controller or data processor may be subject to civil sanctions by the person affected. Ordinarily, the "injury" suffered by a data subject will be damage to his or her reputation, possible financial loss and mental distress. The data subject concerned may have adequate remedies under the existing law – for example, breach of confidentiality and so on. Insofar as a data controller or data processor may not be subject to an existing duty of care, section 7 remedies this by ensuring that such a duty will be implied in all cases where personal information is kept or processed.

♦ **Forfeitures, etc.:** Where a court convicts a person of an offence under the Data Protection Acts, section 31(2) provides that the court has discretion to order any data material, that is, any document or other material used in connection with, or produced by, data equipment connected with the commission of the offence, to be forfeited or destroyed. The court may also order any relevant data to be erased. A court would use this power to prevent any further damage being done by the use of the material or of the data. When exercising this power, the court must give any party (other than the convicted party) who has an interest in, or would be affected by, the destruction or forfeiture an opportunity to show cause why a forfeiture, etc. order should not be made.

♦ **Offences under S.I. No.535 of 2003:** Summary proceedings for an offence under these Regulations may be brought and prosecuted by the Commissioner. The maximum fine on conviction for such an offence is €3,000. The sending of each offending message constitutes a separate offence. The court may also order the destruction of data connected with the commission of an offence.

Court Proceedings

Section 28 provides that the whole or any part of proceedings under the Data Protection Acts may, at the discretion of the court, be heard otherwise than in public. This might be relevant where the case involves very sensitive personal health information relating to the psychiatric condition or sexual well-being of an individual.

6
FAIR PROCESSING, CONSENT & CONFIDENTIALITY

INTRODUCTION

Data protection law places very considerable emphasis on *fair processing* of information. There are a number of conditions to be met, if processing is to be considered fair. In the case of personal health information, the concept of fair processing relies very heavily on the consent of the individual concerned. The issue of what constitutes consent is, therefore, crucial.

Somewhat separately, it may seem strange to state the requirement that information should be processed lawfully as well as fairly, but the Council of Europe Convention and the EU Directive both felt it necessary to do so. The Irish Data Protection Acts do not contain such a reference to "lawfully" but, given the nature of the State, in particular its legal system, there can be little question of information processed unlawfully meeting the fairness requirement. Specifically, the matter was addressed by the Minister for Justice in the Dáil, in 1988, when he cited the Parliamentary Draftsman's advice on this subject:

> "… I am told that 'fairly' comprehends also obtaining it lawfully with due regard to the data subject's constitutional rights. There would be a particular difficulty in specifically requiring a person to behave lawfully. There is a presumption that people behave lawfully because, if they do not, they incur sanctions under the general law governing false pretences, fraud and so on. A requirement to obtain and process data fairly and lawfully is contained in Article 5 of the Convention but, when the Bill was being drafted, the Parliamentary Draftsman considered that a specific reference to 'lawfully' was unnecessary. The point was put to the

Parliamentary Draftsman and he advised that a specific reference to 'lawfully' was unnecessary and inappropriate."[230]

The matter was addressed again in 2003, when the words "and lawfully" were contained in the Data Protection (Amendment) Bill 2002, as initiated. However, they were deleted at Committee Stage, with the Minister of State at the Department of Justice, Equality & Law Reform stating it was:

"... not necessary to state that data shall be processed lawfully ... because the Bill ... sets out the detailed conditions under which non-sensitive and sensitive personal data may be processed ... We are just reverting to the original terminology [in the 1998 Act]."[231]

The Data Protection Acts, therefore, state clearly the conditions under which processing is fair. However, it has never been suggested that either the 1988 Act or the 2003 version lessened the common law requirements relating to the duty of confidence owed by one party to another and this is why informed consent is so important in the health area. There is a useful consideration of this issue by the United Kingdom Information Commissioner in his guide on the *Use & Disclosure of Health Data*.[232]

CONDITIONS FOR FAIR PROCESSING

The Data Protection Acts do not define the meaning of "fairly". However, it seems reasonable to conclude that fairness must take into account the intentions of the data controller in relation to the information, especially at the time of obtaining it, and how the processing of the information is likely to affect the data subject. Since the Acts distinguish between sensitive and non-sensitive personal information, and provide for higher standards in relation to the

---

[230] Data Protection Bill 1987, Dáil Éireann, Committee Stage, Vol.382, 29 June 1988.

[231] Data Protection (Amendment) Bill 2002, Select Committee on Justice, Equality, Defence & Women's Rights, 12 February 2003.

[232] Information Commissioner (UK) (2002).

former, certain conditions must be met for the processing of (non-sensitive) personal data, with additional requirements in relation to the processing of sensitive personal data. Specifically, the fair processing principle, as enunciated in the Data Protection Acts, requires that any person proposing to process sensitive personal data must meet at least one requirement from each of two lists set out in sections 2A and 2B:[233]

Section 2A (Processing of Personal Data) List 1:

♦ The data subject has given his or her consent[234] to the processing or, if the data subject has not the competency to do so, then someone appropriate acting on his or her behalf, such as a guardian, parent or other close relative has done so.

♦ The processing is necessary:

◊ For the performance of a contract to which the data subject is a party.

◊ In order to take steps at the request of the data subject prior to entering into a contract.

◊ For compliance with a legal obligation to which the data controller is subject other than an obligation imposed by contract.

◊ To prevent injury or other damage to the health of the data subject, or serious loss or damage to property of the data subject, or otherwise to protect his or her vital interests, where the seeking of the consent of the data subject or another person referred to in the consent paragraph above is likely to result in those interests being damaged.

♦ The processing is necessary for a public purpose, namely:

◊ For the administration of justice.

◊ For the performance of a statutory function.

◊ For the performance of a function of the Government or of a Government Minister.

---

[233] A data controller keeping non-sensitive personal data is required only to meet one condition from the first list to meet the fair processing requirement.

[234] The giving of such consent must not be prohibited by law.

◊ For the performance of any other function of a public nature carried out in the public interest.

♦ The processing is necessary for the legitimate interests of a data controller or a third party to which the data are disclosed, except where the processing is unwarranted in any particular case, having regard to the fundamental rights, freedom and interests of the data subject.[235]

Section 2B (Processing of Sensitive Personal Data) List 2:
Sensitive personal data shall not be processed by a data controller unless a minimum of one of the above conditions (List 1) is met along with one, at least, of the following:

♦ The consent referred to in List 1 is explicit.

♦ The processing is necessary for the purpose of exercising or performing any right or obligation which is conferred or imposed by law on the data controller in connection with employment.[236]

♦ The processing is necessary to prevent injury or other damage to the health of the data subject or another person or serious loss in respect of, or damage to, property or otherwise to protect the vital interests of the data subject or of another person in a case where:

◊ Consent to the processing cannot be given by or on behalf of the data subject.

◊ The data controller cannot reasonably be expected to obtain such consent.

◊ The processing is necessary to prevent injury to, or damage to the health of, another person, or serious loss in respect of or damage to, the property of another person, in a case where the data subject's consent has been unreasonably withheld.

---

[235] Under section 2A(2), the Minister for Justice, Equality & Law Reform can regulate the operation of this provision.

[236] The Minister for Justice, Equality & Law Reform, after consultation with the Commissioner, may exclude by Regulations the application of this provision in such cases as may be specified or alternatively provide that, in such cases as may be specified, the condition imposed by the provision is not to be regarded as satisfied unless such further conditions as may be statutorily prescribed are also satisfied.

♦ The processing is carried out by a non-profit organisation existing for political, philosophical, religious or trade union purposes in the course of its legitimate activities[237] involving its members, or involving other individuals with whom the organisation has regular contact.

♦ The information contained in the data has been made public deliberately by the data subject.

♦ The processing is necessary for a specified public purpose, namely:

◊ For the administration of justice.

◊ For the performance of a statutory function.

◊ For the performance of a function of the Government or of a Government Minister.

♦ The processing is required for the purpose of obtaining legal advice or for the purposes of, or in connection with, legal proceedings or prospective legal proceedings or is otherwise necessary for the purposes of establishing, exercising or defending legal rights.

♦ The processing is necessary in order to obtain information for use, in accordance with the Statistics Act 1993, only for statistical, compilation and analysis purposes.

♦ The processing is carried out by political parties or candidates for election to, or holders of, elective political office in the course of electoral activities for the purpose of compiling data on people's political opinions and complies with such requirements (if any) as may be prescribed for the purpose of safeguarding the fundamental rights and freedoms of data subjects.

♦ The processing is authorised by regulations that are made by the Minister for Justice, Equality & Law Reform and are made for reasons of substantial public interest.

♦ The processing is necessary for the purpose of the assessment, collection or payment of any tax, duty, levy or other moneys

---

[237] This means no third-party disclosure without the consent of the data subject concerned and that there must be appropriate safeguards for the fundamental rights and freedoms of data subjects.

owed or payable to the State and the data has been provided by the data subject solely for that purpose.

♦ The processing is necessary for the purposes of determining entitlement to or control of or any other purpose connected with the administration of any benefit, pension, assistance, allowance, supplement or payment under the Social Welfare (Consolidation) Act 1993 or any non-statutory scheme administered by the Minister for Social & Family Affairs.

♦ The processing is necessary for medical purposes and is undertaken by either a health professional or a person who, in the circumstances, owes a duty of confidentiality to the data subject that is equivalent to that which would exist if that person were a health professional. In this regard, "health professional" includes a registered medical practitioner, within the meaning of the Medical Practitioners Act 1978, a registered dentist, within the meaning of the Dentists Act 1985, or a member of any other class of health worker or social worker standing specified by regulations made by the Minister for Justice, Equality & Law Reform after consultation with the Minister for Health & Children and any other Minister of the Government who, having regard to his or her functions, ought, in the opinion of the Minister, to be consulted. "Medical purposes" includes the purpose of preventive medicine, medical diagnosis, medical research, the provision of care and treatment and the management of healthcare services.[238]

---

[238] In Department of Health (UK) (2003), a distinction is drawn between healthcare purposes and medical purposes. The former is defined to include "all activities that directly contribute to the diagnosis, care and treatment of an individual and the audit / assurance of the quality of the healthcare provided. They do not include research, teaching, financial audit and other management activities". The latter, as defined in the Data Protection Act 1998 include, but are wider than, healthcare purposes. They include preventative medicine, medical research, financial audit and management of healthcare services. Subsequent to the 1998 Act, the Health & Social Care Act 2001 explicitly broadened the definition to include social care.

CONSENT & THE DUTY OF CONFIDENCE

From the above, it is evident that consent is a significant principle in processing all types of personal information. The collection, use and disclosure of personal health information has traditionally been subject to a variety of ethical and common law rules that place an emphasis on consent and confidentiality.[239] These important principles continue to apply, and the application of data protection law to personal health information must have full regard to them if the processing is to be fair.

The Guide to Ethical Conduct & Behaviour produced by the Medical Council reflects the importance that the Council attaches to confidentiality and consent. According to the *Guide*,

> "Confidentiality is a time-honoured principle of medical ethics. It extends after death and is fundamental to the doctor / patient relationship. While the concern of relatives and close friends is understandable, the doctor must not disclose information to any person without the consent of the patient ..."[240]

The *Guide* also provides that:

> "... all medical records in whatever format and wherever kept must be safeguarded [and that] doctors should take all reasonable steps to ensure that other health professionals and ancillary staff maintain confidentiality".

Similarly, the *Code of Professional Conduct for Each Nurse & Midwife*,[241] produced by An Bord Altranais (Irish Nursing Board), places

---

[239] It is very important to bear in mind that consent, as discussed in privacy law, applies to issues about how an individual's health information is handled. The Data Protection Acts, for example, do not deal with consent to medical treatment. In practice, consent to the handling of information and consent to medical treatment often occur at the same time. However, they are distinct authorisations by the individual to do different things: to provide or not provide certain treatments and to use or not use the related health information in particular ways.

[240] Medical Council (2004), p.29.

[241] An Bord Altranais (1998). See http://www.nursingboard.ie.

considerable emphasis on confidentiality as well as noting the potential threat of computerisation to this principle:

> "Information regarding a patient's history, treatment and state of health is privileged and confidential. It is accepted nursing practice that nursing care is communicated and recorded as part of the patient's care and treatment. Professional judgement and responsibility should be exercised in the sharing of such information with professional colleagues. The confidentiality of patient's records must be safeguarded. In certain circumstances, the nurse may be required by a court of law to divulge information held. A nurse called to give evidence in court should seek in advance legal and / or professional advice as to the response to be made if required by the court to divulge confidential information.
>
> It is appropriate to highlight the potential dangers to confidentiality of computers and electronic processing in the field of health services administration."

Indeed, it is common practice among most professional and regulatory bodies in the Irish health system to have express references in their codes of conduct and ethics to the need to respect and safeguard client information. It is indicative of the degree to which confidentiality is observed by healthcare professionals in Ireland that there are so few reported incidents of breach of confidence. One case that ended in court – and attracted some media attention mainly due to the personalities involved – featured a psychiatrist who had sent his bill to the separated husband of his client. The judge noted that the psychiatrist had, at all times, adopted a candid and apologetic approach about the matter.[242]

Exceptions to Duty of Confidence

There are exceptions to the duty of confidence that may make the use or disclosure of confidential information appropriate beyond the

---

[242] "Murphy's wife gets £1,500 nominal damages", *The Irish Times*, 16 April 1994, p.4.

original intention or purpose. Apart from specific statutory exceptions, there are common law public interest or public good exemptions. Courts may also order disclosure of confidential information. However, a major consideration for any person revealing confidential information and relying on a public interest or public good exemption is that they are confident they have sufficient applicable grounds for the exemption to apply. The various rules governing exceptions to the general principle of confidentiality are discussed further in this chapter after the matter of consent is fully addressed.

Valid Consent[243]

There is no single definition of consent in Irish law. However, the EU Data Protection Directive defines consent as:

> "… any freely given specific and informed indication of his [or her] wishes by which the data subject signifies his [or her] agreement to personal data relating to him [or her] being processed."[244]

It is accepted that certain elements must be present, if the consent is to be regarded as valid, including:

- ◆ Awareness and understanding of the nature and extent of the processing, especially in terms of intended and likely uses and disclosures of the information involved.

- ◆ Awareness of option(s) to prevent such processing either in whole or in relation to any particular aspect.

- ◆ The existence of a mechanism to enable the option of withholding consent to be effective.

---

[243] Consent can never be valid, if prohibited by law.

[244] On one reading, this definition suggests that the giving of consent may not legitimately be made a condition of receiving a service such as healthcare, since to impose conditions might mean that consent had not been "freely given". Were a data controller to seek to rely upon consent as a condition of processing medical data (rather than one of the other possible conditions), such a strict reading of the definition in the Directive might invalidate the consent that had apparently been obtained.

In considering the common law duty of confidence, however, the courts have not generally found that consent is rendered invalid by having conditions attached, providing that those conditions are not unduly onerous. Generally, this will be identifiable by reference to the data subject having some degree of choice.

"Consent" given under duress or coercion is not consent at all. By contrast, consent which is entirely optional, and may be withheld without any consequences, is clearly valid (if informed). Between these two extremes is consent that is more or less conditional upon agreement to some other term or condition. In that regard, it would not necessarily be unfair that a medical card patient should be asked to consent to the disclosure of *certain* personal health information by, for example, a GP to the Health Service Executive for specified administrative or audit purposes as a condition of receiving treatment from that GP. By contrast, it is much more unlikely that a patient's consent to the disclosure of his or her hospital medical record to a medical student as a condition of receipt of treatment in a public hospital would be fair. Similarly, consent for administrative staff to access medical data for legitimate administrative purposes might generally be a condition of treatment. However, in a particular case, a patient might object, if the member of the administrative team was personally known to him or her. The significance of this objection must be judged on its merits, which would include the sensitivity of the medical condition involved, but clearly there is a balance to be struck between the concerns of the patient in such a situation and the legitimate business management of the healthcare practice or hospital involved.

Implicit Consent

Consent can be implicit (implied) or explicit (express). Where consent can validly be inferred, implied consent is not a lesser form of consent than express consent.[245] However, it is indisputable that express consent provides clearer verification. Closely related to the idea of implied consent are the notions of tacit and presumed consent. Tacit

---

[245] For example, the UK Information Commissioner stated "It is a mistake to assume that implied consent is a less valid form of consent than express. Both must be equally informed and both must express the wishes of the patient." (Information Commissioner (UK) (2002), p.14).

consent is a passive notion based on the idea that, if persons do not object to something, it can be reasonably assumed that they have silently consented. Presumed consent is similar to tacit consent in that consent is taken for granted, but it is based on what is known about patients and their values and desires.

In the Data Protection Bill 2002, as published, it was provided that consent should be explicit in relation to non-sensitive and sensitive personal data, even though the EU Directive did not prescribe explicit consent for the processing of non-sensitive data.[246] The Bill was amended during its passage through the Oireachtas to drop the requirement for explicit consent in relation to non-sensitive data.[247]

On implicit consent, Jennifer Stoddart, the Privacy Commissioner for Canada, stated that:

> "... [her] office recognises and understands the need for information to flow from healthcare provider A to healthcare provider B in order to ensure the best level of patient care. We recognise the principle of implied consent for information to flow freely within the 'circle of care'. The definitions around the 'circle of care' relate to the care and treatment of the patient and healthcare services for the therapeutic benefit of the patient. This would include laboratory work and professional case consultation with other healthcare providers."[248]

---

[246] The EU Directive does, however, require consent to be "unambiguous".
Writing in the *Irish Medical News* (Madden, 2002), Dr Deirdre Madden (Lecturer in Law at UCC) stated that it is important to note that this would rule out implied consent, and it may also mean that the current situation where a person is asked to mark a box if he objects to his data being processed will have to be replaced with a box to be marked if he consents to his data being processed. This will obviously make it more difficult to gather information about individuals.

[247] At Committee Stage, the Minister of State at the Department of Justice, Equality & Law Reform stated "the Bill as it stands exceeds what is required by the Directive. Following concerns expressed by a range of interests including, most recently, the legal affairs group of the Information Society Commission, I propose to drop the requirement for explicit consent in relation to non-sensitive data".

[248] This speech can be found in the Resource sub-menu of the Canadian Privacy Commissioner's website, http://www.privcom.gc.ca.

Implied consent, therefore, covers the sharing of information within a primary care team, or beyond to secondary or tertiary care providers, where such sharing is related only to the care of the patient concerned. Implied consent normally would also cover business and administrative purposes that arise from, and are directly related to, the treatment and care of the patient. In these situations, the amount of personal information used and disclosed must be kept to the minimum necessary. It does not cover anything outside the above, such as the communication of information for teaching, third-party research or management purposes.

There are situations when healthcare service providers may reasonably rely on implied consent by individuals to handle health information in certain ways. For example, an individual presents to a medical practitioner, discloses health information, and this is written down by the practitioner during the consultation – generally, this will be regarded as giving implied consent to the practitioner to collect the information for certain purposes. The extent of these purposes should usually be evident from the discussion during the consultation. Similarly, if a medical practitioner collects a specimen to send to a pathology laboratory for testing, it would be reasonable to consider that the individual is giving implied consent to the passing of necessary information to that laboratory.

Where there is open communication and information-sharing between the healthcare service provider and the individual, consent issues will usually be addressed during the course of the consultation. If the discussion has provided the individual with an understanding about how their health information may be used, then it would be reasonable for the healthcare service provider to rely on implied consent. This is certainly consistent with the view expressed by the Australian Privacy Commissioner, in his *Foreword* to *Private Health Sector Guidelines*, when he summed up concisely the nature and value of an open communication process between healthcare service providers and patients:

> "Clear and open communication between the health service provider and health consumer is integral to good privacy. This document recognises that when such communication occurs, then ordinarily, many of the privacy obligations of

health service providers will be met. When providers are open about the health information they hold, and how they use and disclose it, surprises are unlikely and with fewer surprises there are likely to be fewer complaints." [249]

Before looking at explicit consent, it must be emphasised again that implied consent must always be informed. In the case of any dispute arising at a subsequent date the onus will be on the healthcare data controller to demonstrate the manner in which such consent was informed.

Explicit Consent

Express or explicit consent is consent that is clearly and unmistakably stated. It may be obtained in writing, orally, or in any other form where the consent is clearly communicated. Where such consent is required, it should *always* be recorded and dated and preferably signed and witnessed. This precaution will prevent future disputes.

The *NHS Code of Practice on Confidentiality* provides that:

"... when seeking explicit consent from patients, the approach must be to provide:

(a) honest, clear, objective information about information uses and their choices – this information may be multi-layered, allowing patients to seek as much detail as they require;

(b) an opportunity for patients to talk to someone they can trust and of whom they can ask questions;

(c) reasonable time (and privacy) to reach decisions;

(d) support and explanations about any form that they may be required to sign;

(e) a choice as to whether to be contacted in the future about further uses, and how such contacts should be made; and

---

[249] Federal Privacy Commissioner (Australia) (2001).

(f) evidence that consent has been given, either by noting this within a patient's health record or by including a consent form signed by the patient."[250]

Further, the information provided must allow for disabilities, illiteracy, diverse cultural conditions and language differences and must cover:

♦ A basic explanation of what information is recorded and why, and what further uses may be made of it.

♦ A description of the benefits that may result from the proposed use or disclosure of the information.

♦ How the information and its future uses will be protected and assured, including how long the information is likely to be retained, and under what circumstances it will be destroyed.

♦ Any outcomes, implications, or risks, if consent is withheld (this must be honest, clear, and objective – it must not be or appear to be coercive in any way).

♦ An explanation that any consent can be withdrawn in the future (including any difficulties in withdrawing information that has already been shared).

Issues with Explicit Consent

While explicit consent for *all* healthcare purposes would resolve doubts about the uses and disclosures of personal health information, such an approach is not an option for the following reasons:

♦ Too expensive and bureaucratic – there would be a significant cost in retaining paper records of consent.

♦ Cost out of all proportion to risk of challenge.

♦ Not possible to reach whole sample population.

♦ Likely disruption to healthcare services.

♦ Diversion of resources from primary purpose of healthcare.

Moreover, in reality, explicit consent would not eliminate the potential for arguments: a signed consent form would not always prove

---

[250] Department of Health (UK) (2003).

informed consent – a patient might not fully understand what he or she was agreeing to and might still dispute the matter in the future. In addition, there is the problem of validating the circumstances of taking consent.

Informed Consent

Whether implied or explicit, consent cannot be valid unless it is informed and voluntary. Informed consent can be summarised as "the right to know and the right to say no". The Canadian Privacy Commissioner, describes informed consent as:

> "… the backbone of our net of privacy principles and practices — the glue that holds the fair information principles together."[251]

Informed consent is predicated on having sufficient intelligible information upon which to base a decision. It is axiomatic that consent cannot be valid, if material facts are withheld as to the potential uses and intended disclosures of the information concerned. Further, withholding such facts, irrespective of the reasons, is a breach of the ethical trust between the healthcare professional and patient.

Information Required for Consent to be Informed & Processing to be Fair

We have already looked at certain information requirements in relation to informed consent: in particular, the NHS *Code of Practice on Confidentiality* and its advice on explicit consent.

The information required for consent to be informed, and the means of providing it, are discussed further in **Chapter 7**, since such information should normally be provided when the information in question is being obtained.

Capacity & Competency to Give Consent

An individual cannot give valid consent if they lack the capacity to make an informed decision. In healthcare, the general presumption is that an adult has the capacity to decide whether to consent to, or

---

[251] This speech can be found in the Resource sub-menu of the Canadian Privacy Commissioner's website, http://www.privcom.gc.ca.

refuse, proposed medical intervention, unless it reasonably can be determined that there is a temporary or permanent (mental) incapacity involved. The same framework applies to consent by patients on the use of their health information. However, as with treatment, there are potentially very problematic issues in the capacity and competency[252] areas, especially in the mental health area and in the case of teenage children.[253] These are discussed below.

The Data Protection Bill 2002, as introduced to the Oireachtas, provided that the consent of a parent or guardian was required where the data subject was under the age of 18. But this was changed before the Bill was enacted, as a result of a Government amendment. The reason given was that "many people of this age are in third-level education or working and parental consent is neither feasible nor necessary".[254] Instead, the consent of a parent or guardian (or other close relative, as appropriate) is required, only where the data subject is unable to do so for reasons of physical or mental incapacity or age. It was recognised that the age will vary according to the subject.

Subject to the above, an individual may be assumed to be competent, under Irish law, to give consent on reaching the age of 16, in line with current medical practice.[255] Where the individual is below

---

[252] Competence is understood in terms of the patient's ability to understand the choices and their consequences.

[253] Indeed, given our Constitution, the information rights of the unborn may require some consideration too.

[254] Minister of State at the Department of Justice, Equality & Law Reform, Data Protection Bill 2002, Committee Stage, Select Committee on Justice, Equality & Law Reform.

[255] In Ireland, the Age of Majority Act 1985 provides that an individual attains full age on reaching 18 (unless married before this age, in which case majority is attained on marriage). Accordingly, unless the law provides otherwise in particular cases, a child is anyone under the age of 18. One such exception is found in the Non-Fatal Offences Against the Person Act 1997, section 23(1) of which states that: "The consent of a minor who has attained the age of 16 years to any surgical, medical or dental treatment which, in the absence of consent, would constitute a trespass to his or her person, shall be as effective as it would be if he or she were of full age; and where a minor has by virtue of this section given an effective consent to any treatment it shall not be necessary to obtain any consent for it from his or her parent or guardian …". It seems reasonable to conclude that, if an individual of 16 can give full consent to surgical, medical or dental treatments, then he or she must be similarly empowered as regards all the

that age, consent may still be given, but the medical practitioner involved must assess whether a child or young person has the maturity to understand and make their own decisions about the handling of their personal health information.[256]

Similarly, there are some patients who, because of certain types of illness or disability, are not competent to give consent for the collection, use or disclosure of their personal health information. Where guardianship law is applicable, its rules for consent on behalf of incompetent patients should be followed. In other cases, the medical practitioner should speak to the patient's relatives or carers to obtain their agreement to the proposed use or disclosure of the personal health information or the patient may have nominated some specified individual in writing to act on his or her behalf.

In situations where there is no one available to act for an individual, the healthcare service provider may have to make decisions about appropriate handling of the individual's health information. Professional and ethical obligations and current accepted practices should provide guidance in these circumstances.

When considering matters of competency, it is very important to bear in mind that most people with disabilities are able to make their own privacy decisions and have the legal (and moral) right to do so. Accordingly, there is a responsibility on healthcare service providers to ensure that privacy issues are discussed with the individual concerned in a way that is understandable and comprehensible, to the

---

information aspects relating to such treatments (and by extension to all his or her medical records generally).

[256] In England & Wales, this position was considered by the House of Lords in 1985 in Gillick *v.* West Norfolk & Wisbech Area Health Authority. The Lords decided that, with regard to medical treatment, a child under 16 could give informed consent *'if and when the child achieves sufficient understanding and intelligence to enable him to understand fully what is proposed'*. However, the Court also felt that the child should be encouraged to involve parents or other legal guardians in the decision. This test, known as "Gillick competence", still prevails, although it is a complex area that has provoked legal debate ever since. Later case law has held that what must be considered is the level of understanding of a particular child in relation to the particular treatment proposed; on occasion, 17-year olds have been found insufficiently competent, while much younger children have been accepted to be 'Gillick competent' and able to take important decisions for themselves.

greatest extent possible in the circumstances. Moreover, even if an individual lacks actual legal capacity, they should be involved as far as is practical in decision-making processes.

Obtaining, Withholding & Withdrawing Consent

As a general rule, consent should be obtained at the beginning of any healthcare relationship. It is important to emphasise that where consent – express or implied – is required for the use or disclosure of personal health information, it can always be withdrawn, even after it has initially been given. This may be problematic for healthcare data controllers, but must be acknowledged.

The matter of consent can be addressed with new patients at the time of their first visit to, or contact with, the healthcare service provider and, with existing patients, normally at the time of their next visit. Consent is not required at the time of every subsequent visit / contact, but only when there is a material change in the anticipated use or disclosure of the patient's information.

Some patients may refuse to provide certain personal health information or may withhold consent for particular uses or disclosure of that information. Where there is a concern that the patient may suffer adversely if certain information is not collected, used or disclosed, this should be explained to the patient and the matter formally recorded. Where patients are competent to make such a choice and where the consequences of the choice have been fully explained, the decision should be respected. This is no different from a patient exercising his or her right to refuse treatment. In other situations, eligibility or entitlement to a health-related service or allowance can only be determined if the individual seeking the service or allowance provides certain personal medical details. The implications for the application of failing to provide the required details should be fully explained. In every situation, reasonable efforts should be made to identify and resolve any legitimate concerns of the individual.

EXCEPTIONS TO CONSENT

It has long been the case that certain disclosures of personal health information without consent have been authorised or required by law or have been necessary for proper medical care. Invariably, the justification is either the interests of the individual involved or other parties or the public interest generally.

Emergencies & Consent

It is an accepted healthcare and legal principle that, in an emergency, where consent cannot be obtained, such patient information as is necessary to treating the person involved can, and should, be disclosed. But even this general rule is subject to the proviso that there must still be respect for any known advance refusal by the patient to allow all or some of his or her information to be released, even in an emergency.

Disclosing Confidential Information in the Public Interest or to Protect the Public Good

Under common law, an organisation or individual is permitted to disclose personal information in order to prevent and support detection, investigation and punishment of serious crime and / or to prevent abuse or serious harm to others, where they judge that the public good that would be achieved by the disclosure outweighs both the obligation of confidentiality to the individual patient concerned and the broader public interest in the provision of a confidential service. Each case must be considered on its own individual merits and decisions may often be finely balanced between conflicting interests, making it difficult to make a judgement. Accordingly, when faced with such a situation, it is advisable to seek legal or other specialist advice (for example, from professional, regulatory or indemnifying bodies).

Disclosures in the public interest should also be proportionate and be limited to relevant details. As it may be necessary to justify subsequently such disclosures to the courts or to regulatory bodies, a clear record of the decision-making process and the advice sought is in the interest of everyone involved. For that and other reasons, healthcare data controllers should give consideration to initiating a formal policy that creates a set of procedural steps to deal with such situations.

It is further advisable that any such policy should ensure that, wherever possible, the issue of disclosure should be discussed with the individual concerned and consent sought. Where this is not forthcoming, the individual should be told of any decision to disclose against his or her wishes. However, this may not be feasible in certain circumstances – for example, where the likelihood of a violent response is significant and immediate.

Medical Council & Disclosures

The Medical Council has identified four instances where patient consent may be over-ridden:

♦ When ordered by a judge in a court of law or by a Tribunal established by an Act of the Oireachtas.

♦ When necessary to protect the interest of the patient.

♦ When necessary to protect the welfare of society.

♦ When necessary to safeguard the welfare of another individual or patient.[257]

Section 8 Exceptions

Section 8 of the Data Protection Act 1988 contained a number of exceptions to the normal rules on disclosure. In the 2003 Amendment Act, those special cases are repeated but, this time, they apply not just to disclosures but to the whole range of processing activities (including collection, use, etc., as well as disclosure). This is a wide-ranging change to the earlier position.

Specifically, it is now provided that any restrictions imposed by the Data Protection Acts on the processing of personal data do not apply if the processing is:

♦ In the opinion of a senior member of either An Garda Síochána or the Permanent Defence Force required for the purpose of safeguarding the security of the State.

---

[257] Medical Council (2004), p.29.

♦ Required for the purpose of preventing, detecting or investigating offences, apprehending or prosecuting offenders or assessing or collecting any tax, duty or other moneys owed or payable to the State, a local authority or a health board, in any case in which the application of those restrictions would be likely to prejudice any of the matters aforesaid.

♦ Required in the interests of protecting the international relations of the State.

♦ Required urgently to prevent injury or other damage to the health of a person or serious loss of or damage to property.

♦ Required by or under any enactment[258] or by a rule of law or order of a court.

♦ Required for the purposes of obtaining legal advice or for the purposes of, or in the course of, legal proceedings in which the person making the disclosure is a party or a witness.

♦ Made at the request, or with the consent, of the data subject or a person acting on his or her behalf.

♦ Made to the data subject concerned or to a person acting on his or her behalf.

Operation of the Section 8 Exceptions in the Health Sector

It is not difficult to imagine situations where the exceptions would be relevant to personal health information. The detection of crime proviso could be of relevance in the context of combating fraud in the health system, for example, in investigations for excessive claims by healthcare professionals. Similarly, a hospital may consider the disclosure of medical information would be justified to the Gardaí in

---

[258] Administrative law governs the actions of public bodies, including most hospitals and health agencies. According to well-established rules, a public authority must possess the power to carry out what it intends to do. If not, its action is *ultra vires*, that is, it is beyond its lawful powers. It is also necessary that the power be exercised for the purpose for which it was created or be "reasonably incidental" to the defined purpose. An approach adopted by Government to address situations where a disclosure of information is prevented by lack of function (the *ultra vires* rule) is to create, through legislation, new statutory gateways that provide public sector bodies with the appropriate information disclosure function.

the event of an assault on a member of staff, or to an internal disciplinary board formed to investigate an alleged assault on a patient, but unjustified in the context of a minor theft. However, it is important to note that this exception applies only where fair processing would prejudice or jeopardise the matter in question. Protecting the international relations of the State could be used to permit disclosure of personal health information to another Government where the individuals involved might be carrying a possible infectious disease to the other country.

The particular issues associated with consent and the use, sharing and disclosure of personal health information for health service management and research are discussed in **Chapter 10**.

THE FAÇADE OF PATIENT CONTROL

Commenting on the power relationship inherent in the health system, the New Zealand Privacy Commissioner, observed that:

> "... some suggested [health] information systems purport to give the patient control: give the patient the opportunity to dictate who may access the information ... On the surface, that seems fine ... But ... it must never be forgotten that in healthcare, patients are at the receiving end of an unequal power relationship. Knowledge is power, and the knowledge rests with the health professional."[259]

He went on to give the example of an individual seeing a specialist, who says she cannot really treat you without checking your history. She asks you to authorise her to have full access to your medical records. Do you say that she will only be allowed to see certain parts of the information? Do you refuse and walk away with the problem unresolved? Probably, like many others, you would give the authorisation, in spite of your misgivings.

Interestingly, the New Zealand Commissioner saw the increasing use of electronic records as being a major contributor to this problem of blanket authorisations based on unequal power relationships, not

---

[259] Privacy Commissioner (New Zealand) (1998).

just between the patient and clinicians, but also between the patient and government, employers, the legal profession and insurance companies.

At another level, the modern State is already in a powerful position to decide what should happen to our health information. For example, as part of the English NHS's National Programme for Information Technology, a new centralised Care Record System will allow instant access to any patient's medical records from anywhere within the English NHS. This should make treating patients throughout the service more efficient and reliable – in addition, immediate access to data could be life-saving in emergency situations. However, the matter of who actually decides on what is recorded and who should have access is critical to the matter of control.

Initially, it was stated by government that the patients would have the right (i) to specify that detailed information recorded at the point of contact with the NHS should not be available to other NHS organisations via the summary record held on their NHS care record and (ii) to define some information as especially sensitive and only accessible under terms of explicit consent. Subsequently, it emerged that patients' rights would be restricted to simply discussing what details might be recorded, with their doctor having the final decision on what to record. [260]

The position has since been clarified by the publication in May 2005 of *The Care Record Guarantee: Our Guarantee for NHS Care Records in England* by the English National Health Service.[261] The document was drawn up by the Care Record Development Board, an advisory body of patients, members of the public, healthcare professionals, social workers and researchers. It provides that patients will keep control over access to their health records in the NHS patient health record system being rolled out across England in 2006. Commitments made include:

♦ Access to records by NHS staff will be strictly limited to those having a "need to know" to provide effective treatment to a patient.

---

[260] *Today*, Radio 4, 30 March 2005, http://news.bbc.co.uk/1/hi/health/4392555.stm.

[261] Department of Health (UK) (2005). Available at http://www.connectingforhealth.nhs.uk.

♦ In due course, patients will be able to block off parts of their record to stop it being shared with anyone in the NHS, except in an emergency.

♦ Individuals will even be able to stop their information being seen by anyone outside the organisation that created it – although doing so may have an impact on the quality of care they receive.

In a *Press Statement* accompanying the release of the guarantee document, the Health Minister, Lord Warner, said:

> "The new electronic record system has enormous potential benefits for patients. In time, it will allow staff caring for them – wherever they may be in England – to have instant, accurate access to their essential health history, including allergies, current medication, pre-existing conditions and recent treatment. There will be very strict controls on who has access to a patient's records. However, we recognise that some people may have particular concerns about how their personal health information will be kept confidential in the new system. We understand that, which is why we are today setting out clearly what they can expect from the NHS and their rights to control who has access to their personal information. These rules will be backed up with tough security measures to prevent unauthorised access to records, ensuring everyone can have confidence in the new system."[262]

---

[262] "Clear Rules Set Out for Patients' Electronic Records", *Press Release,* Department of Health (UK), 23 May 2005, Reference number: 2005/0185. Available at http://www.dh.gov.uk/PublicationsAndStatistics/PressReleases.

7
OBTAINING PERSONAL HEALTH INFORMATION

INTRODUCTION[263]

Fair obtaining is perhaps the single most important data protection principle because, if the information is obtained unfairly, then it taints the information, the collector, the use and anyone who comes into contact with it. As a rule, fair obtaining is most likely where personal information is collected directly from the individual to whom it relates. Traditionally, in the health system, most information is obtained in this way through the process of direct engagement between individuals and health professionals or agencies.

However, increasingly, health information collected for one purpose from one person is communicated beyond the original episode to a number of persons for different purposes. Sometimes, these disclosures go far beyond what was envisaged at the time of the initial encounter. Data protection rules (together with the common law principle of confidentiality) govern this area to ensure that the data subject retains some degree of control, especially as regards subsequent use and disclosure.

The principle of fair obtaining is closely associated with what is known as the "purpose specification principle": that is, that personal information must be kept only for one or more specified and lawful purposes. In his *Annual Report* for 1990, the Data Protection Commissioner spelt out what this meant:

> "If a data controller, who collects personal data for a particular purpose, subsequently decides to use those data

---

[263] For a full appreciation of all the issues associated with fair obtaining, readers are recommended to read this Chapter in conjunction with **Chapter 6**.

for an entirely different purpose, then he must first obtain the consent of the data subject concerned before doing so." [264]

OBTAINING INFORMATION

A healthcare service provider, health agency or any other data controller obtains personal health information if it collects, gathers or otherwise acquires it directly or indirectly from the individual concerned or someone else and either then or subsequently records it (or has the intention to so do). Information is deemed to be obtained even where the data controller comes across it by accident, or has not asked for, but nevertheless keeps it.

It is most important to note that information is obtained at the point where the data controller first receives it, and includes all situations where the data controller obtains any new information from or about an individual.

Personal health information can be obtained in a wide variety of situations, including where a person:

♦ Records what an individual says, and includes any opinion about, or interpretation of, what is said.

♦ Records third-party information about the individual.

♦ Receives a form, a letter, or email from an individual, with a view to that correspondence being stored and used.

♦ Re-identifies previously de-identified information.

♦ Downloads and retains personal information from another computer or Internet server.

♦ Stores video tapes or photographic images of procedures (for example, colonoscopy) in ways that identify individuals.

---

[264] Data Protection Commissioner (1991), p.27.

INFORMATION REQUIRED FOR CONSENT TO BE INFORMED

The Data Protection Acts provide guidance in section 2D[265] as to what information should be provided to individuals in order to make the processing of their data fair. Clearly, this will vary from case to case, and from person to person, depending upon a number of factors, including the age and mental capacity of the individual, the range of intended purposes of the information, any possible non-routine disclosures of the information and the sensitivity of the information concerned.

Under the fair processing principle, the information provided should meet two criteria. First, it should be sufficient to allow the patients to exercise their rights in relation to their data. Second, it should be adequate to allow the patient to assess the risks to him or her in providing their information, in consenting to its wider use, in choosing not to object to its processing, etc.

Where a data controller obtains health information directly from the individual or from the individual's representative (for example, a parent or guardian), it must take all reasonable steps to ensure that the individual concerned or his or her representative is made aware of:[266]

♦ The fact that the information is being collected with a view to it being kept.

♦ The identity and contact details of the data controller by which, and / or for which, it is being obtained;

♦ The purpose, or purposes, for which the information is being collected.

♦ The intended third party recipients of the information, if any, and their likely uses of the information.

♦ Whether the supply of the information is voluntary or mandatory and the consequences, if any, of not providing any, some or all of the information.

---

[265] Section 2D sets out the information requirements for fair processing as well as the exemptions to those requirements.

[266] Section 2D(2).

♦ Any statutory or other legal provision that requires the information to be collected or specifically authorises its collection.

♦ Any right of the individual not to provide the information or to do so anonymously.

♦ The legal, ethical and organisational rights of access, correction, blocking, etc. that apply in relation to the data.[267]

Where the information is not collected directly from the individual or his or her representative, the data controller involved must also comply with the above as well as making the data subject aware of the categories of information involved and the name of the original data controller.[268] This should happen (i) not later than the time the data controller first processes the information or (ii) if disclosure of the information to a third party is envisaged, not later than the time of such disclosure.[269] However, this requirement does not apply:[270]

♦ Where, in particular, the processing is for statistical historical or scientific research and the provision of the specified information would be impossible or involve disproportionate effort.

♦ In any case where the processing is necessary for compliance with a legal obligation to which the data controller is subject other than a contractual one and any conditions prescribed by Ministerial Regulations are met.

It is likely that there will be a number of standard purposes for which the personal data of all patients entering a hospital, or registering with a healthcare provider, will be processed, information about which can be provided to patients at the outset of the episode of care. In particular, data subjects should be advised of typical information flows between various parts of the health system *and* the reasons for such communications. This information is relatively timeless and it is

---

[267] A data controller would not be required to take the steps, if it already has taken those steps in relation to the collection, from that individual or his or her representative, of the same information or information of the same kind for the same or a related purpose, on a recent previous occasion.

[268] Section 2D(3).

[269] Section 2D(1)(b).

[270] Section 2D(4).

appropriate that patients are given it at an early opportunity. Further, it would certainly be best practice to remind patients of this information from time to time – for instance, by ensuring that leaflets containing the relevant information are readily available to existing and potential users of health services.

Some patients subsequently may have their personal information processed for a number of additional purposes (for example, certain information may be passed to social services). Those patients who will have their personal data processed for these additional purposes will need to be provided with this further information, in order to satisfy the fair processing requirements, in particular the consent element. This type of information is specific to particular patients at particular times and should be given in context, at a time when individuals are able to make sense of it.

Accordingly, when explaining the purpose or purposes for which information is to be processed, data controllers must strike a balance between providing an unnecessary amount of detail and providing information in too general terms. In that regard, an explanation to the effect that personal information is to be processed for "healthcare purposes" would be too general. On the other hand, an explanation that explained, at length, all the administrative systems in which patient data might potentially be recorded would be likely to be excessive. However, it is recommended that where explicit consent is relied on for processing personal health information, the information provided should err on the side of too much, rather than too little, if subsequent disputes are to be avoided.

Means of Providing Information to Patients

Methods by which the information may be provided include a standard information leaflet, information provided face-to-face in the course of a consultation, information included with an appointment letter from a hospital or clinic, or a letter sent to a patient's home. The effort involved in providing this information may be reduced by integrating the process with existing procedures. Many healthcare service entities already provide leaflets to patients about how the practice, hospital, centre, etc. operates – such leaflets can help meet the fair processing information requirement, if suitably detailed and accessible. In addition, practitioners should be able to provide readily specific information to patients in the course of consultations. However, the data controller must bear in mind that the onus is always on it to ensure that the required information is provided to individuals in an appropriate manner. Clearly, where explicit consent is required for any use or disclosure, there will have to be a one-to-one engagement with the data subject.

The provision of information by means of a poster in a hospital's Admissions area or in a surgery or waiting room, by a notice in the local paper or on the data controller's website is very unlikely to be sufficient to meet the necessary standard requirements, since not all data subjects will see, or be able to understand, such information. Such methods may, of course, be used to supplement other forms of communication. All of this points to the need for healthcare data controllers to have a pro-active patient information policy.

Identity of the Data Controller

It would be a mistake to think that the identity of the data controller is so obvious as to not require identification. The name and address of the doctor collecting the information may be clear to the individual when that doctor is obtaining it in a single-handed practice. However, if the practice is a group or partnership entity, or if the doctor is carrying out the service on behalf of another party (such as an insurance company), the identity of the data controller involved may not be so clear.

Fair processing requires that care should be taken to ensure that the data subject knows the identity of the data controller that will process his or her data. In addition, there may be more than one data controller, in which case the identity of all data controllers should be communicated to data subjects. Increased multi-agency working and joint services initiatives may make the identity of the data controller less evident, not just to the patients, but even to the persons engaged in a particular project. Finally, it is important also to repeat that a data controller must have a legal personality.

Information as to the identity of the data controller should always be specific and never so broad as to be meaningless – for example, stating that the Health Service Executive is the data controller covers a potential multitude of divisions, agencies, projects and persons at numerous locations across the country.

Ideally, all the above steps should be taken when the information is being collected or, if that is not practicable, as soon as practicable thereafter.

Obtain Necessary Information Only

Information collected should be limited to what is necessary for the data controller's functions and activities. In assessing what is necessary, professional practice standards and organisational guidelines will be relevant.

The aim should be to minimise situations where unnecessary information is collected, even unintentionally. For example, a hospital may have a form with spaces to collect much standard information, particularly where the form serves a number of purposes. Often, people may have the impression that they must fill in all fields, even if this is unnecessary. The design of healthcare forms should be proofed from a data protection perspective.

A healthcare service provider may only collect health information about an individual where they have that individual's express or implied consent to do so or in those scenarios where consent is not required. In situations where health information is collected directly from the individual, the individual's consent to the collection generally can be inferred, but only where it is clear to him or her what information is being recorded and for what purposes. Again, this relates directly to all consent needing to be informed.

There are a limited number of situations where a healthcare service provider is permitted, under data protection law, to collect information about an individual without consent. For the most part, those scenarios have been framed specifically because consent is not a realistic option – for example, in an emergency situation where an individual is unconscious, or in significant distress or confusion, and urgent medical treatment is required. In other cases, a healthcare data controller can collect information without consent if there is a law requiring it to do so but, in these situations, the matter should be explained to the individual so that he or she is placed in an informed position regarding his or her information and the necessary trust between a health professional and client is not undermined by what a patient might regard as an unacceptable use or disclosure.

Secret Collection

It certainly would not be fair to tape-record a conversation without the individual's knowledge, even if the reason for doing so was simply to have as full a record as possible of the medical consultation. Collection of information is considered to be "fair", only if the approach taken is open and not misleading, and if the individual is not coerced or tricked into providing information against his or her will or knowledge.

Intrusive Collection

An example of intrusive collection is when an individual is required to disclose delicate information in a situation where they can be easily overheard. This might occur where a practice receptionist, admission office staff in a hospital, pharmacy staff, etc. ask questions about, or otherwise discuss, the nature of the individual's condition in an open area. Some individuals may be particularly concerned or embarrassed about discussing health issues in a public area, so the data controller should, as a matter of good practice and respect for clients, ensure its employees are aware of the need for discretion and provide proper space for private conversations – for example, by taking the individual to one side or by using a private room if one is available.

Obtain Information from the Individual Directly

As already stated – but worth emphasising – it will always be easier to ensure fair processing when the information is collected from the patient directly, because that affords the best opportunity to outline all the material facts relating to its proposed use, retention and disclosure. Accordingly, whenever and wherever it is reasonable and practicable to do so, a data controller should collect health information about an individual only from that individual.[271] Deciding whether it is

---

[271] Rule 2 (Source of Information) of the *New Zealand Health Information Privacy Code* (Privacy Commissioner (New Zealand) (2000)) provides that, where a health agency collects health information, the health agency must collect the

reasonable and practicable to do so depends on the circumstances and involves balancing a number of possible factors, especially whether a reasonable person might expect their information to be collected directly or indirectly, how sensitive the information is and what is accepted practice within the health sector (not just by data controllers, but by clients too).

In practice, health information will mostly be obtained directly from the patient, either because it has been supplied by him or her (for example, a description of symptoms) or generated by the person creating the record (for example, a medical opinion based on symptoms presented). In other instances, information about patients will clearly and necessarily be provided by a person other than the individual concerned – for example, if a GP sends a patient to see a consultant for further diagnosis or treatment, the GP will receive a reply that will be added to the patient record. In such a case, the consultant is the direct source of the information.

Further, there are a number of situations where collecting information directly from the individual may not be reasonable or practical – for example, in an emergency situation where background health information is collected from relatives.

As a general rule, in any circumstances where health information is not collected directly from an individual, the data controller should be sure that it can justify this course. Further, the data controller must treat the information collected as governed by the same rules of confidentiality as if obtained from the individual directly.[272] Finally, in every case where personal information is obtained from a third party, it is highly advisable for the data controller to inform the information provider that his or her identity may have to be released to the data subject together with the information supplied.

---

information directly from the individual concerned, except in certain specified circumstances.

[272] This is certainly the view of the Medical Council, which, in its *Ethical Guide*, deals with third-party information as follows: "Sometimes it may be necessary to obtain information about a patient from a third party e.g. a relative. This information is also governed by the same rules of confidentiality as [if obtained from the individual directly]".

FAMILY HISTORIES

Family information exists to a greater or lesser extent in the health record of everyone who has contact with the health system. This is particularly so with psychiatric records, genetics records and paediatric records. Indeed, not only is the taking of certain family history details seen as good professional practice, it is also possible that failure to take a history (at least in some circumstances) could be used as evidence in negligence or professional standards cases.

Collecting information about an individual's family members may involve collecting identifiable personal information about those people. It is difficult to be dogmatic as to whether their individual consents should be obtained. Generally, this is not in line with the traditional practice of medical history-taking, but it seems difficult to escape the conclusion that recording information about other *identifiable* living family members raises potentially problematic issues, particularly where their consent cannot, at least, be inferred. This is most likely to be the case where a patient is discussing sensitive health-related issues with his or her medical practitioner and the other individual is not presented in a positive light. Healthcare data controllers should be careful about recording information about third parties that indicate that he or she is engaged in any activity that is socially, morally, legally or otherwise unacceptable. This is even more applicable when it comes to using or disclosing such information. There is nothing to stop healthcare professionals listening to such information from a patient, but it will fall within the Data Protection Acts as soon as the information is recorded or the intention to so record arises. All of these issues should be fully explained to the consulting patient.

An important consideration is a health professional's obligation of confidentiality. There may be situations where a person gives information to a healthcare professional regarding an identifiable individual, and would not wish that other individual ever to know that the subject has been discussed. Obvious examples include people discussing troubles in close personal relationships, or between parents and children.

The issue has been considered in Britain, where the Department of Health established in 2002 the Health Records & Data Protection

Review Group to consider a number of privacy in healthcare issues, including treatment of family history information in health records. The Review Group has produced a research paper on the subject,[273] arising from concerns about genetics practices but going on to consider the matter in a much wider context. The British view was:

> "... that information about family histories would appear to include personal data as defined by the Data Protection Act 1998 and be subject to the provisions of the Data Protection Act 1998".

Accordingly, it was concluded that the fair processing obligation seems to require that third-party family members should be provided with basic information as described in their 1998 Act and, whilst the NHS might be able to claim disproportionate effort in some cases, in many others, this would not apply.

Arguably, the question of family member notification only arises where information is (or is recorded in order to be) processed electronically. This is because, so it is claimed, manual recording of family history information is unlikely to be filed in a way that would bring the information about that family member within the scope of the data protection statutes, in that it is not "readily accessible".

As a result of their conclusions, the Review Group has been asked to consider the need for an Order under the Data Protection Act 1998 to exclude, or make special provision for, family history data in relation to fair processing requirements.

These issues have also been considered in Australia, where it has been recognised formally that collecting information about an individual's family members – for example, when taking a medical history – may involve collecting identifiable personal information about those people that, in some circumstances, may require that family members' consents be sought before collection occurs, and that they are informed of the collection.

The Australian Privacy Commissioner had committed himself publicly to ensuring that the necessary collection of family medical history information could continue through the use of other provisions in their privacy legislation.

---

[273] Department of Health (UK) (2002).

Notwithstanding this, there was considerable concern among the Australian medical profession that the accepted practice of collecting social and medical histories during the course of providing a healthcare service breached the National Privacy Principles set out in the privacy legislation. Accordingly, they made representations to the Privacy Commissioner and, having considered the matter, the Commissioner issued two *Public Interest Determinations* in 2002,[274] aimed at resolving difficulties in collecting family-related information for medical purposes. The Determinations provide that a healthcare service provider may now collect health information from a client about a third party (for example, a family member) without that party's consent when:

♦ Information about a client's social, family or medical history is necessary to provide a health service directly to the consumer.

♦ The third party's information is relevant to the family, social or medical history of that client.

Silence as Consent & Small Print

A major practical consideration is whether so-called passive consent mechanisms are acceptable as a means of obtaining valid consent.

Such an approach arises when a data controller communicates with a data subject, advising that he intends to use the data subject's information in some way unless the individual indicates otherwise. In his 1997 *Annual Report*, the then Data Protection Commissioner stated that:

> "… this approach undermines the data subject's autonomy as a decision maker. It also ignores the fact that silence may simply mean that the data subject has not received the communication from the data controller".[275]

---

[274] Public Interest Determinations 9 and 9A (Family Medical History Determinations, December 2002). The Determinations, as well as some background information, can be viewed at http://www.privacy.gov.au/health/determinations/index.html.

[275] Data Protection Commissioner (1998).

The Commissioner then referred to an EU Consumer Survey that established that 89% of respondents were concerned about passive consent being regarded as acceptable.

In the same *Annual Report,* one of the case studies featured the matter of obtaining consent through small print on application forms.[276] In the case involved, there was a statement explaining that the customer's information might be used for direct marketing and giving him or her the opportunity to decline such use. However, the statement was printed in very small type, whereas the details and purported advantages of the product and the service were presented in a much clearer and more attractive way. The Commissioner:

> "… cautioned the data controllers involved that there was a significant risk of contravening the Act in the course of action they had pursued".

He then went on to set out his general views on fair obtaining and small print:

> "It is necessary for the individual to be made aware, clearly and unambiguously, of the purposes for which his or her data are being obtained and the manner in which it is proposed to use and disclose them. I question whether the presentation in 'small print' of information which has an important bearing on the information privacy choices of a data subject meets the fair obtaining requirements of the Act. This is especially the case where other information extolling the merits of the product or service on offer uses clear language and striking graphics. I am putting data controllers on notice that such practice, in my view, is unacceptable and, in the event of complaints, is likely to lead to a finding that the data in question have not been fairly obtained. This in turn may have serious consequences for the data controller concerned, not least being the inability to legally use any personal data obtained in reliance on the small print in question."

---

[276] Data Protection Commissioner (1998), Case Study 4: *"Small print" on application forms – inadequate for fair obtaining,* pp.25-26.

Fair Obtaining & Registration

From the outset, the *Annual Reports* of successive Irish Data Protection Commissioners have repeatedly highlighted the importance they place on fair obtaining and their "strong commitment to vigorous enforcement" of this principle.[277]

In his *Annual Report* for 1994, for example, the Commissioner stated that he considered the fair obtaining principle to be "at the heart of data protection law".[278] Similarly, in the 1997 *Annual Report*, the Commissioner expressed his view that "fair obtaining is an active duty".[279] He went on to emphasise the importance of this principle:

> "It is up to the data controller, not the data subject, to make sure that it takes place ... The primary relationship under the Act is that between the data controller and the data subject, and the terms of that relationship are largely governed by what takes place at the time the data controller obtains the data subject's information (significant subsequent modifications of that relationship require the positive and fully informed consent of the data subject). Any cases brought to my attention which may involve incompatible uses or disclosures, or unfair processing, will be judged in the light of what has taken place during that transaction."

It is again important to underline that the information provided by a registered data controller in its registration entry has very little to do with meeting the "fair obtaining" principle:

> "What a data controller does about his obligations in respect of registration has little bearing on the primary relationship with the data subject. If he has not, in the first place, fulfilled his active duty to make the data subject aware of the intended uses and disclosure of personal data in such a way that the data subject can give informed consent, specifying them in the registration does not make up for that and will

---

[277] Data Protection Commissioner (1994), p.9.
[278] Data Protection Commissioner (1995), p.8.
[279] Data Protection Commissioner (1998).

not, in my opinion, constitute an adequate defence against a complaint in relation to section 2 of the Act."[280]

Case Studies on Obtaining Information Fairly

In his *Annual Report* for 1997, the Data Protection Commissioner examined the issues of hospital patient information being disclosed for research purposes, where it was not collected for that purpose. [281] The details of the particular case are outlined in **Chapter 10.**

---

[280] Data Protection Commissioner (1998).
[281] Data Protection Commissioner (1998), *Case Study 1.*

8

RETAINING & SAFEGUARDING PERSONAL HEALTH INFORMATION

INTRODUCTION

Persons collecting, obtaining, using and disclosing personal health information need to take reasonable steps to ensure the quality, security and integrity of such information. Further, there is an important requirement to ensure that information is kept only for as long as necessary and that it is properly safeguarded during that period before being anonymised or destroyed. Benefits in maintaining quality health information can include its reliability in supporting informed decisions about healthcare and treatment and its role in facilitating the continuity of care when a new healthcare service provider becomes involved, whether temporarily or permanently. If health records are inaccurate, insufficient or outdated, decisions may be wrong and thus harm the patient. If information is recorded inconsistently, then records are harder to interpret, resulting in delays and possible errors. In some cases also, the information may be needed not only for the immediate treatment of the patient and the audit of that care, but also to support research that can lead to better treatments in the future. In all of this, the practical value of privacy-enhancing measures and anonymisation techniques will be undermined, if the information they are designed to safeguard is unreliable.

Accordingly, all persons holding personal health information should think about where inaccuracy, incompleteness and lack of currency of personal information will most likely detrimentally affect data subjects.

MEETING THE QUALITY STANDARDS

Quality Considerations

Patient files should be:

- **Factual, consistent and accurate,** which means that information should be:
  - ◊ Recorded as soon as possible after an event has occurred, providing current information on the care and condition of the patient.
  - ◊ Recorded clearly, legibly and in such a manner that it cannot be erased.
  - ◊ Recorded in such a manner that any alterations or additions are dated, timed and signed in such a way that the original entry can still be accessed, as required.
  - ◊ Accurately dated, timed and signed or otherwise identified, with the name of the author being printed alongside the first entry.
  - ◊ Recorded, wherever applicable, with the involvement of the patient or carer.
  - ◊ Clear, unambiguous, (preferably concise) and written in terms that the patient can understand. Abbreviations, if used, should follow common conventions.
  - ◊ Consecutive.
  - ◊ Organised by the data controller in a manner that minimises the potential for the personal health information of one individual being confused with another.
  - ◊ Organised for efficient retrieval, including for advising the individual of preventive services provided by the healthcare agency or service provider and (for electronic records) use standard coding techniques and protocols.
  - ◊ Detailed as necessary (which does not prevent the compilation of patient summaries for certain purposes).
  - ◊ Recorded in a manner compliant with equality and disability law.

♦ **Relevant and useful**, which involves:

◊ Identifying problems that have arisen and the action taken to rectify them.

◊ Providing evidence of the care planned, the decisions made, the care delivered and the information shared.

◊ Providing evidence of actions agreed with the patient (including consent to treatment and / or consent to disclose information).

and includes:

◊ Medical observations: examinations, tests, diagnoses, prognoses, prescriptions and other treatments.

◊ Relevant disclosures by the patient – pertinent to understanding cause or effecting cure / treatment.

◊ Facts presented to the patient.

◊ Correspondence from the patient or other parties.

Patient records should *not* include:

♦ Unnecessary abbreviations or jargon.

♦ Meaningless phrases, irrelevant speculation or offensive subjective statements.

♦ Improper personal opinions regarding the patient.

View of the Medical Council

Not surprisingly, the Medical Council has stated that is in the interest of both doctors and patients that accurate records are always kept.[282] Records should be retained for an adequate period (this may be for periods in excess of 21 years) and eventual disposal may be subject to advice from legal and insurance bodies.[283]

The Medical Council's *Guide* goes on to remind doctors:

"… of their responsibility in advising administrative authorities of the importance of medical records being stored in such a manner that ensures confidentiality, security and

---

[282] Medical Council (2004).

[283] Medical Council (2004), pp.16-17.

ready accessibility for clinical staff when required for patient management".

Retention of Information

Proper management of any information system requires procedures to be put in place to ensure that information is not retained beyond the date when it is no longer of value to the organisation. Consistent with that criterion, the Data Protection Acts require that personal information should not be retained for longer than is necessary. No time limit is set, reflecting the reality that a variety of legitimate factors determine the valid retention period in particular cases and within organisations. However, in every situation, personal health information should be retained by healthcare providers only for as long as it is required for use or disclosure in order to provide necessary and proper treatment to the individual concerned or to meet medico-legal and other professional requirements. At the very least, it is recommended that individual patient medical records be retained for a *minimum* of eight years from the date of last contact or for any period prescribed by law. (In the case of children's records, the period of eight years generally begins from the time they reach the age of majority).

In other cases, healthcare professionals or agencies holding personal health information may decide that it is in the patient's, and their own, best interests that it should be retained indefinitely. Further, different types of organisations and practitioners within the health system may take different views on what is appropriate. For example, VHI holds claims data on-line for seven years and off-line indefinitely.[284]

---

[284] Molony (2004).

HEALTH BOARDS' GUIDE TO RECORDS MANAGEMENT

Freedom of Information Liaison Group

Recognising the range and complexity of the issues involved, the National Freedom of Information Liaison Group (Health Boards) published, in October 1999, a document entitled *Policy for Health Boards on Record Retention Periods*.[285] The document, which is very detailed, deals with definitions and classification of records, essentials of records management, storage, security and destruction issues and legislation relating to and advice on retention periods. It gives considerable attention to personal health records kept by, and in, a variety of bodies and locations.

The report states that (then) current practices in relation to record retention vary widely throughout the health service and that:

> "... as medical technologies in the health services continue to accelerate there is increasing pressure to hold records indefinitely (for example, in the case of genetic engineering, frozen embryos etc.)".

Consequently, the stated principal purpose of the paper was to set out "the minimum periods for which records should be retained". It added that:

> "... where there are local considerations or where resources allow, records may be retained in their original format or alternatively stored for periods in excess of the minimum recommended".

Recognising the realities of the volume of records generated within the Irish health system, and consistent with legal requirements on records, it advocated a best practice approach to:

> "... assisting managers in controlling the potential problem of holding large amounts of records:
>
> ◊   in easily accessible form,

---

[285]   National Freedom of Information Liaison Group (Health Boards) (1999).

◊ securely, and

◊ confidentially."[286]

The preparation by the Health Boards of the *Records* document was undoubtedly influenced by the application of the Freedom of Information Act 1997 to Health Boards in 1998[287] and clearly is heavily influenced by the implications of that legislation for health agencies. In particular, the definition of record used covers:

"... any memorandum, book, plan, map, drawing, diagram, pictorial or graphic work or other document, any photograph, film or recording (whether of sound or images or both), any form in which data (within the meaning of the Data Protection Act 1988) are held, any other form (including machine-readable form) or thing in which information is held or stored manually, mechanically or electronically and anything that is a part or a copy, in any form of any of the foregoing or is a combination of two or more of the foregoing ..."

and is taken from the Freedom of Information Act 1997.

Essentials of Records Management

The Health Boards' *Records* document defined the parameters of records management as the systematic collection, classification, indexing, retention, safeguarding and disposal of corporate records (in particular those in paper or electronic form relating to people). It proposes, therefore, that procedures should be in put in place to ensure that:

---

[286] The document did not attempt to cover every type of record held by health service agencies but instead focussed on the following important categories: (i) Acute Hospitals & Records of Residential Services, (ii) Community Health & Welfare Services, (iii) Personnel Records and (iv) Financial Records.

[287] The document states that "the Freedom of Information Act 1997 has granted new legal rights to the public, which will undoubtedly lead to an increasing number of requests for information held by all public bodies. To facilitate these requests, it is timely that all health service agencies should examine their methods of record storage and retrieval".

- Complete and accurate records of the data controller's activities and decisions are created as soon as possible after the event.

- A new record (whether created internally or received from elsewhere) is associated to its correct file.

- Essential and significant records should bear the unique index number of the file where they are stored.

- Records are attached in the appropriate order for that file.

- Non-record documentary material, where appropriate, is associated with the official file.

The document identified two matters that should determine the duration of the retention period:

- Any legal requirement relating to the record (which might also determine the form in which the record must be kept).

- An assessment of the value to the organisation of continuing to hold the record (including statistical and research purposes).

In assessing the value, it recommended the common-sense application of the following criteria:

- Avoid trying to accommodate every conceivable need.

- Retain information, if it is likely to be needed in the future and if the consequences of not having it would be substantial.

- Be conservative – avoid inordinate degrees of risk.

- Ensure systematic disposal of records immediately after their retention period expires

- Base retention periods on the consensus of opinions of knowledgeable / experienced people.

It identified that a wide variety of personal health records would arise in acute hospitals and other residential services, including medical charts, casualty records, pathology records, x-ray films and reports and general administrative documents. It acknowledged that the requirements for holding medical records vary according to the purpose for which they are originally collected and proposed the following criteria for determining retention:

- **Patient care:** Records are maintained primarily for the treatment of patients during current and subsequent periods of medical attention. The retention period should be subject to consultation with the appropriate health professional. The period, of course, must span at least the duration of treatment. Failure to retain a record for a sufficient period of time could be considered negligent, if the patient were injured by treatment that would have conflicted with recorded information, had it been available.

- **Legislative criteria:** All statutory retention periods should be regarded as minimum periods only. Hospital and healthcare facilities have the option to establish longer periods, where necessary. Where no legislative guidance exists, retention periods must be set internally after careful examination of the purposes for which records are maintained.

- **Other legal criteria:** Medical records should be retained as long as there is a possibility of legal action being brought by the patient, or on behalf of the patient. A healthcare agency or service provider must examine whether the cost of indefinite retention of records would exceed the liabilities likely to be incurred in cases where defence to an action for damages is handicapped by the absence of records.

- **To facilitate research and statistical analysis:**[288] In the light of the latest trends in medical and historical research, it may be appropriate to select some records for permanent preservation. Selection should be performed in consultation with health professionals and records management personnel. If records are to be sampled, specialist advice should be sought from the same health professionals and records management personnel. If a health service agency has taken on a leading role in the development of specialised treatments, then the patient records relating to these treatments may be especially worthy of permanent preservation. If a number of patient records are not considered worthy of permanent preservation, but nevertheless contains some material of research value, then the option of retaining individual records should be considered.

---

[288] This includes its possible importance in relation to new reproductive and genetic technologies, although this again raises other privacy issues.

Most usefully, the document gave specific guidance on retention periods in relation to a wide range of specified personal health records, detailed in **Appendix 2**.

SECURITY & INTEGRITY OF INFORMATION

Central to the whole area of keeping and retaining information is the matter of providing appropriate security for the information. Put simply, security is concerned with the protection of information in any manual or automated system against unauthorised access, disclosure, alteration, or destruction and with granting access to information of varying degrees of importance or sensitivity to authorised users only.

Where information is shared (as, increasingly, it is in the health system), there is a need for security mechanisms (including audit trails) to restrict users to those portions of database required for their legitimate activities, and a need to control the changes that users can make. Equally, security is about having a proper recovery system.

Other security issues relate to:

♦ Operating system and hardware.

♦ Physical controls – locked rooms / terminals, etc.

♦ Fireproof safes for back-ups.

♦ Policy questions:

◊ How to decide who sees what?

◊ What about computer staff?

♦ Legal / social / ethical issues.

Integrity is concerned with preserving the consistency and the accuracy of data; protecting against both malicious and accidental interference, even by authorised users. It applies both to correctness of data and to mechanisms that help to ensure the correctness of data. System integrity is the ability of the system (whether manual or electronic) to function according to specification, even in the face of "hacking". Semantic integrity is concerned with the correctness, especially the internal consistency, of the data in the database, in the presence of user updates. The data model used may impose specific integrity constraints.

Quite apart from data protection considerations, any data controller in any sector is well-advised to pay attention to security and integrity issues. It can be difficult to quantify the value of information: often it does not have a clear economic value, but, in a hospital, data corruption might lead to patients receiving the wrong treatment, or none at all, with potentially fatal consequences.

Considerations under the Data Protection Acts

The Data Protection Acts 1988 to 2003 do not detail specific security measures that a data controller or data processor must have in place. Section 2(1)(d) of the 1988 Act introduced the general obligation on persons to have appropriate measures in place to prevent:

> "...unauthorised access to, or alteration, disclosure or destruction of, the data and against their accidental loss or destruction".

The European Communities (Data Protection) Regulations 2001 (S.I. No.626 of 2001) and, subsequently, the Data Protection (Amendment) Act 2003, introduced a new section 2C into the 1988 Act, which set out the security considerations in much more detail. Specifically, the legislation now requires that the following factors should be considered when developing security policies:

- ♦ The state of technological development.
- ♦ The cost of implementing measures.
- ♦ The harm that might result from unauthorised or unlawful processing.
- ♦ The nature of the data concerned (since health information is sensitive, by definition, it requires a higher level of security).

A further development introduced by the 2003 Act is the obligation on data controllers and data processors to ensure that their staff are aware of security measures and comply with them.

Having regard to the above, the Office of the Data Protection Commissioner has produced *Security Guidelines*[289] providing practical advice on:

♦ **Access Control:** The obligation to prevent unauthorised access to information can be met, at the simplest level, by placing a password onto a computer. This would certainly be the minimum measure acceptable. However, it is only effective if staff keep the password secure, and the password is reviewed and changed regularly. A more advanced form of authentication is the use of a token (such as a smart card), or biometrics (such as an iris scan or a finger print scan). Where all three are used in combination, this would offer a high level of authentication.

Network administrators can add a level of security beyond mere authentication. Users tend to develop unique profiles, depending on what they normally do on their computers – a combination of the time and frequency of access, location, or nature of data accessed. Where a user seeks to access data in an unusual manner, which conflicts with an established profile, a challenge response question can be asked by the system. This type of authentication prevents a person who has found a password from accessing the system.

In conjunction with authentication, the nature of access allowed to an individual user should be set and reviewed on a regular basis. Ideally, users should only have access to data that they require in order to perform their duties. Reviews are necessary in order to increase, if necessary, as well as to restrict, previous access where a user role changes.

A logging and reporting system can also be a valuable tool in assisting the network administrator in identifying abuses and developing appropriate responses.

♦ **Encryption:** There are a variety of tools available with which to encrypt data. These can be useful in closed systems, where all users can have access to the key with which to decrypt data. Providing such a key is held securely, encryption offers a high degree of protection against external attack.

---

[289] See http://www.dataprivacy.ie.

Where encryption currently does not work satisfactorily is in sending data to the outside world. Use of a Public Key Infrastructure (PKI) requires that both sender and recipient use the same encryption system. Until such time as a market leader or industry standard exists, such PKIs will be slow to develop.

♦ **Anti-Virus Software:** Anti-virus software is not only required to prevent infection from the Internet (either e-mail- or web-sourced), but also from diskettes or CDs. No anti-virus package will prevent all infections, as they are only updated in response to infections. It is essential that users update such software on a frequent basis, but also keep vigilant for potential threats. A policy of not opening e-mail attachments from unexpected sources can be a practical way of preventing infection.

♦ **Firewalls:** A firewall is useful where there is any external connectivity, either to other networks or to the Internet. It is important that firewalls are properly configured. As firewalls are available for free download from the Internet, they should routinely be installed by all data controllers and processors. This will become more important as computer users progress to "always-on" Internet connections, exposing themselves to a greater possibility of attack.

♦ **Automatic screen savers:** Most systems allow screensavers to activate after a period of inactivity on the computer. This automatic activation is useful, as the alternative manual locking of a workstation requires positive action by the user every time he / she leaves the computer unattended. Regardless of which method an organisation employs, computers should be locked when unattended. This not only applies to computers in public areas, but to all computers. It is pointless having an access control system in place, if unattended computers may be accessed by any staff member.

♦ **Logs and audit trails:** It is, of course, worthless having an access control system and security policy if the system cannot identify any potential abuses. Consequently, a system should be able to identify the user name that accessed a file, as well as the time of the access. A log of alterations made, along with author / editor, should also be created. Not only can this help in the effective administration of the security system, its existence should also act as a deterrent to those staff tempted to abuse the system.

◆ **Human factors:** No matter what technical or physical controls are adopted, the most important security measure is to ensure that staff are fully aware of their responsibilities.

◆ **IS17799 Certification:**[290] The National Standards Authority of Ireland has set a standard for information security management systems. An organisation certified to be IS17799-compliant demonstrates compliance with the security requirements of the Data Protection Acts 1988 to 2003.

◆ **Remote access:** Where a worker is allowed to access the network from a remote location (for example, from home or from an off-site visit), such access creates a potential weakness in the system. Therefore, the need for such access, and appropriate security measures, should be properly assessed before this facility is granted.

◆ **Wireless networks:** Access to a server by means of a wireless connection (such as infrared or radio signals) can expose the network to novel means of attack. The physical environment in which such systems are used may also be a factor in determining any weakness in the system security. As with remote access, wireless networks should be assessed on security grounds rather than solely on apparent ease of use.

◆ **Laptops:** Laptops, personal organisers and other form of portable computers are especially vulnerable, as there is not only a higher risk of theft, but also a new risk of accidental loss. It would be a sensible precaution not only to have adequate security measures, but also to limit what information is placed on such machines in the first place. Where laptops are the personal property of an individual, the data controller should have a contract in place to detail the conditions under which information may be processed on personally-owned computers. A contract might also be advisable to cover all employee use of portable computers, especially concerning use of personal information, where a person leaves the employment of a data controller. Even where data are

---

[290] Further information on IS17799 may be found on http://www.nsai.ie.

not routinely deleted from portable computers, such data should be backed up onto the network. This will assist in keeping the data on the network accurate and up-to-date, as well as defending against the accidental loss or destruction of data on portable computers.

♦ **Back-up systems:** A back-up system is an essential means of recovering from the loss or destruction of data. While some system should be in place, the frequency and nature of back-up will depend, amongst other factors, on the organisation concerned and the nature of data being processed. The security standards for back-up data are the same as for live data.

♦ **Physical security:** Physical security includes issues like perimeter security (office locked and alarmed when not in use); computer location (so that the screen may not be viewed by members of the public); disposal (so that computer print-outs containing sensitive data are securely disposed of). A case study published in the Data Protection Commissioner's *Annual Report* for 1996 concerning the position of a computer screen in a public area demonstrated some of the issues that can arise in this area.[291] The complainant wanted to buy a fridge in a shop. She enquired whether she could avail of an instalment payment scheme. The assistant checked some information about her on a computer screen. The complainant was upset, because her information was visible to other customers who were free to circulate around the computer. An investigation established that the screen was badly situated, and it was possible for customers to see details on screen, although staff tried to be discreet. In a subsequent remodelling of the retail space, the computer screen was placed in a more private and secure position and staff were reminded to be careful in accessing customer data.

Security of Personal Health Information

All the above are relevant to personal health information. Consequently, it is particularly important that data controllers who keep such information have well-established security policies in place that reflect the importance they attach to proper safeguards.

---

[291] Data Protection Commissioner (1997), *Case Study 1.*

Practices that may lead to breaches of security include:

♦ Leaving medical notes unattended at a public counter.

♦ Not disposing of health records in a secure manner.

♦ Inadequate controls regarding which staff can access health information – this might include inadequate password control on a database.

♦ Storing sensitive data on a laptop computer that is taken off-site and not stored securely.

Determining reasonable security measures will depend on the circumstances. Relevant factors to consider include:

♦ The sensitivity of the health information held by the health service provider.

♦ The harm likely to result, if there is a breach of security.

♦ The form in which the information is stored (on paper, electronically or video), processed and transmitted.

♦ The size of the organisation and the cost-effectiveness of the options available.

Examples of reasonable steps include:

♦ Implementing computer system safeguards, including password protection, with required regular changes to passwords, and electronic audit trails.

♦ Providing lockable physical security for paper records.

♦ Ensuring information is communicated securely (for example, not transmitting health information via non-secure e-mail).

♦ Monitoring information systems to test and evaluate data security.

SOME SPECIFIC ISSUES

Having regard to the matters outlined in the Chapter, the following advice is tendered in relation to some frequently-asked questions: namely, what is the position in relation to:

- ◆ Scanned medical records?
- ◆ Patient transfers to another doctor?
- ◆ Closure or sale of a practice?
- ◆ Medical smart-cards and security?
- ◆ Electronic communication of personal health information?
- ◆ Destruction or permanent de-identification of personal health information.

Scanned Records & Retention of Originals

If an original paper copy of medical correspondence or an existing manual patient record is scanned into a computer, and the scanned document (whether retained in the computer or copied to a disk, etc.) cannot be edited in any way whatsoever except by reference to a provable and verifiable audit trail that records all attempts at accessing or attempted modification, then there is no need for the original to be retained. Apart from having appropriate security, the data controller should have a full back-up procedure in case of computer failure, etc.

In addition, the destruction of original records (especially healthcare records) must always be done in a way that ensures that they are properly, completely and confidentially destroyed. It is important for doctors and other health professionals to remember that, under data protection legislation and the law generally, responsibility for patient records (irrespective of the form they are kept in), including their destruction, is invariably on them.

Patient Transfer to Another Doctor

Where a patient decides to transfer to another doctor (or indeed, any other healthcare professional), the existing doctor should facilitate that decision by making available to the patient's new doctor a copy of the patient's health information, in accordance with data protection law and ethical guidelines. However, the original doctor should maintain the patient information record accumulated up to the date of transfer for an adequate future period, consistent with medico-legal and other professional responsibilities. During that period, the provisions of the Data Protection Acts (and FOI legislation, if the patient is a public patient) continue to apply to the information.

Closure or Sale of a GP Practice[292]

In the event of the closure of a GP practice through the retirement (or death) of a general practitioner operating in a single-handed practice, the medical practitioner (or executor, in the case of the medical practitioner being deceased) should take prompt and reasonable steps to notify patients and to allow them the opportunity to transfer their records to another provider. If any patient cannot be contacted, or does not respond within a reasonable period, the medical practitioner (or executor) should maintain the records with due safeguards for an appropriate period and then securely destroy them.

In the case of a retirement or death within a partnership or group practice, the practice should inform the patients of the general practitioner involved of his or her retirement or death and advise that the patients' records will be retained within the practice for the benefit and continued care of the patient (unless the patient explicitly directs that they should be transferred to another practice). Where the patient advises that he or she wishes to transfer to another practice, the procedure to be followed by the practice is as set out in the above paragraph on *Patient Transfer to Another Doctor*.

Medical Smart Cards & Security

Smart card technology is a part of modern life and the development of the Electronic Health Record may well see individuals carry their health records around in the same way they currently carry credit cards.

In such a situation, while the smart card may be issued by a central authority, there may be, depending on the information content, several data controllers involved – general practitioners, pharmacists, hospitals, consultants, Health Boards and others. Accordingly, the use

---

[292] In **Chapter 4**, we identified the relevant provisions in the GMS Scheme contract applicable to the records of a medical card patient in the event of the death, retirement or resignation of his or her doctor.

of smart cards raises issues of identifying who is, in any situation, the data controller. As in every situation, the answer will be determined by the application of the data protection provisions to the facts of the particular situation.

In terms of security, the use of medical smart cards is likely to give rise to a particular set of security considerations that health authorities and the Data Protection Commissioner will have to agree on.[293] One matter is certain, security will need to be specific and robust enough to ensure access on a need to know basis only. Equally, the patient should be made aware of (i) the information content of the card, (ii) the card's intended uses and (iii) persons having card editing facilities.

Electronic Communication of Personal Health Information

There are already a number of initiatives underway in Ireland between general practice, hospitals and other agencies involving the communication of personal health information electronically.

This matter has already been considered briefly in **Chapter 4**. It is recommended that, in other similar situations, the type of agreement that Healthlink enters into with its participating data controllers (GPs) should be followed and include an appropriate security clause.

Destruction or Permanent De-identification of Health Information

When original records are re-configured – for example, by committing them to microfilm, CD, etc. – or destroyed when no alternative storage is available – a clear destruction procedure should be applied. In relation to personal records for patients, clients and staff, a log of files destroyed containing the person's name, date of birth, file number and date of last contact with the service should be maintained. This log should be completed by an employee of the data controller supervising the removal process and by a senior employee authorising the removal and destruction of the records. The date of destruction

---

[293] Data Protection Commissioner (1996). The Commissioner described how his Office had been involved in lengthy consultations with the Department of Health and the Eastern Health Board before the introduction in Bray of a pilot project on the use of medical smart cards.

and the manner in which the records were destroyed should also be recorded.

The destruction should be carried out by shredding, pulping or incineration. Where a contractor is used to carry out any of these processes, he or she should be required to sign confidentiality undertakings and to produce written certification as proof of destruction. Direct supervision of this exercise may be important, especially where the personal health information in any record being destroyed is particularly sensitive.

In many cases, feasible alternatives to destroying health information should be considered and may include archiving data securely or keeping summary or statistical information, where this is sufficient, or de-personalising it.

Concluding Observations

It is worth repeating the conclusion in the Health Board's *Records* document that:

> "... many organisations lack effective mechanisms for handling their records. This has resulted in significant amounts of information either being incorrectly filed or being recorded in unmanaged files. Active management of such information is necessary to facilitate the efficient operation of the organisation and to comply with statutory requirements."[294]

Information no longer needed for further use or disclosure, including records no longer required for treatment and care, or for health service management, monitoring or evaluation, or for legal reasons, should be destroyed, securely archived or permanently de-identified.

Health information is highly valuable for many reasons, most importantly for an individual's on-going healthcare, but sometimes also for wider public health and safety reasons.

There is a need to balance, amongst other things, benefits to healthcare with privacy when deciding how to proceed with the destruction of health information. However, healthcare service

---

[294] National Freedom of Information Liaison Group (Health Boards) (1999).

providers will need to consider the risks in keeping health information for longer than is necessary, as this may increase the risk of privacy breaches.

Considerations regarding the retention or destruction of health information include:

♦ The legal or professional requirements to retain it.

♦ The benefits and risks of keeping the information.

♦ The likely significance of the information for the individual's future care or for future public health knowledge or research.

♦ Its possible importance in relation to new reproductive and genetic technologies.

♦ Possible alternatives to destruction, such as de-personalisation.

Finally, writing in 2001, Dr. Brian Meade made the point that:

> "... with a few precautions, electronic records held on computer are actually safer than manual records. The ability to retain a spare copy of all your patient data at home provides great peace of mind. In the event of your practice suffering damage due to a fire, flood or burglary, a spare copy of your patient files is available to keep you functioning."[295]

---

[295] Meade (2001).

9

USING & DISCLOSING PERSONAL HEALTH INFORMATION

INTRODUCTION

The guiding principle governing the use and disclosure[296] of all personal health information is that the data subject should understand what the data controller proposes to do with it and be agreeable to those intentions. Only in certain limited circumstances is it lawful or ethical to use personal health information inconsistently with the wishes of the patient.

Further, privacy advocates argue that a health information system or network should allow patients to opt out, without compromising their access to healthcare. For example, Saskatchewan's Health Information Protection Act 1999 upholds patient autonomy and consent. Persons can choose not to have their personal information on the Province Health Information Network or any prescribed network.

---

[296] The definition of disclosure has already been set out. However, since the concepts of "use" and "disclosure" are central to this Chapter, it is worth elaborating on them briefly. Under the Data Protection Acts, communication of information made directly or indirectly by a data controller or data processor to an employee or agent for the purpose of enabling that person to carry out his or her duties is essentially a use, rather than a disclosure of information. For example, in a hospital, this means that administrative information communicated by the A&E Department to Accounts about a patient's stay for billing purposes represents an internal use of personal health information. A disclosure of information for the purposes of the Data Protection Acts can occur in a variety of ways – for example, telephone, letter, email, etc. – and everyone in the data controller's organisation should be made fully aware of the need to guard against the unauthorised or inadvertent release of information.

Patients control where their information is kept and who has access to it. This is commonly referred to as a "locked box" provision.

We have already seen, in **Chapter 6**, that consent can generally be implied for a patient's health information to flow freely within the "circle of care". Implied consent is normally also applicable in other situations, where the proposed use or disclosure by the data controller is clearly and directly related to, or arises from, the patient's treatment and would have been within the reasonable and informed expectation of the patient at the time the information was collected from him or her.

It may not be so easy to argue implied consent where the information in question is obtained from another party. In such instances, the legitimacy of relying on informed consent will be determined by the circumstances of each case, in particular the reason why the information could not have been obtained directly from the data subject.

In any other case of intended use or disclosure that strays beyond the above, such as making personal health information available to a third party researcher, express consent is invariably required.

Accordingly, patients' consent and their reasonable expectations regarding the use of their health information are crucial. This again emphasises the importance of open communication between healthcare data controllers and their clients. In that context, the final section of this chapter looks at the Scottish NHS's approach as a model for openness.

PRIMARY & SECONDARY PURPOSES

Primary Purpose

The primary purpose is the main reason a data controller keeps personal information about an individual. It would be a cause of concern if a data controller could not readily identify what the primary purpose was in relation to any personal information obtained or kept by it. Apart from data protection considerations, such a situation would suggest that the data controller has ineffective management information arrangements.

In the health sector, where an individual visits a healthcare service provider for advice or treatment, the *primary* purpose for which information is recorded, used or disclosed by the provider is that of the patient's care. In practice, certain details may also be recorded for internal management and related purposes – for example, whether the patient has medical insurance or a medical card, what consultation fee was paid, etc. These are *secondary* purposes. Moreover, the health provider visited may envisage using some or all the information recorded for its own research or statistical analysis. These are also secondary purposes. As with primary purposes, data controllers should be able to enumerate secondary purposes.

It is most important, especially in relation to sensitive categories of information such as health, that there should be a common view between the data controller and the data subject on the primary and secondary purposes for which information is processed. To that end, the data controller should prepare and make widely available a patient information leaflet that gives as much detail as possible, in an easy-to-understand manner, about the way personal health information is obtained, used, retained, secured and disclosed by it. This should be complemented and supplemented by a positive approach to identifying and resolving particular issues that certain clients may have.

Primary Purposes: Integrated Care & Sharing

It is recognised that the development of primary care teams and other multi-disciplinary structures provide the opportunity for the provision of a wider range of, and more integrated, patient services. These can be delivered either in a single purpose-built healthcare centre or in a number of related centres and locations, as local circumstances and resources dictate. (In a somewhat similar fashion, group and partnership practices allow general practitioners to come together and pool clinical and administrative resources for enhanced patient care.)

In order for the concept of integrated care involving a number of members of a primary care team to work effectively, the sharing of certain personal health information may well be necessary for proper patient treatment and, where this is the case, it would come within the "circle of care" concept.

As a general rule, whenever personal health information is to be shared with, or made available to, another health professional in a team, centre or hospital, it should be on a need-to-know basis and, importantly, the patient must understand the circumstances in which this may occur.

The Australian *Guidelines on Privacy in the Private Health Sector* reflect this view:

> "The key to making this principle easy to meet is ensuring alignment between the expectations and understanding of the health service provider and those of the individual about what will be done with personal information collected. Providers need to pay most attention to those circumstances where expectations are not shared."[297]

In that regard, healthcare providers should recognise that some individuals want to use health services in particular and limited ways. For instance, someone may seek care and treatment through a particular healthcare service provider, wanting to tell certain information only to that provider. This may happen where an individual attends a specialist sexual centre and is seeking advice and treatment on that one issue only, and does not want the information disclosed to anyone, including his or her general practitioner. Consequently, it is possible that, even within the "circle of care" context, there will be some circumstances where a healthcare service provider needs to seek express consent before sharing information with another provider. This may include some second opinions. For these reasons, when collecting information, it is always advisable to discuss with the individual how the team-based approach to treatment will affect the handling of personal information.

Secondary Purposes: Non-Treatment Uses & Disclosures (Implied Consent)

Secondary purposes include certain activities or processes not directly related to patient care but which arise from the provision of such care and are necessary to the proper operation of the data controller's

---

[297] Federal Privacy Commissioner (Australia) (2001).

organisation or business. If implied consent is to be relied on then, as a matter of data protection law and good administrative practice, (a) the individual should be advised, of these possible uses or disclosures of his or her information and (b) the amount of information that is used or released should be limited to the minimum necessary for the particular activity involved. These secondary purposes can include:

♦ Management and administrative functions within the data controller's organisation

♦ Audit and control uses.

Management & Administrative Functions

Healthcare service providers come in many forms and sizes. They range from a single-handed healthcare practitioner operating from his or her home to a modern state-of-the-art hi-tech hospital facility. In every case, the data controller will be required to maintain certain organisational records that may contain certain personal health information.

Data subjects have the right to expect – and data controllers are obliged to see – that the use and flow of personal health information within any organisation should be regulated to ensure that it is available only to the extent necessary to enable the clerical, executive and management staff perform their tasks for the legitimate functioning of the organisation. In that regard, patients can be reasonably expected to understand that such personnel are likely to have access to their records for billing, appointment and other administrative purposes. It is a matter of good practice that all persons in any organisation keeping personal health information (not already covered by a professional confidentiality code) should sign a confidentiality agreement that explicitly makes clear both their duties in relation to personal health information and the consequences of breaching that duty.

Audit & Control Uses

Financial auditing or other external verification of records is a standard legal requirement that applies to most data controllers. The purpose is to ensure that the records give a true and fair view of the data controller's activities, especially for tax and other financial purposes. In carrying out their tasks, auditors or inspectors examining the accounts of health service providers may wish to confirm certain visits and payments with the individuals against whose name they are recorded.

In Scotland, in the aftermath of the implementation of the EU Data Protection Directive, staff undertaking payment verification of primary care practitioners' claims for payment were prevented by a number of practitioners from carrying out their work, because of a stated fear that allowing access to patients' personal health information for such audit purposes would breach their Data Protection Act. On consultation, the Information Commissioner took the view that implied consent is sufficient for GP practices making disclosures of patient data for the purpose of being paid for treatment provided. The Scottish NHS accepted this view and the related need for primary care practitioners to inform their patients in order to infer their consent to use personal health information for the purposes of fee payment. The same arrangements then operate for dataflows intended to assure the verification of services, their provision and quality. Accordingly, both payment verification and practice visits for the purposes of audit are legitimate activities under this heading.

A similar interpretation would appear appropriate under Irish data protection law. However, once again, it is most advisable that patients are made aware in the practice information leaflet that certain services attract payments which their practice needs to claim and verify, and that routine checks will be made for this purpose by HSE or other regulatory staff. The leaflet should also take the opportunity to detail the nature and level of the information that the audit or verification body will have access to for its purposes. Prominently displayed posters can be used in addition to, but not as a substitute for, leaflets.

Secondary Purposes: Non-Treatment Uses & Disclosures (Express Consent)

Other secondary purposes require express consent, because it would be unreasonable to expect that an individual would regard them as being part of, or arising from, his or her treatment arrangement with the healthcare service provider. These include use or disclosure of patient information for:

- ◆ Training and education.
- ◆ Teaching purposes.
- ◆ Quality assurance and continuing professional development.
- ◆ Disclosures to religious chaplains in hospitals, etc.
- ◆ Direct marketing.
- ◆ Fundraising.
- ◆ Bad debt recovery.

Training & Education

It is important for healthcare practitioners to be able to train in "real life" environments, although equally effective training and education, in some cases, may be provided by using de-identified case studies or, in the case of IT training, through using simulated data. If a healthcare professional uses de-identified information for training, consent is not required. However, where the use of personal health information is necessary for training purposes, the sensitivity of such information needs recognition. Some individuals seeking healthcare may not want their information disclosed any more widely than is necessary to receive treatment. These individuals will certainly not want their information used for training or education activities and more importantly, if they were asked, they would not give their consent to its use or disclosure for any purpose other than their own healthcare.[298]

Teaching Purposes

Wherever possible, personal health information should be anonymised before it is used for teaching purposes. Where this is not possible, the doctor should be certain that the patient understands and agrees to this use.

Quality Assurance & Continuing Professional Development

Quality assurance can be defined as all activities that contribute to defining, designing, assessing, monitoring, and improving the quality of care both for individual patients and the healthcare system

---

[298] In Australia, the *Guidelines* state that "the use of information for training and education will therefore usually require the individual's consent".

generally. These activities can be performed as part of the accreditation of facilities, supervision of health workers, or other efforts to improve the performance of health workers and the quality of health services.

Continuing Professional Development is usually taken to mean learning and related activities, especially formal arrangements, that update existing skills. It is generally regarded as essential to good patient care that healthcare professionals are committed to ongoing development of their skills and knowledge.

Personal health information can be used for quality assurance and continuing professional development activities within the practice or hospital where:

♦ The patient has given consent for the use of personal health information for these activities, or

♦ The personal health information has been anonymised.

Disclosures to Religious Chaplains in Hospitals, etc.

Disclosures of personal information relating to a patient to religious chaplains in hospitals, etc., or to other clerical persons, is not permitted, in normal circumstances, under data protection law, without the consent of the patient. This does not prevent hospital chaplains from making themselves readily accessible to any patient who wishes to see them. In exceptional circumstances, such as where a patient is brought into hospital in a serious and unconscious state, a friend or relative can act to give or withhold consent. The situation is more complex where there is no person to give consent. Rather than placing the onus on the medical staff involved, hospitals and medical centres should have a clearly articulated policy in this area.

Direct Marketing

Direct marketing by a data controller, using health information collected by it in the course of treating patients, would not fall within the reasonable expectations of most individuals, and some might even be upset by it. Accordingly, as a matter of good sense, considerable care should always be exercised with uses that may be seen by the data subject as direct marketing. It should be emphasised that, in no case, can personal health information be disclosed to an outside party for its commercial marketing use without the clearest express consent of the individual involved.

Fundraising

Ordinarily, information collected by a healthcare service provider during the provision of health services cannot be used for fundraising without consent. A healthcare service provider may use personal information for fundraising, only if it was collected primarily for that purpose. For example, the fundraising section of a private hospital may want to write to former patients asking for donations. The section requires only the names and addresses of former patients to do so. However, an individual's name and address, collected in the course of providing a health service, is regarded as "health information" and is therefore sensitive. Seeking donations using this information would not be a directly-related secondary purpose, nor within reasonable expectations. The hospital would need consent to use the information in this way.

Bad Debt Recovery

While the use and disclosure of limited personal health information by a data controller for routine internal financial management and independent auditing can rely on implied consent, the potential communication of personal details to a debt recovery firm would come as a surprise to many patients. Therefore, it requires express consent.

Increasingly, Irish healthcare bodies look to debt recovery firms to pursue patients who have not paid their bills. For example, several of the Health Boards, in their data protection registration entries for 2004/5, listed debt recovery agencies as disclosees.

Expectations & Awareness

It is worth explaining that expectation is more than awareness – telling someone about proposed secondary uses or disclosures may not necessarily create a reasonable expectation. A healthcare data controller needs to consider the kind of person they are talking to, what their understanding is likely to be and therefore what they may reasonably expect. This means having regard to factors such as the individual's age, sex or cultural, linguistic and socio-economic background. If an individual expresses negative views, when made aware of a proposed secondary use or disclosure of their personal information, this would indicate ordinarily that they would not reasonably expect that use or disclosure to occur. All in all, a reasonable expectation is what a reasonable individual with no special knowledge of the health sector would expect to happen to their health information.

Commonsense & Special Rules

Sometimes the impression can be given mistakenly that the rules on use and disclosure of personal health information are so inflexible as to be bizarre, unworkable and even likely to endanger life. This is not so and the file notes of the New Zealand Privacy Commissioner give an excellent example:

> "A nurse saw a patient who had had a general anaesthetic not long before driving away from the hospital. She was very worried about the patient's safety and wanted to contact the police. However, she was told by ill-informed hospital management that they could not do that 'because of the Privacy Act'. The nurse did not agree, being of the view that the appropriate authorities could be notified if people were a danger to themselves or to others. She was correct as the Privacy Code is explicit. If there is a serious and imminent threat to the life or health of a person, and obtaining authorisation is not practicable or desirable, then personal health information (but only as much as necessary) can be disclosed to a person who can act to prevent or lessen the threat."[299]

Personal Health Information & Automated Decision-Making Processes

A particular provision on use worth noting was introduced by the Data Protection Act 2003. It provides that decisions which produce legal effects, or otherwise significantly affect an individual, should not be based solely on automated processing of information, where the purpose is to evaluate certain matters relating to the individual.[300]

---

[299] Privacy Commissioner (New Zealand) (2001).
[300] Section 6B of the Data Protection Acts 1998 to 2003.

In healthcare, in the future, an increasing number of decisions (both clinical and other) will be based on tests and processes involving computer-based risk assessment and stratification. The value of this approach usually is supported by clear evidence and its use is for the undisputed benefit of the patient. In any such situations, the agreement of the patient overrides the prohibition and this can be obtained in the normal course of explaining the test or process to the individual involved.

Summary of Implications for Health Service Data Controllers

Healthcare data controllers need to take care not to go beyond the expectations of the individual, when it comes to using or disclosing information. If a healthcare provider is uncertain, it should make sure the individual understands and expects the proposed uses and disclosures. In most situations, an individual's expectations will be apparent through normal communication. Where the individual's expectations are reasonably clear, and the healthcare provider works within them, there are likely to be fewer privacy problems.

Chapters 6 and **7** (fair processing and obtaining of information) are clearly relevant in this whole area of use and disclosure. It is necessary only to summarise the key points here: namely, that at a minimum:

- ◆ Individuals should be made fully aware of the proposed uses and intended disclosures of their personal health information as early as possible.

- ◆ They should be able to question such uses and disclosures.

- ◆ They should understand the essential purposes of sharing information and the consequences of not doing so.

- ◆ They should be advised of safeguards that are in place and their ability to object to potential misuses of data where use is mandatory.

PARTICULAR ISSUES ARISING IN GENERAL PRACTICE

Given the importance of general practice in the Irish health system and its uniqueness, it is worthwhile considering several issues relating to use and disclosure of personal health information that arise in that sector. (Some of these scenarios may be relevant to other healthcare service providers in the wider primary care field.)

Locums

Making clinical patient records available to a locum doctor, so that the locum may provide medical care to patients, is compatible with the purpose for which the general practitioner keeps the patient record.

Change of Doctor in a Practice

In cases where a medical practice is taken over by a new medical practitioner, or a new medical practitioner joins an existing group practice, a question arises as to whether the new medical practitioner can have access to the patient records of the practice. Access is only appropriate where the patient concerned has given consent. Generally, consent can be inferred from the fact that the patient has sought a consultation with (or has not objected to being seen by) the new medical practitioner.

Sale of a Medical Practice

Where a practice has been sold to another practitioner, all patients should be notified individually within a reasonable time of the change of ownership. This can be done by means of a letter that offers the patient the choice of remaining with the practice and the new general practitioner or having their personal information sent to another GP of their choosing. In the event of the patient not responding negatively within a certain specified time of being so advised, it can be reasonably presumed that he or she is satisfied that their personal health information should remain with the practice and the new general practitioner.

Third-party Disclosures

General practitioners make daily disclosures of patient information to third parties, either as part of the treatment process (for example, to hospital consultants) or at the direct request of the patient, and therefore consent is not normally problematic. However, difficulties can arise where the nature of the disclosure, or the consequences of it, are not fully understood by the patient.

The following are situations where particular difficulties can arise:

♦ Referral letters to specialists.

♦ Private medical attendant reports.

♦ Reports to employers.

♦ Request for copies of medical records by solicitors.

Referral Letters to Specialists

Patients may not be aware that details of past medical history, as well as other personal information, may be included in a referral letter. With electronic patient records, this information is inserted automatically from the patient's electronic file and sensitive information can be included that is not necessary for the specialist to see.

It is therefore good practice to:

♦ Check the contents of the medical history section in referral letters and omit sensitive or unnecessary details from them.

♦ Give referral letters, or copies thereof, to patients when making referrals, for their own information.

♦ Use computer software to "hide" especially sensitive information (for example, pregnancy terminations), so that it appears in the record but not in referral letters, unless the GP chooses to put it there and the patient agrees.

♦ Inform patients, *via* the practice information leaflet, that it is standard practice to include a list of their major medical illnesses, current medications and drug allergies in all referral letters to specialists.

Private Medical Attendant Reports

Private medical attendant (PMA) reports are requested from general practitioners by insurance companies to assess a person's insurance risk for pensions, mortgages and other financial products.

The PMA report involves a series of detailed questions about a patient's current and past medical history. Disclosure by the general practitioner of any significant illness in the PMA is likely to lead to refusal by the company to insure, or to offer premium rates above those normally quoted. In certain instances, the first insurance company may also wish to share the names of clients who have been refused with other insurance companies, thereby making it extremely difficult for some individuals to get protective cover with any insurer.

General practitioners are part of this process and, although patients have consented to the release of data by their doctor, not all patients actually appreciate the detail of information released and the likely consequences of certain disclosures. There is also the possibility that patients may fail to report certain problems to their general practitioner for fear that it may affect insurance premiums, which can create potentially serious problems for both patients and doctors in care provision over time.

Having regard to the complex and sensitive issues involved in this area, the following approach should be adopted:

♦ General practitioners should inform patients of the type, and possible consequences, of private health information they disclose to insurance companies. This can be done in the form of a letter sent to the patient when a PMA request is received by the practice.

♦ Patients should be given a period of time to view the contents of the PMA report before it is sent to the insurance company.

♦ General practitioners should respond only to written requests for clarification regarding PMA reports and should also only reply in writing to the chief medical officer of the insurance company.

♦ General practitioners should not send actual copies of consultation notes to insurance companies. Only the nature of a complaint, treatment offered and outcome should be included.

♦ Consultants' reports concerning patients should not be sent to insurance companies. Insurance companies can approach the consultants directly for these, if they believe they are necessary.

It is recommended that the all above matters should be outlined for the benefit of patients in a patient information leaflet.

Reports to Employers

While, in most instances, medical certificates should only provide a confirmation that the patient is unfit for work, together with an indication of when he or she may be able to return, on occasions there may be proper business and employment reasons that require the employer to be advised of the general nature of the employee's illness or condition.

In any such situation, the matter should be discussed with the employee by the medical practitioner, and the employee should be advised of what information is intended to be provided. Further, where the employee is concerned that his or her health illness or condition is of a particularly sensitive nature, the medical practitioner should consider releasing the information only to the employing firm's occupational health doctor.

General practitioners retained by businesses as an occupational health advisor should also exercise care in their dealings with employers. Patients asked to attend the general practitioner in order that a report can be prepared for forwarding to an employer should be made aware of the reason for the visit and any implications that would flow from unwillingness either to undergo an examination or to allow the examination results to go to his or her employer.

Requests for Medical Records by Solicitors

It is common for solicitors to request copies of clients' medical records in order to assess the strength or otherwise of a personal injuries claim. This request is generally made, on behalf of the patient, pursuant to section 8(h) of the Data Protection Acts, which provides for disclosures, at the discretion of the data controller, with the consent of the data subject.

The general practitioner should try to ensure that the patient fully understands the implication of such disclosure. Patients may not appreciate that the entire medical record is usually requested by the solicitor – in any such cases, there should be grounds justifying the need for complete records – and that both parties in the legal case may have access to it subsequently. In every case, the request from the solicitor must be accompanied by a signed consent from the patient.

A GOOD APPROACH TO OPENNESS

Devolution in the United Kingdom has seen the creation of an even more distinctive NHS for Scotland and it is already clear that significant difference are emerging in approaches to patient health information management. In the section of the Scottish NHS website dealing with *Confidentiality & Privacy*,[301] there is a prominent statement about patients' rights to control the use of their information:

> "You also have the right to object to us making use of your information. You can ask us to change or restrict the way we use your information and we are obliged to agree if it is possible to do so."

In addition, the Scottish NHS has produced information leaflets advising patients of the potential uses of their personal health information and their rights. An abridged version is reproduced below:[302]

> *What is this leaflet about?*
>
> It tells you:
>
> ◆ What your personal health information is.
> ◆ How the NHS keeps this information confidential.
> ◆ How this information is used.
> ◆ Who this information is shared with and why.
> ◆ Your rights.

---

[301] www.show.scot.nhs.uk/confidentiality/patientguidance.htm.
[302] The full version is at www.show.scot.nhs.uk/healthrights/leaflets/confid/scotland/confid.htm.

Why has this leaflet been produced?

The NHS must keep your personal health information confidential. It is your right. This leaflet explains how the NHS does this.

What is my personal health information?

It is information that identifies you. It includes things like your name, address, date of birth or postcode. It can be linked to, for example:

♦ Information about any care and treatment you have received.

♦ Information about your health and lifestyle.

♦ Results of tests you have had.

How and where is my personal health information kept?

It is kept in records. Records can be written on paper, held on computer or both. Records are stored securely in different parts of the NHS.

♦ You have a record at your GP surgery.

♦ If your GP refers you to a hospital, the hospital will start a new record and keep it there.

♦ Records can also be held in other places, for example, at your dental surgery or at a clinic you have been to.

How does the NHS keep my personal health information confidential?

♦ All NHS staff have a legal duty to keep information about you confidential.

♦ The NHS stores your personal health information securely.

♦ Only relevant information is shared inside the NHS or with outside organisations. We explain when and why it's shared later in this leaflet.

♦ The NHS will not give information about you to organisations such as benefits agencies, employers or the media without your permission.

How is my personal health information used?

NHS staff use your information to give you the care and treatment you need. They will share relevant information with other NHS staff involved in your care. This makes caring for you safer, easier and faster. For example, information is shared if:

♦ Your GP refers you to a hospital.

♦ You are moved from one hospital to another.

♦ You need support at home, such as a visit from a district nurse.

♦ NHS 24 refers you to a GP or another part of the NHS.

If you are concerned about your information being shared, you can object. We explain how to object later in this leaflet.

How else does the NHS use information about my health?

The NHS uses relevant information about your health to help improve the general public's health and NHS services. They should give you information about how they use it. It can be used, for example:

♦ To count the number of cases of diseases.

♦ To look at how safe and effective a treatment is, for example, flu vaccinations.

♦ To check that the NHS is providing a good service.

♦ To plan how many beds, wards and staff are needed.

♦ To train students and staff.

♦ To check that the NHS spends public money properly.

♦ For research.

Wherever possible, your name, address and other information that identifies you is removed. Sometimes the NHS uses information that does identify you. If they do this, they should explain to you how and why your information will be used. If they use information which identifies you for teaching or research, they must ask your permission.

If you don't want the NHS to use your information to help improve public health and NHS services, you can object. We explain how to object later in this leaflet.

When can my personal health information be shared outside the NHS?

As well as NHS staff, you might receive care from a carer, a home help, a social worker or others. They might need to know relevant information about your health. Usually, it will only be given to them if:

♦ You have agreed, and

♦ They need it to be able to give you care and treatment.

Usually the NHS will not share your personal health information with people such as a relative, carer or friend without your permission. However, there are special cases:

♦ If you are a child, the law may allow someone with parental responsibility for you to see your records and discuss your care.

♦ If you are an adult who cannot make decisions for yourself, or cannot tell others your decisions, the law allows someone to see your records and discuss your care, if:

  ◊ You have appointed them to act on your behalf in a power of attorney, or

  ◊ They have applied to a court and have been granted the power in a guardianship order.

In these special cases, that person will not receive information that:

♦ You have told NHS staff you don't want them to have, or

♦ That staff feel would be harmful to your health or the health of others.

To get more information about the rights of children you can contact the Scottish Child Law Centre. Their contact details are given later in this leaflet.

To get more information about the rights of adults who cannot make their own decisions or tell others their decisions you can contact the Office of the Public Guardian. Their contact details are given later in this leaflet.

Sometimes the law allows the NHS to share your personal health information without your permission, for example, to investigate a serious crime or to protect a child.

What are my rights?

As well as your right to confidentiality, you have the right to:

♦ Know how your personal health information is used. You can ask a member of NHS staff providing your care.

♦ See your health records and, if you choose, to get a copy. The leaflet 'How to see your Health Records' explains how to do this. We explain how to get a copy of 'How to see your Health Records' later in this leaflet.

♦ Object, if you don't want your health information to be used or shared, tell a member of NHS staff providing your care. If you do this, the NHS has to limit how it uses your information where possible.

♦ Complain, if you are not happy about how your health information has been used or protected, first talk to a member of NHS staff providing your care. If you are still not happy after this, and would like to make a complaint, the leaflet 'The NHS Complaints Procedure' explains what to do.

10
HEALTH SERVICE
MANAGEMENT & RESEARCH

INTRODUCTION

One of the key debates in data protection and privacy is the need to balance potentially conflicting rights and needs. The rights relate to individuals and the degree of control they should enjoy over information relating to them. The needs relate to society and the benefits to the public good that greater use and sharing of information may facilitate. In the health sector, this conflict is about the rights of the patient to determine who has access to their medical records and the needs of the health service to use patient information for a range of management and research purposes that stand to benefit society generally, through better service planning and healthcare innovations. Like most data protection issues, the problem is not confined to Ireland.

For example, in England & Wales, a 2002 NHS study on people's attitudes to consent and confidentiality of patient information – *Share with Care: People's Views on Consent & Confidentiality of Patient Information* – stated:

> "Without access to appropriate information, a health system is, at best, inefficient and frustrating and, at worst, dangerous. Modern healthcare services cannot function without those involved having the information they need to provide and receive care. Their needs for information cannot be met without electronic medical records and other computerised systems."[303]

---

[303] National Health Service Information Authority (UK) (2002). This qualitative and quantitative research study was undertaken in conjunction with the Consumers' Association and *Health Which?*.

In the USA, in 1997, Donna Shalala, then Health & Human Resources Secretary, outlined the nature of the challenge in more everyday terms:

> "Twenty-five years ago, our healthcare privacy was protected by our family doctor, whom we trusted not only because of the Hippocratic Oath and the fundamental ethics of medicine – but because we knew them. Today, the revolution in our healthcare delivery system means that instead of Marcus Welby, we have to place our trust in entire networks of insurers and healthcare professionals. The challenge is to balance protection of privacy with our public responsibility to support national priorities – public health, research, quality care, and our fight against healthcare fraud and abuse."[304]

In Ireland, as we saw in **Chapter 1**, the pressures for improved management information systems and greater sharing of information for a variety of health-related purposes, including research, have come to the fore in the debate over improving our health system.

Before going any further, it is important to record the response of the Data Protection Commissioner to this new emphasis on healthcare information systems:

> "Data protection law is no barrier to a proper functioning health service because it provides an assurance that in this delicate area people's privacy rights are protected. In this regard, data protection complements the confidentiality obligations of medical ethics."[305]

---

[304] Shalala (1997).

[305] Data Protection Commissioner (2003).

HEALTH INFORMATION &
RESEARCH STRATEGIES

In 2001, the Deloitte & Touche *Value for Money Review of the Irish Health System* identified inadequate information systems as a critical weakness limiting the capacity for the proper management and performance of the health system.[306] The National Health Strategy[307] published later that year – *Quality & Fairness* – emphasised that improved information management must play a central role in supporting strategic goals (including research) and, for that reason, must not be seen merely as an add-on. Accordingly, it examined the ways in which enhanced information systems and new technologies[308] might be introduced and used to greatest effect. In particular, it saw a crucial role for the proposed Health Information & Quality Authority[309] in promoting a common approach to security, privacy and confidentiality and the development and agreement of guidelines governing access to information from health agencies.

All of this, including the establishment of HIQA, would be facilitated by legislation that would drive and govern the new information frameworks that would emerge from the more detailed consideration of information issues in the National Health Information Strategy. In brief, the envisaged legislation would address concerns about privacy and confidentiality, while ensuring that health information could be utilised for the benefit of all.[310]

Taking its cue from *Quality & Fairness*, the Health Information Strategy is quite clear on what it is seeking to do. Its central aim is to "exploit information to the fullest" in pursuit of the goals of the National Health Strategy. In so doing, it recognised that there is a need

---

[306] Deloitte & Touche (2001).

[307] Department of Health & Children (2001).

[308] The Strategy recognised the value of information and communications technology: Action 116 provided for a sustained programme of investment in the development of national health information systems, while Action 117 asserted that information and communications technology will be fully exploited in service delivery.

[309] Department of Health & Children (2001), Action 111.

[310] Department of Health & Children (2001), Action 121.

for a set of rules to ensure full and proper use of information, while fully protecting the privacy of the individual.

These aims, and their related privacy challenges, are discussed throughout the 2004 National Health Information Strategy but are most clearly articulated in *Chapter 12*, which deals with health information governance, defined as:

> "... a strategic framework that brings coherence and transparency to information initiatives and which is responsive to the spectrum of issues and concerns of those involved" ... [and] ... "includes issues such as information sharing, health surveillance, quality assurance, confidentiality, privacy, records management, freedom of information and data protection".[311]

The chapter is worth reading in its entirety, because it gives a very clear insight into the legal, management and administrative structures that the Department of Health & Children believes should govern personal health information, especially its use for management purposes. Those structures would be created through the introduction of a Health Information Bill,[312] which would then provide:

> "... a comprehensive statutory framework within which to require, permit, or prohibit the sharing of personal health information for purposes beyond the context of treatment or personal services provided by the health professional".[313]

In the same vein, it goes on to say that:

> "... it is essential that the privacy of an individual's information is respected and that, at the same time, health professionals who share health information as a necessary part of their duties are also protected. Both these requirements must be achieved in a way that supports high-quality care of individuals while also allowing essential

---

[311] Department of Health & Children (2004), *Chapter 12*.

[312] That Bill, would, of course, need to pass successfully through the Oireachtas before becoming law.

[313] Department of Health & Children (2004), *Chapter 12*.

service functions to be carried out, such as health surveillance and disease registration and the quality assurance of health services."

All of this is predicated on the view that:

"… individuals in receipt of care presume on a health system that maintains and grows its expertise and ability to protect the public by virtue of its access to the health information of the population. While legislation must protect the individual, it must also enable the maintenance of information systems to support necessary health service functions in the common good."

Identified Management Information Requirements

In support of the general objective of improving the management of the health system and facilitating the development of the Electronic Health Record, the National Health Information Strategy proposed the following specific steps:

- Personal health information will be collected, used and disseminated for defined purposes, including quality assurance purposes, professional audit mechanisms, disease and procedure specific registers, risk management and adverse incident reporting systems and performance measurement systems.
- Notification and monitoring of an increased number of diseases will be provided for in legislation.
- A unique health identifier will be introduced.
- Health research will be facilitated.
- The particular information-related issues that arise in the private side of the health system will be addressed, in order to ensure a comprehensive picture of health needs across the health system.

Privacy Safeguards

The balance with privacy protection would be achieved by:

- Creating a *culture that respects the sensitivity of personal health information,* which will be evident in the fair obtaining of such information, its secure processing and the ready access by the subject, who will be informed as to its purpose and authorised use.

♦ Requiring each health agency to plan, develop, implement and maintain an *enterprise-wide programme* to protect personal information and the interests of the individuals to whom it relates.

♦ The development of a *handbook of good practice* to assist health service staff in the everyday collection and management of personal health information. The handbook will include a Code of Practice,[314] which would put the statutory requirements within a context of good practice and professional ethics, offer practical advice on everyday situations, recognise the range of contexts in which access may be required, and reassure health professionals that practice within the guidelines would be in accord with requirements.

♦ Establishing an independent *Personal Health Information Advisory Group* on a statutory basis, for the expert consideration of client / patient information issues, and as a valuable source of independent advice to the Minister for Health & Children, especially in areas of sensitivity such as balancing the need to safeguard privacy and confidentiality within the wider requirements of achieving the common good.

♦ Designating the chief executive officer (or equivalent), or a named delegate in each health agency, as the *Information Guardian* for that agency, who will be responsible in law for ensuring that agreed processes and procedures are in place for the implementation, operation and evaluation of the information governance framework and that responsibilities have been assigned to appropriately resourced and competent individuals.[315]

♦ Ensuring there will be appropriately trained staff to support the implementation of the governance framework.

---

[314] It appears that the intention is to have the Code (or Codes for different sectors) approved by the Data Protection Commissioner to give them binding effect.

[315] The processes and procedures will be documented and will list those who have access to information, the type of information that such people can access, the circumstances in which they can access it and the manner in which the information will be provided.

♦ Carrying out an *ongoing review of systems, procedures and physical arrangements* to ensure the health system and its professions respect privacy and set considerable store by it.

♦ Ensuring, in the case of statistical analysis, that information systems can separate identifiable from non-identifiable data and placing reliance, where possible, on the latter.

♦ Harmonising freedom of information and data protection regulations, access rules and extending the Freedom of Information Acts to those public health agencies not currently scheduled.

♦ Applying the National Archives Act to the health sector, with the establishment of a national health archive to ensure the proper retention of health records and the preservation of important historical records.

In the context of these proposed privacy steps and the comment that existing "safeguards for individual privacy may not always be sufficient", it appears that the proposed Health Information Bill will seek to provide a higher level of data protection than currently exists. Certainly, its data protection provisions must, at a minimum, be consistent with the EU Directive. Notwithstanding that, the statement that "the Health Information Bill will ... provide authority for requiring the collection and communication of important sets of data, including personally identifiable information where essential, while protecting individual rights" indicates that the special rules that will be introduced in this area of health information will differ materially, in certain respects, from existing data protection principles on collecting, using and disclosing personal health information. This conclusion seems consistent with the general tone and theme of the National Health Information Strategy.

The main advantage of having specific health information legislation is that it can have regard to the unique issues associated with, and needs of, the health system. In particular,

♦ The terminology and language can be specifically structured to reflect health sector usage and understanding.

- Some limited and specific exceptions, tailored to the health sector, can be included where difficulties in complying with the general data protection principles are anticipated.

- Certain exemptions that appear in the general data protection statutes, but which have no relevance to the health sector, can be omitted, which makes the legislation clearer.

- A non-binding, but highly illustrative, commentary can be prepared to accompany the legislation.

The chief disadvantage is that the health system does not operate in isolation from the rest of society or the economy in terms of information flows. Like so much else, it is a question of balance. Overall, a statutory code of practice would have the same regulatory effect as legislation, while providing considerably greater flexibility.

The Role of HIQA

The Health Information & Quality Authority is intended to have a major role in the information governance structures of the reformed health system. Its functions will include:

- Providing advice to the Department of Health & Children and the health agencies on information governance issues, especially in relation to Freedom of Information, data protection and records management.

- Specifying the pertinent information requirements, including access arrangements within service agreements.

- Setting, in consultation with the Central Statistics Office, statistical practice standards for the anonymisation, pseudonymisation and restriction of disclosure of data to safeguard privacy and confidentiality.

- Publishing guidance for use by research and system design teams.

- Assisting in the development of educational and training programmes on information governance.

- Monitoring the implementation of information governance requirements, such as auditing the compliance with client / patient consent practices and systems security processes and procedures.

RESEARCH STRATEGIES & STUDIES

Medical research is fundamental to advances in healthcare and, as such, is an extremely important element in a modern healthcare system. Advances in medical science that benefit the population as a whole, or those parts of the population with particular illnesses or conditions, would not be possible without research that frequently requires information on the medical histories of living identifiable individuals.[316] As with the management of the health service, reconciling the rights of individual to control the use of their information with the greater good to the community that can come from research using personal health information presents a challenge.

National Health Research Strategy

Two recent Irish reports – one on public perceptions towards medical research and the other on research and human tissue material – each give interesting insights into contemporary thinking and attitudes on health-related research in Ireland. Before considering those reports, it is important to realise that there has been a national strategy for health research – *Making Knowledge Work for Health: A Strategy for Health Research* – in place since 2001.[317] The Strategy reflects the legitimate view that knowledge-based innovation and new ways of thinking are required for the future development of the health services, if continued health and social gain are to be realised.

From the information privacy perspective, two factors were expressly identified as hindering research in the Irish health system:

♦ The absence of a unique national patient / client identifier

♦ The implications of data protection law for the creation and maintenance of population databases and registries.

The Strategy stated that the introduction of national patient / client identifiers would:

---

[316] It is worth bearing in mind that even anonymised information might still be capable of being related back to particular persons, especially in the case of small groups of patients with unusual conditions that make their identification easier.

[317] Department of Health & Children (2001b).

"... allow much better assessment of health outcomes and [improve] the quality of care patients and clients receive in the health services. This issue is being addressed in the context of the proposal of the Minister for Social, Community & Family Affairs that every citizen is assigned an RSI number from birth. *The Minister for Health & Children proposes that the same system be used in relation to the health services, with due regard to the need to protect the confidentiality of the professional/client relationship.*"[318]

On databases and registries designed to promote the health and well-being of the population or sectors of the population, the Strategy expressed the view that:

"... these databases and registries, which must be managed on computer, need to achieve maximum coverage of the relevant population if they are to meet their objectives. In addition, with many of these databases and registries, it is essential to record personal information, including name and address, to enable the individuals to be followed up on a regular basis. Under the existing data protection legislation, an individual can refuse to allow personal information to be recorded on computer. Under the proposed amendments to the existing data protection legislation [that is, implementation of the EU Data Protection Directive], this right to refuse consent is protected. *The Minister for Health & Children proposes that, where a database or registry is being developed or maintained for the benefit of the health or wellbeing of the population or a sector of the population, he may exempt that database by order from the consent requirements of the data protection legislation. All other rights of the individual to be informed about the existence of the database and obtain, update or correct the personal information held will be preserved.*"[319]

---

[318] Department of Health & Children (2001b).
[319] Department of Health & Children (2001b).

In several respects, the 2001 National Research Strategy was complemented and supplemented by the 2004 National Health Information Strategy, which took a broader view of the related management and research needs of the Irish health system.

Report on Public Perceptions on Medical Research

A major study on public perceptions in Ireland towards medical research, *Public Perceptions of Biomedical Research: A Survey of the General Population in Ireland*[320] was published in June 2005 by the Health Research Board.[321] The aim of the study was to provide the first nationally-representative profile of public perceptions on use of human tissue in medical research in Ireland. Specifically, the research aimed to provide nationally-representative data on:

- ◆ Public willingness to donate a tissue sample for medical research.
- ◆ Public preferences for informed consent procedures in relation to the use and storage of human tissue for medical research.
- ◆ Public preferences for tissue storage (linked or unlinked model of storage).
- ◆ The level of feedback on research findings considered desirable by the public.
- ◆ Public awareness of, and attitudes towards, the recent organ retention controversy.

The findings included:

- ◆ The introduction of privacy legislation mandating informed consent for access by researchers to medical records has adversely affected cancer registries in England and Germany. The report refers to research by Tu *et al.*, suggesting that collecting de-identified data from all patients' medical records circumvents the necessity of mandatory informed consent, provided appropriate

---

[320] Cousins *et al.* (2005).

[321] The Health Research Board is a statutory body that encourages and funds research that translates into improved diagnosis, understanding, treatment and prevention of disease and improves efficiency and effectiveness of the Irish health system.

confidentiality safeguards are in place.[322] They argued that any
concern regarding access to medical records without consent
should be balanced against the potential harm to future patients,
if they are given an incorrect prognosis (based on data from a
consent-based registry, which is limited due to a selection bias).
The HRB study also referred to other research that argued that
public health is threatened more by incomplete data than
individual privacy is threatened by disease registries.

♦ Almost three quarters of participants (74%) were unaware that
blood or tissue samples are often stored as part of a person's
medical record for their future care or treatment.

♦ Those surveyed were generally quite positive about genetic
research, while there were some reservations regarding the ethics
of genetic research.

♦ Consistent with positive attitudes to medical and genetic research
in general, only 10% felt that researchers were mainly motivated
by selfish factors such as money or fame.

♦ Participants had most confidence in the ability of individuals, in
particular doctors and nurses (82%), and then hospital /
university-based researchers (70%), to evaluate the risks and
benefits of medical research. Sixty per cent of participants
reported having confidence in research ethics committees. Health
boards and researchers in pharmaceutical companies received the
lowest ratings, with over a quarter (28% and 26% respectively) not
confident in their ability to evaluate risks.

♦ Of those surveyed who were willing to allow use of their excess
surgical tissue, the most common motive was for the potential
benefits there may be for the health of the participant's family in
the future (96%).

♦ While anonymisation helps protect patient privacy, it leaves
physicians with the ethical dilemma of not being able to disclose
information that the patient might like to have and / or from
which he or she could potentially benefit.

♦ Advances in knowledge of the causes, clinical characteristics, and
prognosis of diseases following certain treatments would be

---

[322] Tu *et al.* (2004).

impaired, if researchers were unable to link biological samples back to individual medical records. The study referred to work by Beskow et al.[323], which claimed that storing remaining biological material under a linked (or "patient identifiable") model enhances its research value, as it can link it with other clinical and epidemiologic data.

In his *Foreword* to the report, the Chairman of the HRB, Professor Desmond Fitzgerald, made the case for medical research and provided a clear and succinct insight into how to move the engagement process forward:

> "Today's health research is tomorrow's healthcare. So much of what we take for granted in medical diagnosis and treatment today – antibiotics, joint replacements, heart surgery, cancer therapy, pain control – is the result of research undertaken in the past by committed and farsighted health professionals and scientists, supported mainly by public bodies with an interest in improving health through research. Those undertaking and funding research depend on the goodwill and the active participation of the public in the task of pushing back the frontiers of knowledge and developing better ways of protecting health and treating disease. Maintaining and developing this engagement, at a time of major advances in science and great debate about the ethical issues those advances have brought in their wake, will be crucial to ensuring that health research and heath care in Ireland remain in the front rank." [324]

Interestingly, he added:

> "... The survey ... points to the need for better communication between those engaged in research and the public they serve."

---

[323] Beskow *et al.* (2001).
[324] Cousins *et al.* (2005).

Report on Research & Human Biological Material

Just a few weeks after the launch of the above report, the Irish Council for Bioethics launched its report on *Human Biological Material: Recommendations for Collection, Use & Storage in Research.*[325] The Chairperson of the Working Group that prepared the report stated in the *Foreword* that:

> "The proper achievement of medical and scientific progress surely lies in a proper consideration of legal and ethical norms so that an environment of balance is reached within which the dignity and autonomy of individuals is respected, and by which research can expand and flourish."[326]

The report devotes considerable attention to the issue of consent and, while the matter is discussed primarily with regard to participation in the research exercise rather than the processing of a participant's personal information *per se*, it is clear that similar consent principles apply to the latter as to the former. A number of consent-related recommendations are made including:

> "Evidence of free and informed consent should ordinarily be obtained in writing. In cases where it is not possible to obtain consent in writing, procedures used to seek and document informed consent shall be recorded, documented and maintained." (**Recommendation 2**)

The report also deals with confidentiality and privacy and includes two important recommendations:

> "Research participants have a right to expect that identifiable information about themselves, either provided or discovered in the course of research, will not be shared with others without their knowledge or permission. A

---

[325] Irish Council for Bioethics (2005).

[326] Asim A. Sheikh BL, Chairperson, Working Group on Human Biological Material, Irish Council for Bioethics. Asim Sheikh is also author of the Health Research Board publication, *Genetic Research & Human Biological Samples*, which is available on the HRB website (http://www.hrb.ie).

duty of confidentiality is owed to all research participants." (*Recommendation 17*)

"Researchers should be aware of their obligations and duties as prescribed by the Data Protection Acts [and] must ensure the confidentiality and privacy of data obtained directly from individuals, their medical records, or from their biological material. Prospective research participants should be informed what personal information about them will be stored, how it will be used, and if it will be shared with third parties. Details should also be given to research participants about what safeguards are in place to protect their confidentiality." (*Recommendation 18*)

It also proposes that, to safeguard confidential information in prospective research, identified or identifiable biological material or data should be anonymised or coded as early as possible in the research process (*Recommendation 19*).

DATA PROTECTION PROVISIONS ON RESEARCH

Personal Health Information Kept for Research Purposes

It is worth emphasising that personal information kept for research purposes is fully within the scope of the Data Protection Acts and must meet all the relevant data protection principles, subject only to any clear and specific exceptions set out in the legislation. For that reason, it might be useful, at this point, to consider briefly the relevant exemption provisions in the Acts relating to research. It will be evident that they represent a clear attempt to facilitate genuine study and scholarship, while, at the same time, protecting the rights of the individual, especially as regards any harm that he or she might potentially suffer from such studies. However, it is somewhat problematic that two of the key terms used – namely, "historical" and "scientific" – are not elaborated.

Section 1(3)(c) provides that sections 2 (Protection of Privacy with regard to Personal Data), 2A (Processing of Personal Data) and 2B

(Processing of Sensitive Personal Data) do not apply to information kept solely for the purpose of historical research, the keeping of which complies with such requirements (if any) as may be prescribed, in statutory regulations, for the purpose of safeguarding the fundamental rights and freedoms of data subjects. Two important words here are "solely" and "historical". The relevant personal information must be kept by the data controller *only* for historical research purposes. If the data controller holds, uses or discloses it for any other reason, the exception is lost. Further, the exception is strictly limited to historical research purposes.

When personal information is held by a data controller for a particular purpose or purposes and is then subsequently used by that data controller for statistical or research purposes, it is exempt (by virtue of section 2(5)(a) of the Data Protection Acts) from a number of the normal data protection rules. The data subjects do not have to be told that it is being used for research (although it is advisable that they should be), as long as it does not give rise to any distress for them.[327] However, in any situation where it is contemplated that personal information may be disclosed for research activities to a third party outside of the control of the data controller – for example, to a university research team – then there is no alternative to obtaining explicit consent. This has been made clear by the Data Protection Commissioner.[328]

In order to make processing of personal information fair, section 2D (Fair Processing of Personal Data) requires data controllers to make available to data subjects certain facts – discussed in **Chapters 6 and 7** – about any personal information obtained in relation to them. However, there is an exception to this requirement under subsection (4)(a), where, in particular for processing for statistical purposes or for the purposes of historical or scientific research, the provision of the specified information proves impossible or would involve a disproportionate effort, and where such conditions (if any) as may be prescribed by regulations made by the Minister for Justice are complied with by the data controller carrying out the research.

---

[327] In his *Annual Report* for 2004, the Data Protection Commissioner still felt it was good practice to advise individuals of this use of their information.

[328] Data Protection Commissioner (2004), p.31.

Finally, the right of subject access conferred by section 4 of the Data Protection Acts is restricted under section 5(h), where the personal information concerned is kept *only* for the purpose of preparing statistics or carrying out research and:

♦ it is not used or disclosed (other than in line with the specified disclosure exceptions of section 8) for any other purpose, and

♦ the resulting statistics or the results of the research are not made available in a form that identifies any data subjects.

Medical Research & the Need for Consent

Subject to the limited exceptions above, as a general rule, personal health information can be used only for the purpose of medical research with the express consent of the patient, who has an understanding of what the proposed research entails and the ways in which their personal health information will be used. This is especially so where there is any third-party involvement.

In that regard, it is worth revisiting **Chapter 6**, where we set out lists of conditions relevant to fair processing, We saw that, under the Data Protection Acts, apart from explicit consent, one of the other permissible conditions for obtaining, using or disclosing personal health information is that its processing is necessary for medical purposes and is undertaken by a health professional or a person having an equivalent duty of confidentiality. Medical purposes are defined as including the purpose of preventive medicine, medical diagnosis, medical research, the provision of care and treatment and the management of healthcare services. This provision, which originated in the EU Data Protection Directive, was intended to facilitate both proper healthcare service management and legitimate medical research.

However, the fact that processing is being carried out for medical purposes (including medical research) by a health professional or equivalent person is not sufficient on its own to make the processing fair and lawful. It is simply one of the conditions set out in sections 2B. To be fair and lawful, the processing of personal health information must (i) meet the other applicable conditions and requirements set out in sections 2, 2A, 2C and 2D and (ii) be consistent with the common law duty of confidentiality, which prohibits healthcare professionals from disclosing patients' information without their consent. As the UK Information Commissioner stated:

> "There is an overlap ... between the fair processing requirements of the Act and the consent requirements of the common law."[329]

The implications of this overlap in the case of a data controller proposing to disclose personal health information to a third party researcher is that the data controller should obtain the explicit consent of the patients involved, not just to ensure that the release is fair and lawful, but to guard against potential patient complaints and legal actions over inappropriate disclosure.

In data protection law, there is a range of statutory and other exceptions to the consent provision on use and disclosure. Some of those exceptions are specifically related to healthcare management and research purposes – for example, disclosures under the Health (Provision of Information) Act 1997 and the Infectious Diseases Regulations 1981. However, there is no general exception to consent that can be relied on by managers and researchers. Of course, de-personalising personal information may take it outside the scope of data protection law but, even here, there may still be issues of consent[330] and, in any event, in many research exercises, anonymous information may not be appropriate.

As a result, it is argued by many engaged in health service management and research that, while consent is a valid general principle, there are several reasons why it may not be reasonably practicable to gain individual patient consent in certain cases. These include where disproportionate or prohibitive effort or cost is required (for example, research involving thousands of historical records) or because the sensitivity of much needed research is likely to see consent withheld (for example, studies into whether particular groups of people abuse their children).

---

[329] Information Commissioner (2002).

[330] It is arguable that the actual operation to de-personalise the identifiable information is processing within the meaning of the Data Protection Acts and therefore requires consent or, at the very least, that the individual concerned should be advised of what is intended.

More generally, it is sometimes argued that the very fact of having to ask individuals about using their information for a particular research project is likely to make them refuse. However, the Canadian Privacy Commissioner rejected this view:

> "... the Canadian Medical Association survey revealed that almost eight out of 10 Canadians either strongly or somewhat agreed that they would allow their personal health information to be released to governments and researchers, but only if their consent were sought. Without consent, 51 per cent of Canadians would not agree to release their personal health information even if any identifying information were removed." [331]

Health Research, Data Protection & the National Health Information Strategy

We have seen already that the Health Information Strategy identified health research as an area that needed facilitating. Indeed, the comment that "it is essential that there is a robust legislative basis to support appropriate research activities, together with inbuilt safeguards to protect privacy and confidentiality" indicates that specific rules for the use and disclosure of personal information for research purposes will feature prominently in the proposed Health Information Bill. It is not surprising therefore that the Health Research Board, a statutory body that promotes, funds, commissions and conducts medical, epidemiological and health services research, publicly welcomed the Strategy as providing:

> "... a much needed framework to ensure the future integration and governance of information to improve health and health services in Ireland. The strategy recognises the importance of high quality information for health research and the need for a strong R&D function in the development of a world class health service."[332]

---

[331] Privacy Commissioner (Canada) (2000).

[332] "Health Research Board Welcomes Publication of Health Information Strategy", *Press Release*, Health Research Board, 23 July 2004.

The Chief Executive of the Health Research Board added that:

> "... a team of experts has also been brought together to provide guidance on the collection and use of information for health databases and research in the light of data protection legislation".

The work of this Expert Group will involve reconciling the competing merits of facilitating important medical research with safeguarding individual's rights, against a complex backdrop of professional and ethical codes, common law principles of confidentiality and data protection requirements. It is likely that the Group's report will call for some changes in the existing law, based on a consideration of international experience. Accordingly, it is useful to look at the situation in some other countries that have dealt with this issue.

THE POSITION IN OTHER COUNTRIES

Medical Research & Data Protection in the UK

Since Irish data protection law is based on the same Council of Europe Data Protection Convention (1981) and EU Data Protection Directive (1995) as the British model, it is instructive to consider how the matter has been addressed in that country.

In Britain, the implications of data protection law for medical research have given rise to considerable argument. A report in *The Times* in May 2001,[333] quoted Professor Julian Peto, Head of Epidemiology at the Institute of Cancer Research, as saying "it's no understatement to say that the Data Protection Act is killing people", due to its implications for research. This brought a quick response from the Government to clarify the situation, with the Minister of State at the Cabinet Office stating that:

> "... data can be used for any medical research purpose under the [Data Protection] Act without the need for the consent of individuals. So Professor Julian Peto is simply wrong when he states that the Data Protection Act is preventing data from

---

[333] "Data law is a killer", *The Times*, 15 May 2001.

> being passed to medical researchers. Where there are
> problems for medical researchers, they relate to the common
> law duty of confidence, not data protection legislation. The
> effect of the common law of confidence is that patients'
> consent to the disclosure of their medical data is required
> unless there is an overriding public interest."[334]

Far from resolving the matter, the Government's statement simply
added another confusing dimension to the problem. The law of
confidence is certainly relevant, as the Minister of State asserts, but so
too is the data protection law. As stated previously, it is the meeting of
the data protection principles with the duty of confidence that makes
consent so integral to using and disclosing personal health information
fairly and lawfully.

In March 2004, the Director of the Wellcome Trust – Britain's
biggest biomedical research charity – criticised the "extreme rights-
based philosophy" of the data protection regime, especially the
obsession with the minutiae of patient consent, which prevents
researchers from accessing patient records without consent, even on an
anonymous basis, as causing serious problems for scientists and
researchers.[335]

Professor Peto made a further emotional contribution to the debate
in 2004, when his article in the *British Medical Journal* claimed:

> "The deaths that will occur because of the effects of data
> protection law on British medical research attract less
> publicity than child murders; but the pointless obstacles that
> *bona fide* researchers, particularly epidemiologists, face when
> they seek access to individual medical records are now
> causing serious damage." [336]

---

[334] Lord Falconer (now Lord Chancellor), in a letter to *The Times*, "Privacy Law &
Medical Research", 17 May 2001.

[335] "Regulation will kill research", interview with Mark Walport, Director of the
Wellcome Trust, *The Times*, 30 March 2004.

[336] Peto, Fletcher, & Gilham (2004).

An important recommendation of the 2004 Wanless Report, *Securing Good Health for the Whole Population*,[337] is that the proposed White Paper on public health:

> "... should address the possible threat to public health research which arises from the difficulty of obtaining access to data because of the need to strike a balance between individual confidentiality and public health research requirements."[338]

In England & Wales, the Government has made it clear that informed consent is the fundamental principle governing the use of patient-identifiable information by any part of the NHS or research community.[339] Notwithstanding this, the matter of bypassing, or overriding, consent for management and research purposes (whether arising from the common law or data protection law) has been dealt with through section 60 of the Health & Social Care Act 2001. The section creates a legislative override to patient consent. This gives the Secretary of State for Health power to ensure that patient-identifiable information needed to support essential NHS activity can be used without the consent of patients. The power can only be used to support medical purposes that are in the interests of patients or the wider public, where consent is not a practicable alternative and where anonymised information will not suffice. The provision has been asserted to be a transitional measure, while consent or anonymisation procedures are developed. It has come in for considerable criticism from a wide range of groups.

The Section 60 solution has generated a considerable degree of controversy. An article in the *British Medical Journal* in 2001 criticised section 60 for creating new powers to control patient information that contributed nothing to a better health service. The author (a Reader in Security Engineering at the University of Cambridge Computer Laboratory) claimed that the measure upset the established balance between patient privacy, professional autonomy, public health effectiveness, and the needs of scientific research. He pointed out that

---

[337] Wanless (2004).

[338] See http://bmj.bmjjournals.com/cgi/content/full/328/7447/1029#REF3#REF3.

[339] Department of Health (UK) (2001).

past attempts to disturb this balance foundered – on professional resistance, patient rights, and the property rights of healthcare firms – but the side effects of these disputes have often been debilitating. As a result, he argued that section 60 would upset the balance again with potentially damaging effects on both privacy and research.[340]

After considering the issues involved and the use of a section 60 type provision, Scotland decided on a different approach to the issue as a result of a major study.[341] In particular, it was felt that the prime case against legislation of this type is:

> "... that it will restrict in particular circumstances an individual's right to privacy. This might have the effect of causing patients to lose faith in NHS Scotland and to withhold information because of concerns that their confidentiality might be breached. There is also a possibility that permanent legislation would remove some of the current incentives to review practices with the objective of minimising the use of patient identifying information.
>
> There are also technical reasons for not legislating in this way. In short, legislation will not necessarily offer a way of meeting the challenge. Regulations to allow for data to be used without consent in specific circumstances would undoubtedly miss some information flows that are worthy of protection. Alternatively, a new disease may appear in future (as vCJD did in the 1990s) and the data required to investigate the disease may only be partial because no one could predict in advance that regulations were necessary. It is preferable therefore to have in place systems and procedures that enable information to be processed for the whole spectrum of current and potential purposes without relying on a statutory override of the individual's right to confidentiality."

---

[340] Anderson (2001).

[341] Confidentiality & Security Advisory Group for Scotland (2002). CSAGS was set up in September 2000 as an independent committee, supported by the Scottish Executive Health Department, to provide advice on the confidentiality and security of health-related information to the Scottish Executive, the public and healthcare professionals.

The Report concluded that:

> "... in a patient-centred service, the implications of any legislation which restricts rights of individual patients and risks a loss of confidence in the service must be taken seriously".

In Northern Ireland, the Department of Health, Social Services & Public Safety issued a consultation paper in June 2002 entitled *Health & Personal Social Services: Protecting Personal Information.*[342] In the responses published in March 2003, the Department stated:

> "There was no consensus on the question of whether legislation similar to section 60 of the Health & Social Care Act 2001 to override the duty of confidence should be introduced, and if so, whether it should be permanent or temporary."[343]

The Canadian Approach to Medical Research & Privacy

Section 7 of the Canadian Federal Personal Information Protection and Electronic Documents Act exempts organisations from seeking consent for the disclosure and use of information for certain purposes, one of which is scholarly research. Specifically, the Act permits an organisation to use or disclose personal information without the knowledge or consent of the individual to whom it pertains, if each of the following five conditions is met:

- ♦ First, the disclosure or use must be strictly for statistical or scholarly study or research.

- ♦ Second, the purposes cannot be achieved without using or disclosing the information.

- ♦ Third, the information must be used in a manner that safeguards its confidentiality.

- ♦ Fourth, obtaining consent must be impracticable.

---

[342] Department of Health, Social Services & Public Safety (Northern Ireland) (2002).
[343] Department of Health, Social Services & Public Safety (Northern Ireland) (2003).

♦ Fifth, the organisation or party seeking exemption under section 7 must inform the Privacy Commissioner of the proposed use or disclosure beforehand.

The Canadian Federal Privacy Commissioner stated in his 2001 *Annual Report to Parliament* that he intended to interpret very broadly the definition of statistical or scholarly study in the Act. In relation to health research, he stated:

> "Any *bona fide* health research, undertaken by legitimate organisations under appropriate safeguards, will, in my view, constitute 'statistical or scholarly study or research' even if there is an element of pecuniary interest involved ...
>
> I accept that health research, by its nature, requires personal information, although researchers should use the least identifiable information that will accomplish the desired purpose. As for the impracticability of obtaining consent, I accept as a general principle that cost factors and the difficulty of obtaining consent from 100 percent of a target population may make it impracticable to obtain individual consent for many health research studies. I therefore intend to take an expansive and liberal view on the question of impracticability of consent ...
>
> As for the requirement to inform me beforehand of any research for which an exemption under section 7 is sought, this too is something on which I intend to take a very liberal – I should say, reasonable and practical – approach. I and my Office have neither the resources nor the wish to be kept apprised of every single health research project taking place across Canada. Rather, I would want to be made aware of all the organisations carrying out such research, and the safeguards under which they operate."[344]

He made clear that this liberal interpretation was balanced by:

---

[344] Radwanski, G. (2002).

"... an absolutely inflexible requirement: the information used for health research must remain strictly within the confines of the research project and it must be used in a matter that cannot in any way harm the individual to whom it pertains. Under no circumstances whatsoever can it find its way to the individual's employers, insurers, relatives or acquaintances, governmental or law enforcement authorities, marketers or any other third parties. And the individual must not be contacted as a result of this information by anyone other than his or her own physician, or other primary healthcare provider, as the case may be. I will regard any breach whatsoever of this condition as an extremely grave violation of the Act."

THE DATA PROTECTION COMMISSIONER'S VIEW

The Commissioner's *Annual Report* for 2001 contained a section called "Considerations for the Health Sector", which featured *inter alia* some questions on research.[345] These questions and their answers are set out below, but they should be read in the context that the subsequent 2003 Act created stronger rights for data subjects and enhanced the importance of consent:

> **Question:** *Can I use patient data for my own research or statistical purposes?*
>
> **Answer:** Ideally, you should make patients aware in advance, if you intend to use their data for your own research purposes. However, the Act provides that such uses of personal data are permitted, even where the patient was not informed in advance, provided that no damage or distress is likely to be caused to the individual.
>
> **Question:** *Can I disclose patient data to others for their research or statistical purposes?*
>
> **Answer:** You may pass on anonymised or aggregate data, from which individual patients cannot be identified. Ideally,

---

[345] Data Protection Commissioner (2002).

you should inform patients in advance of such uses of their personal data. If you wish to pass on personal data, including identifying details, you will need to obtain patient consent in advance. The "research exemption", mentioned in the question above, only applies to your own use of personal data: it doesn't apply to disclosures to third parties. There is an exception, however, for cancer research and screening as per the Health (Provision of Information) Act 1997.

Question: *How can researchers avoid duplication of data in respect of the same individual?*

Answer: Researchers who obtain anonymised data are sometimes faced with the problem that they may be dealing with two or more data-sets from the same individual. To address this problem, it may be permissible for a data controller to make available anonymous data together with a unique coding, which falls short of actually identifying the individual to the researcher. For example, a data controller might "code" a unique data-set using a patient's initials and date of birth. The key point is that the researcher should not be in a position to associate the data-set with an identifiable individual (unless, of course, the individual has given clear consent for their medical data to be used for research purposes).

In his 2004 *Annual Report*, the Commissioner took the opportunity to outline more fully his position on medical research. He began:

"We all agree that research is necessary in the medical area for the benefit of society. However, in the medical research field, personal data is very often processed and the question of consent can on occasions pose problems for researchers and data controllers and data subjects alike. Transparency is vital in this area. The Data Protection Acts allow for medical research to operate in a pragmatic manner but medical researchers have to appreciate that where personal data is being used attention to patients needs is paramount. In this respect, my comments about anonymisation and pseudonymisation are particularly relevant."[346]

He then went on to refer to individual medical research projects where, after discussions between the researchers and his Office, significant changes were made to the original proposals that allowed them to proceed without the research programmes being hindered or reduced.[347]

SOME SPECIFIC EXAMPLES

The "Guidance" section of the 2004 *Annual Report* of the Data Protection Commissioner had three specific examples of health information being used or disclosed for management and research purposes.

The first related to Patient Registers, the second to Biobanks and the third to disclosure of school lists for immunisation purposes. The "Case Study" section also featured an inadvertent disclosure of information by a Health Board to a research body. These cases are considered below.

Patient Registers

The Commissioner referred to the fact that medical professionals and others frequently make representations to his Office that, in the case of some diseases, it is essential for patient treatment, follow-up and service-management that databases / registers are 100 per cent comprehensive in terms of patient coverage. He pointed out that the Data Protection Acts[348] require explicit consent for the processing of sensitive data and that it is important that the patient is given sufficient information to give an informed consent. He added that the purpose of the database or register, and why it is essential for all patients in their interests to be recorded on it, should be explained fully.

---

[346] Data Protection Commissioner (2005).
[347] The projects were the National Parasuicide Register, the Coombe Hospital Biobank, and the Trinity College DNA Project.
[348] Section 2B(1)(b).

The Commissioner elaborated that, if it is felt that recording on the database / register is an essential aspect of the treatment and management process, then his Office's approach would be that consent to treatment should incorporate consent to going on the database / register, as this is necessary for patient management and follow-up in the patient's interest (and, therefore, can be looked upon as part of the treatment process). However, if it is the case that the recording on the database / register is optional, then it is appropriate to obtain a separate consent. Either way, full information should be given to the patient about the processing involved and privacy-enhancing technologies, and anonymisation and pseudonymisation (reversible anonymisation) should be used in all cases where personal identifiers are not needed for the particular purpose in hand.

He concluded that, to the greatest extent possible, researchers should only have access to anonymised data. The identifier "keys" should be stored on a separate database. The relevant healthcare professionals should hold these and they should not be available to researchers. The database / register should be password-protected and sufficient security measures should be in place to protect the sensitive data in it.

Biobank

In the second example, Coombe Women's Hospital wished to establish a biobank, using blood donated from the mother at the ante-natal stage, blood from the placenta at pre-birth stage and from the baby's umbilical cord (which would otherwise be discarded). The Hospital contacted the Commissioner's Office, as it wished to proceed on the basis of explicit consent and transparency. Advice was given on the procedures to obtain consent (including the mother's right to subsequently withdraw her consent) and security safeguards in relation to both the donated tissue and the personal data.

In this project, all samples are given a unique project number and stored in a secure biological resource bank. A name will never be used on any information relating to the donated samples. The samples will be anonymous (that is, nobody will know who the donor is), and they may only be used for research initiatives that have the prior approval of the (i) Ethics Committee of the Coombe Women's Hospital and (ii) the Board of Trustees of the Biological Resource Bank.

The Commissioner felt that a most important point was that the link between the patient record and the anonymised research file must be hidden. The importance of security and access restrictions were also emphasised and it was suggested that there should be external independent oversight of the database every two years.

Referral of School Class-Lists to Local Health Boards for Immunisation Programmes

The issue of school class-lists being disclosed to local Health Boards in connection with immunisation programmes was raised with the Commissioner. The Data Protection Acts prescribe that, generally, information should only be disclosed, if it meets the compatibility principle or where one of the exemptions in section 8 applies. Section 8(e) provides that personal data may be disclosed, if required by law. However, there is no specific legal obligation on school principals (the data controllers in this case) to make the children's information available to Health Boards.

However, the Commissioner concluded that the disclosure was compatible with data protection law, on the basis of:

♦ The importance of school class lists being available to the school medical team for follow-up, to ensure the protection of children's future health and wider public health.

♦ The absence of any other fully reliable method of obtaining the class lists.

He determined that it was also covered by section 2A(1)(c)(iv) of the Acts, which provides for processing (which includes disclosures) that is necessary "for the performance of any function of a public nature performed in the public interest by a person".

Inadvertent Disclosure of Client Data by the Midland Health Board to a Research Body[349]

The Midland Health Board brought to the attention of the Data Protection Commissioner's Office that there had been a breach of the Data Protection Acts, in that information had been disclosed

---

[349] Data Protection Commissioner (2005), *Case Study 9*.

inadvertently to a research body without the consent of the data subjects concerned. Section 2D(1)(b) of the Data Protection Acts 1988 & 2003 provides that:

> "Personal data shall not be treated, for the purposes of section 2(1)(a) of the Acts, as processed fairly unless ... the data controller ensures, so far as practicable, that the data subject has, is provided with, or has made readily available to him or her ... information relating to recipients or categories of recipients of data."

The Commissioner advised the Board that this requires that data subjects be informed of proposed disclosures of their data and consent obtained, especially as sensitive data may have been involved, for which explicit consent to process is needed. He directed the Midland Health Board to take the following action:

♦ To obtain the return of the material disclosed and destroy any copies.

♦ To notify its own Health Board Compliance Officer of the matter.

♦ To carry out a risk analysis in order to assess the causes of the disclosure.

♦ To set out a programme of remedial action.

The Board complied with these requirements.

Other Cases

Earlier "Case Studies" are also of interest in seeing how data protection principles are applicable in practical healthcare-based situations.

Hospital Disclosure & Risk-Management Investigation

The 2003 *Annual Report,* for example, featured a case involving Drogheda Hospital and an investigation into a consultant's practice.[350] The disclosure of personal health information by the hospital to two risk management groups to facilitate the investigation brought many

---

[350] Data Protection Commissioner (2004), *Case Study 1.*

data protection complaints from the patients involved, as their consent had not been sought.

The information disclosed was actually paper-based and, therefore, then outside the scope of Irish data protection law. However, the Commissioner felt that, given the major issue involved, the matter should be considered as if the data protection principles applied.

The records of 42 patients were involved and, to ensure patient privacy and confidentiality, patients were numbered consecutively. This numbering was used in the management of all subsequent classifications in the review process.

The North Eastern Health Board maintained that it had a duty of care to patients within its region. Consequently, when it was appraised of serious concerns relating to patient care, immediate legal and medical advice was sought and it was, in this regard, that charts were provided in a confidential manner to the Review Group, following consultation with the Institute of Obstetricians & Gynaecologists. The Commissioner felt that it was clear that the Health Board was acting in the best interests of patients and the wider public interest.

The general principle of the Data Protection Acts is that personal data should only be processed and disclosed to other parties with the patient's consent unless one of the provisions of section 8, which lift the restrictions on disclosure in limited and defined circumstances, apply. Section 8(b) and (d) provide that:

> "Any restrictions in this Act on the processing of personal data do not apply if the processing is: …
>
> (b)   Required for the purpose of preventing, detecting or investigating offences, apprehending or prosecuting offenders or assessing or collecting any tax, duty or other moneys owed or payable to the State, a local authority or a health board, in any case in which the application of those restrictions would be likely to prejudice any of the matters aforesaid ... or
>
> (d)   Required urgently to prevent injury or other damage to the health of a person or serious loss of or damage to property."

The key issue was whether the Board could rely on section 8 as a basis for the referral of case files, without the consent of the patients involved. The Commissioner concluded that the Board was justified in disclosing the files in order to protect the health of those who had undergone the procedures carried out by the consultant, and also so that necessary steps could be identified to avoid inappropriate procedures in the future. Having regard to the serious and far-reaching public health issues and circumstances involved, he considered that the Board were justified in making the disclosures under section 8(b) and (d). He also felt that the disclosure by the Board was a compatible one within the meaning of the Acts. Section 2(1)(c)(ii) provides that "data shall not be further processed in a manner incompatible with that purpose or those purposes" (for which it is held). However, he stated that, while names of patients were also included in the charts supplied to the reviewing bodies, it would have been prudent, if it were feasible, given the urgency and importance of the investigation, to delete all references to patients so that only anonymised information was released.

Referral of Clinical Notes for Review

A similar case was reported in the 2003 *Annual Report* and involved the referral of a medical consultant's clinical notes for review, without his or the patients' consent.[351] The consultant complained that a Health Board had sent the clinical notes of five of his patients to a risk management group in England in March 2000. The Health Board involved acknowledged that the patients' consents were not requested, as it was an assessment considered necessary in relation to the concerns raised, and that legal and medical advice was obtained in relation to the matter. The patient charts were treated in a confidential and a sensitive way, with circulation restricted. The Commissioner concluded that the Board was justified in making the disclosures, in order to have the risk assessment carried out, and did not breach the Data Protection Acts.

The Commissioner added, for information purposes, that in this case, and indeed for patients in acute public hospitals, it has to be recognised that the Health Board or the hospital is the data controller

---

[351] Data Protection Commissioner (2004), *Case Study 9*.

and not the consultant. However, where a consultant has private patients, then he or she becomes the controller, if treating them in a private hospital or in his or her private rooms.

Research & Fair Obtaining

In 1997, there was a case involving a complaint made by a patient about a hospital disclosing his personal information for research.[352] The complainant had attended the Accident & Emergency department of a public hospital and, a few months later, she was contacted by an organisation carrying out research. The researchers knew when she had attended the hospital and why, and they asked her to answer some questions. The complainant objected to the fact that the hospital had told the researchers about her visit. She took this up herself with the hospital, but was not satisfied with their response and complained to the Commissioner. The essence of her complaint was that she had not been informed when she attended the hospital that her personal data would be used in this way.

The Commissioner identified the data protection issue in this case as one of fair obtaining: namely, whether, and if so in what way, the complainant's personal information had been fairly obtained for the purpose of the research. Section 2(1)(a) provides that "data or, as the case may be, the information constituting the data shall have been obtained ... fairly". The hospital argued that it had met its obligations under the legislation on two counts. First, it had listed "personnel engaged in medical research" as disclosees in its entry in the public Register of Data Controllers. Secondly, it had sought to make patients aware of the research project by putting a notice in the waiting area of the accident and emergency department. This notice told patients that the hospital intended to disclose their information to the researchers, and invited them to let the receptionist know if they objected.

The Commissioner did not accept these arguments. He stated that the Registration Entry did not, in itself, satisfy the principle of obtaining information fairly. He also determined that the notice placed in the waiting area was, in the particular circumstances, inadequate.

Specifically, he stated:

---

[352] Data Protection Commissioner (1998), *Case Study 1*.

"I am of the opinion that for personal data to be fairly obtained, a data controller must make the data subject aware, directly and at the time his or her data are being obtained, of how such data may be used and to whom they may be disclosed, in order to get the person's informed consent to the uses and disclosures described."

On the hospital's second argument, he took:

"... the view that the intention to disclose should have been brought to the specific attention of the complainant before data relating to her were obtained. This was essential to ensure that she was in a position to make an informed choice whether or not to furnish her information for such a purpose."

Notifiable Diseases, Pharmacists & Fair Obtaining

In the *Annual Report* for 2002, the *Case Studies* section featured a pharmacist and a request from a Health Board for information relating to notifiable diseases.[353] At the heart of the case were public health concerns and the disclosure of personal health information without the data subject's consent.

The pharmacist involved contacted the Commissioner's Office seeking advice in relation to correspondence received from the Director of Public Health, Eastern Health Authority, regarding a proposed scheme for pharmacists to assist in the surveillance of tuberculosis. Pharmacists were asked to submit a form which detailed personal information of patients using anti-tuberculosis therapy prescriptions. The pharmacist was concerned that, while the objectives of the proposal were well-intentioned, he should not disclose sensitive information he held in trust without patient consent.

The Commissioner contacted the Director of Public Health to establish whether this personal information had been fairly obtained, as required under section 2 of the Data Protection Act 1988. The Director explained that one of his functions related to the surveillance and control of infectious diseases and pointed out that tuberculosis

---

[353] Data Protection Commissioner (2003).

was a notifiable disease. He added that significant public health considerations had prompted the Department of Health & Children to instruct Directors of Public Health to seek the applicable personal details from pharmacies.

The Commissioner contacted the Secretary General of the Department of Health & Children and drew his attention to sections 11 & 14 of the Infectious Diseases Regulations 1981 (the statutory basis for reporting notifiable diseases), which provide that the responsibility to notify the Health Authority of an infectious disease falls on a doctor and not on a pharmacist. The Commissioner assured the Secretary General that he appreciated the importance from a public health perspective of having a reliable tuberculosis reporting system in place but his responsibilities, as Data Protection Commissioner, required him to ensure that such a reporting system fully respected the provisions of data protection law. In particular, the Commissioner wanted to establish why it was necessary to require pharmacists to notify Health Authorities of prescriptions, given that only doctors can issue a prescription and that they already have a statutory obligation to report an incidence of a notifiable disease. Such reporting was actually covered by section 8, which expressly permits disclosure if it is "required by or under any enactment or by a rule of law or order of a court".[354]

The Department of Health & Children advised that reporting by pharmacists was introduced following a review by a Working Party on Tuberculosis in 1996, so as to enhance the tuberculosis surveillance system and to ensure that appropriate contact tracing could be achieved. However, having considered the issues raised by the Commissioner, the Department decided that the reporting of this information by pharmacists should cease.

The Commissioner's general finding was that, while accepting the public importance of the pharmacy reporting programme, the principles of "fair obtaining", which includes transparency, required that personal details obtained for prescription purposes cannot be used subsequently for other purposes without express consent or , if there is a real public health need, a clear statutory basis.

---

[354] Section 8(e).

Some General Conclusions

In reading the 2004 *Annual Report*,[355] it seems that the Data Protection Commissioner has reached three general conclusions on the current state of data protection and the use of personal health information for medical research and management purposes:

♦ First, that there is a need for "greater awareness amongst health service personnel and medical researchers of the data protection rules regarding research".

♦ Second, that making matters clear to patients regarding the potential use of their information for management and or research purposes is not just a data protection priority but also good professional practice.

♦ Third, to reduce risks of disclosure of sensitive personal data, data should be anonymised (or pseudonymised), in cases where personal identifiers are not needed for the particular purpose in hand. In this context, the Commissioner stated: "privacy-enhancing technologies have a contribution to make in this area and their use needs to be adopted more widely to facilitate necessary health and social research".

DATA PROTECTION, POPULATION HEALTH REGISTERS & THE NATIONAL CANCER REGISTRY

The matter of data protection law and population health registers was expressly considered in the context of developing the National Cancer Registry of Ireland. In brief, certain information about a patient's cancer may be passed to this agency, without consent, as per the Health (Provision of Information) Act 1997.

The background was that, having accepted the medical evidence that the time was right to proceed with national screening programmes for breast and cervical cancer, there was a need to populate the required registers in a manner consistent with data protection law. To operate effectively, both programmes required up-

---

[355] Data Protection Commissioner (2005).

to-date population registers containing names and addresses of women in the target age group, so that they could be invited for screening.[356] The women's details would be retained on the registers until they moved outside the target age group.

The first concern was to ensure the identification of all women who should be offered screening for the first time. As no such population register existed for that purpose, it would have been necessary to draw upon data from a number of other available sources such as the GMS Payments Board, the Department of Social Welfare and health insurance companies. However, data protection rules restricted these sources from passing personal details to a third party, such as a screening programme, since this was not compatible with the purpose for which the data was originally collected (even though the new purpose was highly desirable).

The solution adopted was a legislative one: the Health (Provision of Information) Act 1997. The Act deals with cancer screening programmes and the National Cancer Registry Board. It provides that an organisation participating in any programme of breast or cervical screening authorised by the Minister for Health may request information from any person regarding names, addresses and dates of birth, so that, for public health reasons, women may be invited to participate in that programme. It enables (but does not require) any person requested to provide information for this purpose to do so. Such registries are subject to data protection law in how the information is managed, stored and used.

The National Cancer Registry of Ireland sets out its position on confidentiality very clearly:

> "Preservation of confidentiality, as well as being an obligation, is also essential to maintain the trust of those who provide us with information and ensures that the information gathered will continue to be of high quality. Doctors must be assured that the welfare of their patients will be respected and that the Registry will observe the same strict rules with regard to confidentiality that exist in the doctor-

---

[356] The intention was that women would be invited to attend for screening as soon as they reached the appropriate age and, therefore, that the registers would need to be updated constantly.

patient relationship. Finally, we have a legal and moral duty to avoid acts that might cause suffering or distress to any individual, whether patient or doctor." [357]

As the Data Protection Commissioner stated, the Health (Provision of Information) Act is:

"... noteworthy, in that it limits the protection afforded by the Data Protection Act, in the light of new circumstances that could not have been foreseen when the Act was passed. It identifies an overriding public interest – cancer prevention – and enables an exchange of personal data between data controllers which would not otherwise be permissible."[358]

Concluding Comment

Personal health information is collected principally through engagements between patients and healthcare professionals. As already emphasised, its use and disclosure has traditionally been subject to a variety of ethical and common law rules that place the emphasis on consent and confidentiality.[359] Since it would be unreasonable to expect healthcare providers to leave themselves open to legal action for breach of confidence or action under the data protection statutes, health service managers and medical researchers cannot, therefore, expect personal health information to be released to them unless they have secured patient consent.

On the other hand, it is indisputable that effective modern healthcare systems providing integrated and quality patient care are in both the public interest and the interest of any individual needing care. Such systems rely heavily on information from current and former patients. The NHS study, *Share with Care*, reported that people gave much higher priority to spending NHS money on patient care than on schemes to enable better information-sharing, to protect their confidentiality or to give them access to their own health records.[360] Of

---

[357] See http://www.ncri.ie for the full statement on confidentiality and the treatment of personal health information by the NCRI.

[358] Data Protection Commissioner (1997), p.32.

[359] See, for example, Medical Council (2004).

[360] National Health Service Information Authority (UK) (2004).

course, as the authors of the study concluded, the real challenge is to achieve all of these desirable goals without compromising any of them. A similar conclusion was reached in the National Health Information Strategy, with legislation seen as essential to create the proper framework.

11
UNIQUE HEALTH IDENTIFIERS

INTRODUCTION

Arguments about National Unique Health Identifiers (UHIs) are invariably tied up with the wider debate on the allocation, use and abuse of universal State-backed Unique Personal Identifiers (UPIs). More than any other privacy issue, UPIs have been the subject of intense debate in any democratic country where they have been mooted. The topic has tended to polarise views between those who see UPIs as a fundamental threat to civil liberties and human rights and those who argue that such identifiers simply represent a major contribution to citizen security and safety and better public services.

In his *Annual Report* for 1999-2000, the Privacy Commissioner of Canada summed up his fears about the introduction and use of State-backed universal personal identifiers:

> "At the heart of our apprehension is our loss of control: control over what information others have about us, control over how they use that information, control over our ability to influence events and decisions that affect our lives, and ultimately control over our ability to make choices based on our own rational self interest. A universal system of identification threatens to undermine our control by allowing organisations to use the identifier to obtain information about us without our knowledge or consent. It greatly increases governments' ability to gather information from various sources and assemble profiles, as well as to monitor and track an individual's behaviour. When the identifier is compulsory – almost unavoidable when it is widely used and required by all government departments and agencies – the identifier

effectively becomes an 'internal passport' without which we are nobody."[361]

A full consideration of the issues surrounding a universal personal identifier for all State (and possibly private sector) transactions lies outside the scope of a book concerned primarily with the protection of personal health information. However, the related matter of a UHI for all health activities also raises challenging arguments.[362]

A UNIQUE HEALTH SERVICE IDENTIFIER

The *Standard Guide for Properties of a Universal Healthcare Identifier*,[363] outlines four basic functions for a health service client unique identifier:

- **Positive identification of clients when clinical care and advice are provided:** In order to deliver health services to the right person, it is imperative to be able to confirm the identity of the individual. This is especially so in today's healthcare system, where numerous healthcare providers are involved in patient care in a variety of settings, with a corresponding need to be able to positively identify and track clients throughout the case process.

- **Automated linkage of electronic health records:** Linking information and records on the same client facilitates the creation of electronic health records. This not only supports the continuum of care for individuals, but also can provide a source of longitudinal (anonymised) information for analysis and reporting purposes.

- **Streamlining records management:** Technology can make health records management more efficient. The health record can be

---

361 Privacy Commissioner (Canada) (2000).

362 The background, at an international level, to the extended use of personal identification numbers (PINs) is clearly set out in a report from the Council of Europe, *The Introduction & Use of Personal Identification Numbers: the Data Protection Issues.*

363 ASTM International (2000).

simplified by replacing many elements of personal identifying information (such as name, address, sex, birth date, phone numbers, etc.) with a unique identifier, to provide a practical method of easily filing and accessing records associated with an individual. Administrative processing such as eligibility determination, service reimbursement, record transfer and detection of fraud and abuse can also be expedited.

♦ **Provision of a mechanism to strengthen data security:** The protection of privileged clinical information is enhanced by providing the ability to sever commonly-used personal identifiers from sensitive records, to scramble randomly-generated numerical identifiers easily, or to replace them with a numerical pseudonym. The use of client demographic information (such as name, address, gender, birth date, phone numbers, etc.) for identification increases the level of exposure and subjects clients to greater confidentiality risks. As such, a unique health service recipient identifier strengthens access control.

The Case for a Unique Health Identifier for Individuals

Despite significant differences in health systems world-wide, there are common factors driving the implementation of a national unique client identifier in most developed healthcare systems.[364] These include:

♦ To facilitate a changing model of healthcare.

♦ The goal of an electronic health record.

♦ Management and research.

Facilitate a Changing Model of Healthcare

The goal of a more integrated, quality-based and patient-centred health system will be greatly facilitated by a UHI. For the vast majority of people today, health records no longer consist of a paper file in a single healthcare provider's office. Rather, they consist of many records, some paper but an increasing number electronic, as patients visit multiple providers for a range of preventive, primary, secondary,

---

[364] A useful general discussion on the issues, which shows their universality, can be found in Canadian Institute for Health Information (2000).

tertiary and holistic services. The common practice is for each healthcare provider or agency to use different identifiers for the same individual. It is argued that efforts to assure integrated continuity of care, accurate record-keeping, effective follow-up and preventive care as well as detection of fraud, waste and abuse could all benefit from the availability of a single unique identifier for individuals, with appropriate protections against misuse and unauthorised use outside of healthcare.

A unique identifier is necessary because the constellation of personal attributes commonly used to identify an individual (for example, name, birth date, and sex) is rarely captured in the same manner by each entity in the diverse (private and public) healthcare system. Indisputably, the potential for enhancing healthcare depends on the clinician's ability to synthesise information from a variety of sources into an accurate picture of the patient's state of health. A unique identifier would allow for the rapid and accurate identification of the proper records and their integration for the purpose of providing integrated, high quality, patient-focused care.

Having multiple identifiers for the same individual within, or across, organisations prevents or inhibits timely access to integrated and important patient information. Unique identifiers for individuals would facilitate ordering tests and reporting results; posting results, diagnoses, procedures, and observations to charts; updating, maintaining, and retrieving medical records; as well as integrating information across the various internal information systems. For some highly-sensitive records (for example, records of mental health diagnoses or treatment, HIV antibody tests, or genetic tests) unique identifiers for individuals could be critical components of administrative procedures designed to protect such information from inadvertent disclosure.

A unique identifier for individuals could serve multiple purposes even within a single healthcare centre. For some clinical interventions, a reliable means of identifying the patient is important for safety as well as for record-keeping purposes. For example, ensuring safe and effective medication administration requires integrated information about the drug and dose being ordered, other medications being taken or recently ordered, and known drug allergies. Accurate and efficient integration of this clinical information, sometimes from different systems within one organisation, would be assisted by having a unique identifier for individuals associated with each piece of information.

The Goal of an Electronic Health Record

Very much related to the above, the development of an Electronic Health Record would be greatly facilitated by a UHI.

Management & Research

The current reform of healthcare management processes has featured a strong focus on system-wide efficiency, effectiveness, accountability, and needs-based resource allocation. These tenets are extremely information-intensive, requiring sophisticated data in order to support measurements – for example, measuring a distinct population's size and consistency, service and individual outcomes. This kind of activity at a system-wide level is inhibited, and gains for the entire health system are reduced, because of the current inability to link information consistently and easily.

In addition, clinical researchers, public health specialists and health service managers are increasingly seeking greater access to personal health information. Such information, identified and linked by a unique identifier, has added value from their perspective. Health management focused on quality, value for money and accountability will require research to substantiate its decision-making, actions and outcomes. This type of research is often best performed at a macro level and is currently hampered by the inability of the health system to link and provide longitudinal information and data at the national level.

Privacy Concerns

Controversy over the adoption of a standard for the universal UHI for individuals has focused, to a large degree, on privacy concerns. Frequently, these views appear to contrast sharply with the previous discussion of the value that a unique identifier for individuals would have in clinical and administrative practice. Some believe that threats to privacy are inherent in any unique identifier for individuals and claim that privacy threats outweigh any practical benefits of improved patient care or administrative savings. For others, privacy concerns are significant, but can be managed.

Another view is that having different identifiers for the same individual across organisations is sometimes perceived to be protective of individual privacy, because potential linkages across data systems are impeded. Having all healthcare organisations use the same identifier increases the threat to privacy, by facilitating unauthorised linkages of information about an individual within, and across, organisations. This is why some believe that an electronic environment poses greater risks than one that relies on paper records.

Finally, there is the view that the present fragmented and diverse procedures for recording personal health information poses greater privacy risks because of the possibility of error through confusion.

In the midst of the differing opinions over what unique identifier might be acceptable, and whether it is necessary, it is easy to overlook the implications of current practices. Because identifiers differ across organisations, it is indisputable that most healthcare records and transactions contain more elements of identifying information than might be necessary if a single unique identifier were used.

In addition, it is arguable that protection of health information from inadvertent or unauthorised disclosure would become easier with a unique individual identifier that is used for healthcare, but not for other purposes. Such an identifier would be used in a similar manner to the way that HIV testing is often conducted anonymously, by assigning an individual a number that is not otherwise known or used. This number, which is used to track and retrieve the test result, cannot easily be used to identify the individual, whereas name and other identifiers could be. A test result bearing only a protected number cannot be associated easily with an individual. From this perspective, an identifier that could replace other items of identifying information, and that would be used only in healthcare, might yield greater privacy protection than alternatives that do not share these properties.

Other privacy properties for identifiers have been suggested: A check digit that could be used to validate an identifier might further reduce the need for other identifying information. An identifier with no embedded intelligence (for example, initials or a location code) would be more protective than one containing intelligence. A longer identifier would be less easily transcribed or remembered than a shorter one. Encryption of an identifier under controlled conditions might add protection. A decentralized method of issuing identifiers that required no central database would offer other protections.

It is also generally agreed that, at the very least, any identifier must not:

♦ Contain substantive information about an individual.

♦ Be used to establish a single national database of all health records

♦ Be used as a basis for a national identity card system.

Approved Uses of an Identifier for Individuals

It is clear that any adoption of a UHI would make it necessary to prohibit expressly uses of the individual identifier outside the healthcare system. This leaves open the question of what uses within the healthcare system might be approved or disapproved, as well as the need to define the boundaries of the healthcare system itself.

Defining the boundaries of the Irish healthcare system, which is a mix of the private and the public, would require serious thought – for example, should the disclosure of personal health information to an insurance company using the UHI be permitted and, if it is, then would the insurance company not reasonably argue that it makes administrative sense for it to be allowed use the UHI for all other purposes connected with the individual and his or her relationship with the company.

It is also considered important that the individual should have the right to object to having a UHI generally or to block its use for particular purposes or disclosures.

Other Criteria for Evaluation of Possible Identifiers

Irrespective of the merits of adopting or rejecting a UHI, there is consensus that the criteria underlying the selection of any identifier should include not just privacy considerations, but also practicality and cost-effectiveness. In order for a unique individual identifier to be effective, every individual should have an identifier from birth, that applies only to that individual, and that does not change over time. An identifier or identifier system that is not practical to implement or that does not meet the requirements of administrative simplification is impossible to justify. Equally, the costs of implementation and use of the identifier must be within an acceptable range.

These issues were considered in a 1997 study commissioned by the US Department of Health & Human Sciences.[365] It concluded that a workable health service recipient unique identifier had the following six critical, and inter-dependent, components:

- **An identifier:** Usually based on a numeric or alphanumeric scheme.

- **Identifying information:** Permanent (unchanging) personal data such as name, date of birth, place of birth, mother's maiden name; a longitudinal data segment that contains corroborating information that occurs over the lifetime of a person such as address, profession, spouse; and a health service data segment with information that helps locate the individual's previous health records.

- **An index:** Linking the unique identifier and the identification information of the client

- **Mechanism to hide or encrypt the identifier:** Protection of the identity of a client, when sensitive information is being communicated, can be accomplished with the use of technology, such as encryption.

- **Technology infrastructure:** Computer systems, a communication network, and powerful software applications to issue, maintain, and manage the unique identifiers.

- **Administrative infrastructure:** To manage and control various functions relating to the issue, use, and maintenance of the identifier.

---

[365] Appavu (1999).

THE NATIONAL HEALTH INFORMATION STRATEGY & A UNIQUE HEALTH IDENTIFIER

The consideration of the case for a UHI in the National Health Information Strategy had regard to the challenge of finding an identifier option that could achieve an appropriate balance among privacy, practicality and cost-effectiveness.

In introducing the discussion, the National Health Information Strategy stated:

> "The provision of client-centred services is one of the key principles of *Quality & Fairness: A Health System for You* (2001). This places a special emphasis on the importance of being able to associate, through unique identification, all relevant health information about a given client / patient as and when required. It is important to note that the use of a particular identifier does not in any way presume the sharing of information with other users of that identifier. Information sharing is a completely separate issue and is discussed in Chapter 12 (*Information Governance and Legislation*). Rather, the use of a unique identifier should be considered as a logical extension of the use of a person's name for identification purposes."[366]

Advantages of a UHI

Not surprisingly, therefore, the National Health Information Strategy came down firmly on the side of having a UHI (assigned at birth) used in, and for, both private and public patient treatment, as well as management-related purposes. It argued that "unique identification promotes the quality and safety of client/patient care in many ways":

♦ Providing for a more definite association to be made between the client / patient and his / her records, which, in turn, promotes client / patient safety through the correct identification of the individual.

---

[366] Department of Health & Children (2004).

- ◆ As a key requirement for the proper implementation of the electronic healthcare record, upon which many other benefits will accrue.[367]

- ◆ Supporting the provision of shared care, by allowing records for one individual to be associated or collated, thus enabling different care providers to 'see' all or parts of the same health record. This attribute is especially important for the management of chronic diseases such as diabetes, cancer and heart disease that involve many contacts with different health professionals in a range of settings over long time periods.

- ◆ Enabling good record management that, in turn, supports clinical audit and risk management processes.

Other advantages identified in the *Strategy* were:

- ◆ Largely obviating the need for clients / patients to provide personal details at every contact with the health service, a procedure that clients / patients can find quite irksome, unnecessary and time-consuming.

- ◆ Allowing the identification of duplicates from repeat contacts by the same individual with primary and secondary care services. This is an essential requirement for epidemiological purposes, screening and vaccination services, in service planning and evaluation and in the management of waiting lists, etc.

- ◆ Supporting the tracking and recall of patients or products, if necessary – for example, for vaccines, medical devices and blood products.

- ◆ Reducing wastage of resources – for example, by reducing the number of repeated diagnostic tests.

Accordingly, it concluded that:

> "The only safe and practical method of being able to draw together the separate parts of an individual's health record is through the use of unique identification. In the absence of this, it is not feasible to plan, manage, deliver or evaluate

---

[367] See Department of Health & Children (2001), Action 118.

services on a person-centred basis, since this can only be achieved by associating records belonging to the same client / patient."

Options for Unique Health Identification in Ireland

A national approach to unique health identification is therefore considered essential. The two main approaches are:

♦ Use of the Personal Public Services Number[368] together with its supporting inter-sectoral infrastructure.

♦ Development of an entirely separate national identifier, specific to the health sector, with its own supporting infrastructure.

The Health Information Strategy considered these two options and felt that, given the scale and complexity of developing and maintaining a comprehensive and up-to-date client / patient database, the use of an entirely separate national identifier specific to the health sector with its own supporting infrastructure would convey few, if any, advantages and create several disadvantages, including poorer data quality in terms of narrower coverage and slower updating of information, as well as the cost of duplicating the effort being expended by other sectors. For those reasons, it considered such an approach impractical and opted instead for an identifier "based upon the PPSN and its supportive infrastructure".[369]

A key consideration in this area was the need to recognise the significant interplay between the public and private health sectors. For example, a patient may attend a general practitioner privately, receive healthcare in a public ward or clinic in a hospital, and later undergo surgery in a private hospital. To support the quality and continuity of care, it is essential that unique identification enables health information to "follow the patient" as appropriate, especially with regard to bridging the hospital (primarily public) and primary care (primarily private) domains.

---

[368] The PPSN is managed by the Department of Social & Family Affairs, as discussed in **Chapter 1**. The number is already used in the public health sector for a number of purposes by a range of authorised users.

[369] Department of Health & Children (2004), Action 16, Chapter 12.

Using the PPSN as the Health Identifier

At the time the PPSN was introduced in the Social Welfare Bill 1998, the then Data Protection Commissioner gave evidence to the Dáil Select Committee considering the Bill, in which he set out the range of data protection concerns he had "about what is undoubtedly the most important data protection issue you have been asked to consider since enacting the 1988 legislation".[370] In particular, he anticipated in his evidence its extended use over time.

In other countries, the extension of their Social Insurance Numbers to new areas has engendered considerable debate. For example, in Canada, the 1987 *Report of the Standing Committee on Justice and of the Solicitor General*[371] made strong recommendations on the need to contain the use of the Canadian social insurance number. The report noted that the number was so important, so special and so much a symbol of the need for data protection that it demanded certain controls over its use. In its response to the committee, the Federal Government indicated that it would act to ensure that the SIN did not become a universal identification number. Nonetheless, in Canada, successive Privacy Commissioners have sounded warnings in regard to the creeping general application of the social security number. This matter of function creep has been of concern to the Irish Data Protection Commissioner too.

Similarly, in Australia, the 1988 Privacy Act was foreshadowed by a vigorous campaign against the surveillance possibilities of a proposed so-called "Australia card", equipped with a number for each holder of the card. The project was dropped, and the Privacy Act has considerably circumscribed the use of the tax file number.

In Ireland, the use of the PPSN as a UHI has created two main opposing schools of thought. On the one hand, it is claimed that preserving the ability to link healthcare records with records from other sources using the number is essential. The choice of an identifier used only in healthcare could constrain important clinical and public health research that depends on such linking. On the other hand, it is

---

[370] Evidence of the Data Protection Commissioner on the Social Welfare Bill 1988 to the Dáil Select Committee on Social, Community & Family Affairs, 4 March 1988.

[371] Standing Committee on Justice & of the Solicitor General (Canada) (1987).

asserted that, if the PPSN were to become the unique health identifier for individuals, the potential for linkages expands to include not only all aspects of an individual's medical data but also employment, tax, social security and a range of other personal information. The availability and widespread use of the PPSN, combined with the increasing use of electronic databases, and the lack of adequate legal and social controls, lend support to these concerns. To some, therefore, the PPSN is simply unacceptable for identifying health records.

Data Protection Concerns about the Use of the PPSN

In *Chapter 12* of the National Health Information Strategy, it is stated:

"Any proposed use of the PPS Number in relation to health information must address, in consultation with the Data Protection Commissioner, the current legal position that this number is for public service use only and factors which could unintentionally result in the PPS Number, *de facto*, becoming a national identifier."[372]

It was also noted that the Data Protection Commissioner had already expressed concerns about the use of the PPSN as a UHI.[373] The Commissioner made it clear that he understood the necessity for a unique personal identifier in the context of the development of an Electronic Health Record and could see the attractiveness, from a health administrator's perspective, of basing it on the PPSN. However, he was opposed to its use for the following reasons:

"... there are fundamental data protection problems with a number that is established for one purpose by legislation being used for other purposes, including private sector ones ... the proposal could be characteristic of the phenomenon of 'information and function creep', which is of general concern to me and many individuals and which has been observed in other countries, where a limited proposal is extended to purposes beyond those originally envisaged, with consequent implications for the privacy of citizens ... [and] ...

---

[372] Department of Health & Children (2004).
[373] Data Protection Commissioner (2003), *Appendix 3*.

> Notwithstanding the importance of the health area, the proposed extension of the use of the PPSN into the private health sector – unless it is proven that there is a necessary 'public' element to that service – would potentially make it very difficult in the future to resist its use by other sectors, giving rise to the very real possibility that it could become a National Identification number by stealth ... "

However, the Commissioner made it clear that he had no difficulty with the introduction by the government of a unique health identity number – combined with sufficient safeguards – on the basis of properly debated and enacted stand-alone legislation. This is where the publication and Parliamentary progress of the proposed Health Information Bill will provide a key stimulus to, and a valuable forum for, a public debate on the UHI, both in terms of health service reform and wider societal concerns.

THE SITUATION IN OTHER COUNTRIES

The debate on UHIs is frequently an emotive one and usually strongly influenced by a country's political history and cultural traditions. Equally, the same pragmatic reasons for and against as outlined above are also made.

USA

In the United States, a White Paper was published on a Unique Health Identifier for Individuals.[374] The UHI was seen as part of a process to achieve uniform national health data standards and health information privacy that would support the efficient electronic exchange of specified administrative and financial healthcare transactions.[375]

The Health Insurance Portability & Accountability Act 1996 (HIPAA) recognised the unique identifier for individuals as an essential component of administrative simplification. The specific arguments advanced for its introduction were as follows. There is evidence that a unique identifier for individuals in the health system

---

[374] Department of Health & Human Services (USA) (1998).
[375] The Health Insurance Portability & Accountability Act 1996.

would have many benefits, including improved quality of care and reduced administrative costs. Being able to identify an individual uniquely is highly desirable in both the delivery and administration of healthcare. Today, various healthcare organisations and insurance companies, integrated delivery systems, health plans, managed care organisations, public programmes, clinics, hospitals, physicians, and pharmacies routinely assign identifiers to individuals for use within their systems.

However, the level of controversy surrounding this standard identifier has caused much national debate and a delay in its implementation. The initiative came to a halt when Congress passed legislation prohibiting the use of any funds in 1999 to address the need for a unique client identifier. The National Committee on Vital & Health Statistics has recommended that a standard for a unique identifier for individuals is not adopted until privacy legislation has been fully implemented. One US commentator has referred to the Universal Health Identifier as "Big Help or Big Brother?".[376]

Australia

In Australia, in June 1995, the Australian Health Ministers' Advisory Council established a Task Force on Quality in Australian Healthcare. Among the recommendations in its final report in June 1996 was that:

> "… the introduction of a voluntary patient-held 'smart card' for health records be the subject of feasibility and pilot studies".[377]

This idea was incorporated into the 1999 National Plan of Action for Information Management in the Health Sector over the next five years.[378] Under the present Health Connect Project – which involves a major network of electronic health records that aims to improve the flow of information across the Australian health sector – the need for a foolproof system of unique identification to prevent people receiving incorrect treatments is regarded as imperative. The issue is currently

---

[376] Jeffrey P. Kahn, Director, Center for Bioethics, University of Minnesota, http://www.cnn.com/HEALTH/bioethics/9807/natl.medical.id/.

[377] Task Force on Quality in Australian Healthcare (1996).

[378] National Health Information Management Advisory Council (Australia) (1999).

being examined and remains a high priority for action by the National Information Management Advisory Committee. The exact nature of the smart card is yet to be determined, as are the "strict privacy protocols" to support it, although it is anticipated that they will be implemented concurrently with the proposed national health information network.[379]

New Zealand

In New Zealand, in 1996, the government developed and released a new *Health Information Strategy for the Year 2000*.[380] The first two issues recognised as being important in the development of the strategy were:

♦ The need to identify individuals uniquely.

♦ The security, confidentiality and privacy of personal health information.

It argued that the positive and unique identification of an individual is a critical principle that lays out a foundation for quality healthcare and significantly lessens the probability of potentially dangerous mistreatment. The Privacy Act of 1993 placed restrictions on the use of unique identifiers, and on the use of the National Health Index (NHI)[381] – an online population-based register that includes a unique random-generated identifier. The Privacy Act safeguards NHI numbers from being used for any purpose, other than in conjunction with the provision of healthcare services, and of information relating to those services. NHI numbers cannot be related to databases from other sectors of the economy, or databases used for different purposes. According to the law, few individuals other than healthcare providers may be allowed to access NHI data.

The NHI has been in use in the hospital sector for almost a decade, and most New Zealanders are on the Index, but it is only recently that NHI use has gained momentum in the primary healthcare sector. In 2004, the Ministry of Health launched an NHI Upgrade Programme,

---

[379] For a full description of HealthConnect and related issues, see www.healthconnect.gov.au.

[380] Ministry of Health (New Zealand) (1996).

[381] The register maintains records of names, aliases, addresses and date of birth.

including a series of initiatives to improve information-sharing among health and disability services and to promote wider use of the number.

New Zealand is also currently finalising a Health Practitioner Index (HPI), which will be a central source of core information about every registered health practitioner and provider in New Zealand. The overall goal of the HPI is to help New Zealand's health sector find better and more secure ways to access and transfer health-related information to improve the health and well-being of New Zealanders. The HPI will improve the privacy and security of patient and practitioner information, through the ability to better control access to it. The HPI is intended to make it easier for the right information to be made available to the right person. For example, a medical practitioner involved in the care of a particular patient might be able to access certain information about that patient's care, whereas another type of practitioner may not have the authority to view the same information. Having a single consistent system of identifying practitioners makes this possible and helps protects patient privacy in an environment where patient information is increasingly shared between different healthcare providers.

The UK

The entire UK has had a health service client identifier (the NHS Number) since 1948, when the National Health Service (NHS) began. Despite this, its value as a national unique healthcare identifier was severely limited. Over time, it developed 22 different formats, was liable to transcription error and was not designed for computer use and validation.

In 1995, the implementation of a modern NHS unique client identifier began under the New NHS Number programme. A 10-digit NHS number[382] has been allotted to everyone in England and Wales as a means of patient identification. A phased approach was adopted, initially focused on primary care, then secondary care, then purchasing, and then community care.

As part of this process, from October 2002, newborn babies were given their NHS lifetime health identification number under the so-

---

[382] The first nine digits are the identifier and the 10th is a validation digit, designed to prevent errors when entering the number in electronic databases.

called NHS *Numbers for Babies Scheme*. The unique number stays with each child for the rest of his or her life – the key to his or her clinical history and intended to be a complete record of every visit the individual makes to the doctor, every vaccination received and every illness treated. Under the programme, these NHS numbers are issued centrally and allocated to babies as close to birth as possible, as part of the Birth Notification process carried out by midwives. Previously, infants had to wait several weeks for their registration number to come through from the Registrar of Births & Deaths. During that time, the child might have undergone tests and treatment in different locations, had their name changed or changed address, etc.

A Department of Health / NHS pamphlet, *General Principles in the Use of the NHS Number*,[383] provides guidance on using the number in accessing, verifying, and linking data, and in using it as the common currency of communication. The document also describes the role of the number in promoting security and confidentiality of data on patients, and explains the conditions under which it can be used by non-NHS organisations. An appendix outlines a protocol for the sharing of information with institutions outside the NHS.

Commenting on the history and value of the number, the NHS has stated:

> "In 1948, it was quite simple; you issued a card which patients carried around with all their details on. Every time they used the NHS, they showed the card which would show entitlement to treatment and enable record transfer and linkage. The use of the NHS number today allows electronic access to patient details via secure online access. In turn, this national initiative [National Programme for Information Technology] is the key to improving data quality by allowing speedier updates to take place, therefore impacting on information held on local Patient Administration systems, leading to better communication with patients and in turn helping to improve medical care by reducing the amount of out of date or inaccurate patient data held. Instead of confidential patient information being displayed on all manner of patient notes, the NHS number has reduced the

---

[383] Department of Health (1998).

need for paper records and improved patient confidentiality into the bargain."[384]

In Northern Ireland, the Health & Care Number (which was born out of the Unique Patient Client Identifier Project) is a 10-digit unstructured number, similar to and compatible with the NHS Number in England & Wales. The Health & Care Number is intended to provide a number from birth to death, which can be used for administrative and demographic purposes across all health and personal social care organisations – existing and proposed. The demographic data set for the Health & Care Number Index will include a Health & Care Number, surname, forename, address, postcode, title, sex, date of birth, date of death and registered GP.

In Scotland, the NHS is developing its own Community Health Index (CHI) Number. Currently, the CHI contains the demographic details of the population registered with a GP, or who have made contact with the health service through the Child Health or Screening Systems. The CHI Number is used within primary and secondary care as a patient identifier. Its main purpose is to facilitate the sharing of information across the whole of NHS Scotland, regardless of where patients are admitted and treated.

Canada

Canada currently does not have a national health service unique recipient identifier. In 1997, extensive work on the issue of unique identifiers was undertaken by the Canadian Institute for Health Information Working Group on Health Identification Systems, as part of their work on developing standards for data linkage in Canada.[385] A survey was designed and distributed, which, in part, explored the current state and future plans for unique identifiers. The key points were:

♦ A wide variety of unique identifiers were found to be in use in the Canadian healthcare system, with varying levels of sophistication.

---

[384] NHS Number: *History of the NHS Number* (available at www.nhsia.nhs.uk/nnp/pages/default.asp)

[385] McBride & Burr (1997).

♦ The primary use for numbering systems was for billing, verification of eligibility for benefits and internal record keeping.

The EU

Since 1990, the European Commission has been active in designing systems for unique patient identification. The European approach is centred on smart card technology. These activities were conducted in cooperation with the European Committee for Standardization (CEN). The analysis, conducted by 10 working groups of the EUROCARDS action, showed that many European countries are considering the development of smart cards for their healthcare system. Such a card was not seen as a stand-alone element, but as a key component of an integrated health information system. Issues of confidentiality and security emerged as major concerns. Equally, there was consensus that the decision to use a card containing personal medical information should remain with the person on a voluntary basis.

12
SUBJECT ACCESS & OTHER RIGHTS

INTRODUCTION

Summary of the Rights of Data Subjects

Complementing the obligations imposed on those who keep personal information, there are a series of rights conferred on individuals. In this chapter, we concentrate on the single most important right: the right of a data subject to access information kept about him or her. However, before doing that, this is a timely opportunity to summarise all the rights enjoyed by data subjects (some of which have already been touched on). Under data protection law, an individual is entitled to:

♦ Have information processed fairly *(the fair processing principle: sections 2, 2A, 2B, 2C & 2D).*

♦ Prohibit the use of his or her information for direct marketing *(section 2(7) and (8)).*[386] An individual can request a data controller, prior to processing, not to process personal data for the purpose of direct marketing and it is also provided that individuals must be informed of their right to object. These provisions are not intended to discourage the practice of responsible direct marketing but rather to raise awareness of the right, and give

---

[386] Interestingly, an amendment was introduced to the Data Protection (Amendment) Bill 2002, excluding from the definition of "direct marketing" any direct mailing carried out in the course of political activities by political parties or their members or by candidates for, or holders of, elective political office. The activities of a body established by or under statute are also excluded, for example, mailing by the Referendum Commission in advance of a referendum.

individuals the opportunity, to opt out of receiving direct marketing material if they so wish.

♦ Establish whether a person is a data controller by writing to any person who he or she believes keeps personal information requesting that person to advise whether they are a data controller and, if so, to provide a description of the information kept and the purposes for which it is kept within 21 days *(section 3)*. (Under the 1988 Act, not all data controllers were registerable and this provision was intended to compensate for that situation.)

♦ Establish *(under the subject access right: section 4)* whether a data controller (or the data controller's agent) keeps personal data on him or her, and if so, be supplied with the personal information concerned in an intelligible format together with details on:

◊ the purposes for which the information is kept.

◊ the persons to whom such information has been, or may be, disclosed.

◊ the types of information concerned.

◊ any information on the sources of such information.

◊ the logic[387] involved where the processing of the personal information by automated means has formed or is likely to constitute the sole basis for any significant decision relating to the data subject.

It is further provided that a subject access request relating to any of the aforementioned matters must be interpreted as a request for all of the above in the absence of an indication to the contrary.[388]

However, where a data controller is registered and makes multiple entries in the register in relation to information it controls separate subject access requests may have to be made if a data subject wishes to access all the information the data controller keeps on him or her.

---

[387] Section 4(1)(a)(iv) provides that the explanation of the logic must be made free of any charge.

[388] Section 4(1)(b).

- Protection against enforced subject access in employment situations *(section 4(13))* (Not yet in force as of June 2005).

- Have his or her personal information enhanced, corrected, blocked[389] or otherwise amended (including by deletion where this is not inconsistent with the keeping of a proper record), if it is held in contravention of the data protection principles and, where any of these actions materially modifies the information kept, there is a further requirement on the data controller to notify any person to whom the data were disclosed in the previous 12 months unless such notification proves impossible or involves disproportionate effort *(section 6)*.

- Object to the processing of personal data relating to him or her where the processing of such data is considered necessary for the performance of a task carried out in the public interest or where the processing is for the purposes of the legitimate interests of the controller *(section 6A)*. However, the objection must be on compelling legitimate grounds: namely, that the processing would be likely to cause substantial damage or distress to the data subject or another individual and that such damage or distress is unwarranted. The right to object will not apply in certain circumstances such as where the data subject has given consent to the processing; the processing is necessary in the course of entering into, or performance of, a contract; for compliance with a legal obligation; to protect the data subject's vital interests; and the processing is carried out by political parties or candidates for elective office in the course of electoral activities.

- Benefit from a general ban on decision-making that is based solely on automated processing of data intended to evaluate certain personal aspects where such a decision produces legal effects concerning an individual or otherwise significantly affects an individual (for example, eligibility for a medical

---

[389] Blocking is defined as having personal information marked so as to ensure that it cannot be used for certain particular purposes. The concept of blocking was introduced by the 2003 Act, as an additional right to amendment and erasure. The example of potential blocking given on the Data Protection Commissioner's website is "you might want your data blocked for research purposes where it held for other purposes".

service), except in the circumstances outlined in that section (for example, where the data subject has consented) and where suitable safeguards to protect the person's legitimate interests are in place *(section 6B)*.

♦ Complain to the Data Protection Commissioner about breaches of any of the above by data controllers and data processors *(section 10)*.

♦ Seek compensation in the Courts for damage suffered if data controllers or data processors fail to observe the duty of care placed on them in relation to collecting or dealing with personal information *(section 7)*.

Note: The position in relation to identifying sources and revealing opinions are subject to special rules intended to protect the public interest and are likely to be particularly relevant in the context of personal health information.

The Importance of the Right of Access

Important as the obligations on persons keeping information may be, they are ultimately of value only because they are supported by a right of subject access. Without that right, it would be impossible for individuals to establish the legitimacy and correctness of information held on them. In 1990, the Data Protection Commissioner stated that:

> "Experience has shown that access requests frequently uncover the existence of inaccurate and misleading data and that, even where inaccuracies are not found, the individuals concerned find it helpful to be able to see the kind of personal data kept about them."[390]

Given the importance and sensitivity of personal health information, it is especially appropriate that individuals should feel re-assured that they have a right to access such information and have it amended, deleted or enhanced where it is incorrect as to its content or held improperly. As the New Zealand Privacy Commissioner observed:

---

[390] Data Protection Commissioner (1991), p.8.

> "The right of [subject] access to personal information is an important right for a number of reasons. Amongst other things it increases the accountability of health agencies. It allows patients to challenge what they see as being incorrect or misleading information and to gain a greater insight into the reasons for the treatment they have received."[391]

Separately from data protection law, best practice in medicine has long recognised the need for open and trusting relationships between doctors and their patients. Many of the provisions of the 1992 *Charter of Rights for Hospital Patients*[392] specifically reflect the values of openness and respect in relation to patients and the *Charter* expressly provides for the release of medical records to patients. Further, the Medical Council encourages doctors to engage positively with patients seeking information. Its *Ethical Guidelines* state:

> "A request for information from a patient always requires a positive response. In general, doctors should ensure that a patient and family members, subject to patient consent, are as fully informed as possible about matters relating to an illness. Patients do not always fully understand the information and advice given to them by doctors. They should be encouraged to ask questions. These should be answered carefully in non-technical terms with or without information leaflets. The aim is to promote understanding and compliance with recommended therapy. The doctor should keep a note of such explanation and if it is felt that the patient still does not understand, it may be advisable to ask the patient's permission to speak to a relative."[393]

The *Guide* adds that:

> "Patients are entitled to receive a copy of their own medical records, provided it does not put their health (or the health of others) at risk."[394]

---

[391] Slane (1999).

[392] Department of Health (1992).

[393] Medical Council (2004), p.13.

[394] Medical Council (2004), p.16.

Accordingly, sharing information with the patient is viewed as being integral to good doctor-patient communication and to high quality care. As a general rule, therefore, patient access to his or her personal health information should be facilitated readily.

In that regard, it is important to stress that the existence of data protection law with its formal rights of access should not overshadow a common-sense approach to making health information available to the individuals to whom it relates. For example, where a patient asks a healthcare service provider for a copy of his or her latest test results during the consultation, this request could be handled by simply providing a copy of the information at the time. Even if the request is more complex – for example, because it involves collating data from both paper and electronic sources – it may be preferable to ask for the request in writing as this gives more clarity about the information sought, but even this does not mean that it need be treated as a formal access request under the Data Protection Acts.

PROCEDURES FOR MAKING & DEALING WITH ACCESS REQUESTS

Every data controller should have a formal procedure for dealing with access queries, to enable requests to be met in a timely and proper manner, consistent with section 4.

A recommended approach for handling access requests is to acknowledge any request received as soon as practicable. The acknowledgement should include an indication of any costs involved in processing the request, as well as an indication of any difficulties that the data controller envisages in finding the relevant information. The acknowledgement should also address the issue of proof of identity of the requestor.

The Access Request

The Data Protection Acts provide that a subject access request must be in writing[395] and that the individual making the request must provide to the person keeping the information proof of identification and any

---

[395] Section 4(1)(a).

other details reasonably requested to assist with locating the personal information concerned.[396] The need for the request to be in writing, and to provide proof of identification, is intended to protect the data controller against making an unauthorised disclosure, while the requirement to assist the data controller in locating information was designed to make complying with the access requirement less burdensome. However, these provisions cannot be used to thwart or delay a request for access.

Interestingly, the data protection regime does not contain a similar provision to the one in the freedom of information code, which places a legal duty on public bodies to help members of the public in making requests, so that the requestor can pinpoint the information he or she wants to see. Further, under FOI, there is a specific duty to help those with disabilities to find what they are seeking.

Fees & Compliance Period

In a comment that has global applicability, the New Zealand Privacy Commissioner stated in 1999 that:

> "Health professionals need to deal with access requests promptly and not ignore them in the hope that they will go away. In my experience, people will not go away if they want to see their medical files."[397]

Under the Data Protection Acts, there is no obligation to charge an access fee. Some data controllers may wish to charge a fee to deter access requests, or to help meet the administrative costs involved when access is provided – for example, costs relating to photocopying, copies of x-ray films and for staff time involved in processing a request. However, the fee must not be excessive or act to discourage individual from accessing their records and, in any event, it cannot exceed €6.35.[398] Once a request has been made, and any appropriate fee paid, the information must be given within 40 days of the request

---

[396] Section 4(3).

[397] Slane (1999). He also made the point that too many complaints he received "were in the health sector and it is time for the record to be improved."

[398] The prescribed fee (section 4(1)(c)(i)) has remained unchanged since 1988. See Data Protection (Fees) Regulations 1988 (S.I. No.347 of 1988).

and compliance with any reasonable query from the data controller for information designed to help locate the information concerned.[399]

If a subject access request is not complied with, or if the information concerned has to be materially amended or erased, then the fee must be returned.

Supplying the Information

Once a subject access request has been received, under section 4(5), the data controller cannot amend the information involved even, if on preparing the information for release, it realises that inaccuracies exist. The only amendments possible are those that would have been made in a routine manner. This exception allows normal business processes to continue, notwithstanding the access request. For example, a hospital can continue to routinely update its patient files, etc. but the individual is protected by ensuring that data controllers cannot simply amend, delete or add to information because they discovered problems when responding to the subject access request.

Section 4(1)(a)(iii) requires the data controller to release the information to the data subject in an "intelligible form" and subsection (9) provides that that obligation is met by supplying the individual with a "copy of the information concerned in permanent form". In other words, the right is not to the original papers or records but to hard copies of the information in those records.

Interestingly, the 2003 Act added a proviso to this section 4(9) requirement, where:

- The supply of such a copy is not possible, or would involve disproportionate effort.
- The data subject agrees otherwise.

No one has yet defined "disproportionate effort" and the Data Protection Commissioner has indicated his reluctance to do so, given his obligation to uphold data subjects' rights. However, he has indicated that he would be sympathetic to a case being made, that providing many hundreds or thousands of pages of documentation

---

[399] Section 4(1)(a).

involves disproportionate effort where most of the documentation has already been supplied.

The matter of "disproportionate effort" is likely to be most relevant when it comes to accessing information held in manual records systems. As already discussed, information in manual systems must be part of a relevant filing system, which has as one requirement that "specific information relating to a particular individual is readily accessible". In terms of the "readily accessible" criterion, it may be legitimate for a data controller to ask an individual making an access request to specify (under section 4(3) [400]) the information being sought by date or other reference in order to render it readily accessible.

While a data subject has a right to all of his or her data, the provisions regarding disproportionate effort and readily accessible data give the data controller some scope to address the request in a manner that balances the individual's rights with the administrative and other costs involved.

Further, under section 4(4) of the Data Protection Acts 1988 to 2003, a person holding personal information about an individual, where such information also relates to another identifiable individual, is not obliged[401] to release the information concerned, unless the other person consents or all identifying details of the second individual have been removed. This was amended in the 2003 Act (see below) to provide that, where the personal information relating to the data subject consists of an expression of an opinion about the data subject by another person, the opinion may be released to the data subject without the third party's consent.

Formatting the Information

There is no obligation on a data controller to re-format or summarise the material in response to an access request. However, if the healthcare service provider believes a summary may be more helpful and is willing to prepare it, and the individual wants the information

---

[400] Section 4(3) obliges an individual making a request "… to supply the data controller concerned with such information as he may reasonably require in order ... to locate any relevant personal data or information".

[401] The wording of the proviso does not rule out the possibility that the person holding the information may release it without consulting the other party.

in this form, this could be offered instead of, or as well as, the original record. Depending on the circumstances, the individual may only be seeking a summary of the record and this could usefully be established at the time the data controller acknowledges the subject access request.

Some factors a data controller may wish to consider when deciding how best to give access to information could include an individual's disability (if any), or their age or language skills. These factors should not present a barrier to an individual obtaining meaningful access to their record.

Repeated Access Requests

If a person holding personal information has complied with an access request, there is no obligation to comply with an identical or similar request from the same individual unless a reasonable interval has elapsed.[402] In determining a reasonable interval, regard must be had to the nature of the information involved, the purposes for which the information is held and the frequency with which it is altered.[403]

While the Acts do not specifically refer to such requests as being "frivolous or vexatious", it might be that the Data Protection Commissioner would support the view that information may be withheld where the request is considered frivolous or vexatious.

Access by Children, Parents & Guardians

This area of access in relation to the information of children can be problematic. Speaking in the Dáil in 2001, the then Minister for Health & Children stated that:

> "… it is important that parents are well informed about the health and medical treatment of their children. Parental consent is required for treatment. Clear communication with parents and guardians is a measure of good practice and in so far as it is in the interests of the child, parents should have ready access to records.
>
> Within statute, the general position is that access to the health record of a child must be in the best interests of the child.

---

[402] Section 4(10), Data Protection Acts 1998 to 2003.

[403] Section 4(11), Data Protection Acts 1998 to 2003.

Parents have a qualified right of access in so far as that is the case. The Freedom of Information and Data Protection Acts create rights of access and also protect the privacy of the child.

When parents seek such access under the Freedom of Information Act 1997, hospitals will grant it in accordance with the provisions of that Act. There are regulations and guidelines relating to access by parents and these are available on the website of the Information Commissioner.

Where parents seek such access under the Data Protection Act 1988, although there is no right of access, the data controller may release records to a parent as a person acting on behalf of or with the consent of the subject."[404]

Specifically, the right of access under section 4 of the Data Protection Acts is personal to the individual in question: only that individual is legally entitled to access the data.

Where a person is 16 years or older, unless there are concerns as to competency, the individual should be able to exercise the right of access to his or her personal health information. Where the individual is below that age, the data controller should exercise professional judgement, on a case-by-case basis, on whether the entitlement to access should be exercisable by the individual alone or jointly by the individual and his or her parent or guardian. In making a decision, particular regard should be had to the maturity of the young person concerned and his or her best interests. For transparency and avoidance of doubt, it is recommended that the data controller prepare and make available a patient information leaflet outlining the approach taken.

In his 2001 *Annual Report,* the Commissioner stated:

"In the normal course, parents do not have the right to use the subject access provisions on behalf of their children, irrespective of their age. However, under section 8, the

---

[404] Dáil Éireann, Vol.542, 18 October, 2001, Written Answers: Medical Records. As the Minister's statement indicates, the FOI Acts contain specific provisions in relation to potential access. This issue is considered in greater detail in **Chapter 13**.

restrictions on disclosure of personal data do not apply in certain circumstances – including where a person is acting 'on behalf of' a data subject. This provision allows a data controller to provide details to a parent, but it does not require them to do so. The discretion afforded to medical professionals in this regard need to be exercised in accordance with the requirements of medical ethics, and in accordance with any other relevant laws, including the established role of the parents in their duty of care as laid down in case law."[405]

The challenges faced in this complex area of trying to balance children's rights and parents' responsibilities in a privacy framework have been considered in other fora in this country, as well as abroad. In Ireland, *Children First: National Guidelines for the Protection and Welfare of Children*[406] is a major document that addresses the multiplicity of issues (including confidentiality and information sharing) involved in identifying and reporting child abuse. More generally, for anyone wishing to read more on the privacy dimensions of this subject, a good starting point is an address by Susan Kerkin (of the New Zealand Privacy Commissioner's Office) on *Disclosing Children's Health Information: A Legal & Ethical Framework*.[407] Finally, **Chapter 13** of this book looks at the FOI perspective on parental access, where the key criterion is the best interests of the child.

SUBJECT ACCESS TO PERSONAL HEALTH INFORMATION

Power to Make Health Access Regulations

For the most part, similar access rules apply to health information as apply to other types of personal information. However, there is a provision under section 4(8) for the Minister for Justice, Equality &

---

[405] Data Protection Commissioner (2002).

[406] Department of Health & Children (1999).

[407] Kerkin (1998).

Law Reform to make regulations governing subject access to personal information:

♦ Relating to physical or mental health.

♦ Kept for, or obtained in the course of, carrying out social work by a Minister of the Government, a local authority, a Health Board or a specified voluntary organisation or other body.

In making any such regulations, the Minister must consult with the Minister for Health & Children and any other Minister of the Government, who would have a responsibility in these areas.

Under the Data Protection Act 1988, the Minister is empowered to make health or social work access regulations, only where he or she "considers it desirable in the interests of the data subject". In 1989, such regulations were made – Data Protection (Access Modification) (Health) Regulations 1989 (S.I. No.82 of 1989) – and are discussed below. The Data Protection Act 2003 amended section 4(8) and provides that the grounds for restricting access, under regulations, is broadened to include those of *public interest*. The reason given for the amendment was "concerns raised by the Department of Health & Children".[408] These concerns were not elaborated and, to date, no new access regulations have been made.

Health Access Regulations 1989

The Regulations provide that personal health information shall not be supplied by, or on behalf of, the person holding it to the individual concerned, if it would be likely to cause serious harm to the physical or mental health of the individual. However, nothing in that prohibition excuses the person holding the information from supplying so much of the information sought as can be supplied without causing the harm referred to in that stipulation.

If the person keeping the personal health information is a health professional, then he or she can make the access decision. A health professional is defined in the Regulations to mean:

---

[408] Data Protection Bill, Dáil Éireann, Committee Stage, Select Committee on Justice, Equality, Defence & Women's Rights, 12 February 2003.

♦ A person who is a medical practitioner, dentist, optician, pharmaceutical chemist, nurse or midwife and who is registered under the enactments governing his or her profession, and

♦ A chiropodist, dietician, occupational therapist, orthoptist, physiotherapist, psychologist, child psychotherapist or speech therapist.

Where the person holding the relevant personal health information is not a "health professional", the Regulations require that such a person may not communicate the information requested until after consulting with an "appropriate health professional", who is:

♦ The registered medical practitioner, within the meaning of the Medical Practitioners Act 1978 (S.I. No.4 of 1978), or registered dentist, within the meaning of the Dentists Act 1985 (S.I. No.9 of 1985), currently or most recently responsible for the clinical care of the data subject in connection with the matters to which the information, the subject of the request, relates.

♦ Where there is more than one such person, the person who is the most suitable to advise on those matters.

♦ Where there is no such person available, a health professional who has the necessary experience and qualifications to advise on those matters.

Interestingly, the data controller is not required to heed the advice given but simply to seek it. However, it is difficult to envisage situations where such advice would be ignored without good reason.

The Regulations relating to social work are similar, but not identical. Unlike the health access regulations, the social work equivalent offers no guidance as to who is to exercise the professional judgement on whether the personal data should be withheld.

The Regulations & Third Parties

The Regulations also include another important provision that runs counter to the general rules on access. The section 4(4) provision, which does not oblige the release of third-party information unless the other person consents or all identifying details of the second individual have been removed, is overridden by the Regulations. They provide that the restriction does not apply in relation to personal information of another individual, if that individual is a health professional who has been involved in the care of the data subject and the information relates to him or her in his or her capacity as such. Accordingly, healthcare data controllers are not obliged to approach other health professionals for permission to disclose reports authored by them and contained in the patient record. However, if the report contains information likely to cause difficulties for the other practitioner, it is professional courtesy to advise him or her of the patient access request.

The Regulations & Withholding Access

As already stated, the Regulations provide that information constituting health data shall not be supplied by, or on behalf of, a data controller to the data subject in response to a subject access request, if it would be likely to cause serious harm to the physical health of the data subject. Importantly, it is harm not distress or emotional upset. The threat must be significant – for example, where there is a serious risk an individual may inflict deliberate self-harm. In any situation where access is denied, the data controller or an appropriate healthcare professional (nominated by the data controller) should advise the patient of the reason invoked for the restriction, either at the time access is denied or as soon as is advisable thereafter.

The information may be edited so that its release may not cause serious harm to the individual but any editing must not alter the information so materially as to make it misleading to the data subject.

PROVIDING DETAILS ON SOURCES & RELEASING INFORMATION PROVIDED IN CONFIDENCE

Special subject access rules apply in the important areas of providing personal information to individuals that also identifies or relates to third parties as sources of information, or where the information provided by the third party is an opinion and was given in the expectation that it would be treated in confidence. These exceptions are likely to be particularly relevant in the health and social work areas and will always involve a case-by-case judgment by healthcare professionals, health agencies, hospitals, insurance companies, etc. Accordingly, their scope and implications need very careful consideration.

Protecting Sources

The Data Protection Act 2003 introduced a new right for the data subject to be informed, when making an access request, of any information known or available to the data controller as to the source or sources of the information held on him or her, unless the release of the source-related information is contrary to the public interest. The exception may mean not only that the name of the source is withheld, but that any information contained in the medical or other record that might identify the sources can also be denied.

The case for this exception was set out at Committee Stage of the Data Protection Bill 2002, when the Minister of State at the Department of Justice, Equality & Law Reform advised the Select Committee considering the Bill that he was:

> "... concerned that the new requirements on a data controller to disclose whatever information is available on the sources of data could have unintended and serious consequences. One of these might be a profound reluctance to volunteer information in a variety of situations where the availability of that information could have beneficial consequences. I am referring to situations in which a well-intentioned and concerned person might have a suspicion of wrongdoing of some sort and may wish to bring that to the attention of the authorities. The possibility that sources might be disclosed could deter the giving of such information and this would not be in the public interest. For these reasons I am proposing the insertion of a public interest test in order to protect certain sources of information."[409]

---

[409] Data Protection Bill 2002, Committee Stage, Minister of State at the Department of Justice, Equality & Law Reform to Select Committee on Justice, Equality & Law Reform, 12 February 2003.

In moving the successful amendment, he gave the following example, which shows the relevance of the public interest exemption in the health area:

> "... in the context of social work or abuse of children, somebody making a complaint, raising suspicions or bringing information to the attention of the authorities should be protected. The data controller should have the discretion to protect those sources in order to encourage people to come forward. If the data controller – in this instance, the relevant health board – decides that the information should not be issued in the public interest, the person seeking the information will have an appeal to the Data Protection Commissioner. The public interest test applies under the freedom of information legislation in the same way, resulting in an appeal to the Information Commissioner."[410]

He added, however, that:

> "... the intention is that the source will normally be disclosed, unless it is clearly in the public interest not to do so".

Protecting Opinions Given in Confidence

The 2003 Act also contained a further new provision, providing that, where the information provided to the data controller by another person is an opinion, it may be disclosed to the data subject without obtaining the consent of the provider of the opinion. However, in a similar fashion to the proviso on revealing sources, there was concern expressed by the Minister before the Select Committee that this right:

---

[410] Data Protection Bill 2002, Committee Stage, Minister of State at the Department of Justice, Equality & Law Reform to Select Committee on Justice, Equality & Law Reform, 12 February 2003. The Protections for Persons reporting Child Abuse Act 1998 already gives immunity from civil liability to those who report child abuse "in good faith" to designated officers of Health Boards or any member of An Garda Síochána. There is also protection from dismissal from employment or other sanctions by employers. Finally, it provides for a new criminal offence of false reporting of child abuse "knowing the statement to be false".

"... may create pressure to release material that was given in confidence or under the understanding that it would be treated as confidential."[411]

As a result, another amendment was drafted, providing that, if an opinion is given in confidence to a data controller or on the understanding that it would be treated as confidential, the data controller cannot release the opinion to the data subject without the consent of the person who provided it. It is very important to bear in mind that the confidentiality exception relates only to an opinion, and not to any facts or purported facts surrounding that opinion. Health and social work considerations were clearly behind the amendment, which is clear from the example given to justify its inclusion, namely:

"... to provide for a data controller, such as a health board or hospital, getting an opinion. Part of the data held could contain an expression of opinion from a professional and the dealing between that professional and the data controller was on the understanding that it would be confidential. We are providing that the data controller will not be allowed to release those opinions because the understanding was they were given in confidence. It is straightforward."[412]

The provision may not be as straightforward in practice as in intention. It is inevitable that some data controllers will seek to use the provision

---

[411] The important matter of what is meant by the term "understanding" was elaborated during the course of the passage of the Freedom of Information Act 1997 through the Oireachtas. The Minister of State at the Department of Enterprise, Trade & Employment stated: "I have received further legal advice on the meaning of the term 'understanding'. My legal advice is that it means an understanding by both parties and it would not be open to only one person to have an understanding that it would be treated as confidential; an understanding by one party only could not be treated as an understanding of confidence." Freedom of Information Bill 1996, Report & Final Stages, Seanad Éireann, 12 February 1997.

[412] Data Protection Bill 2002, Committee Stage, Minister of State at the Department of Justice, Equality & Law Reform to Select Committee on Justice, Equality & Law Reform, 12 February 2003.

to overly protect themselves and the provider of opinions. It will be a complex, and perhaps even controversial, area to regulate.

An appeal can be made to the Data Protection Commissioner by the data subject, where he or she considers that the exception is being abused or wrongly applied to withhold information.

Interestingly, the Freedom of Information Acts already restricted access to information given to public bodies in confidence, or on the understanding that it would be treated as confidential, if its disclosure would be likely to prejudice the giving of further information from the same person or other persons.

In his *Annual Report* for 2001, the Information Commissioner (who is responsible for FOI law in Ireland, see **Chapter 13**) considered the issues associated with the exemption dealing with information provided in confidence. One of the first issues he addressed was the presumption by:

> "... some public bodies, regardless of the circumstances, [which] appear to take the view that there is always an implied confidence involved in the supply of information to them".[413]

He stated that in some cases investigated "the supplier had no expectation of confidence". He added that:

> "... in the absence of evidence of a mutual understanding of confidence, the decision to withhold the information cannot be regarded as justified ... [and] even where express assurances of confidentiality are given, this is not the end of the matter".

He felt that some such assurances may be inappropriate, especially since FOI came into effect, or their scope may be misleading, as where, for example, information is given to a public body and it is intended that active use will be made of it to the detriment of another person. He believed that, in such cases, if active use is made of the information then:

---

[413] Information Commissioner (2002), p.18.

"... fair procedures may require disclosure of the substance of the information to the person affected, regardless of any prior assurances given to the provider of the information".

He also sounded a warning about the inappropriate release of third-party information that could arise from lack of consultation. Under section 26(1)(a) of the Freedom of Information Acts, if the public body decided that information had not been given to it in confidence, it could release the record without consultation with the provider of the information. In such a scenario, where a public body makes an error of judgement, or where the provider of the information had not made it sufficiently clear that the information had been provided in confidence, the third-party source has no opportunity to make a case against release to the body concerned.

Issues with the Sources & Confidentiality Exemptions

On the basis that the legal scope of a data controller encompasses employees and agents acting in their official capacities, an employee of a hospital (who collects personal information in the course of his or duties) is not treated as separate from the hospital, but as part of it. Therefore, it is crucial that it is understood that the "sources" and "confidentiality" exceptions are not available to persons within the data controller's organisation who provide information on, or express an opinion on, an individual to another person within the organisation. For example, patient information provided by a hospital-employed psychiatrist to another person (healthcare professional or otherwise) in the same hospital would not benefit from non-identification of the source, even if it were considered that such non-identification was in the public interest. Similarly, any opinion on an individual expressed by the psychiatrist to another person within the same organisation would not benefit from protection as a confidential opinion, even if it were intended to be so.

Further, any personal health information (including opinions) provided by health professionals (in their capacity as such) to other health professionals (or relevant parties) *outside of the data controller's organisation*, would not be likely to have protection from patient access, even where the information was provided in the belief that it would enjoy confidence. This is because, in most cases, such opinions are part of the normal clinical consultation process and seeking to prevent access to them would seriously impede subject access to health records. The Health Access Regulations support this conclusion.

OTHER ACCESS ISSUES

Specific Restrictions on the Right of Access

Apart from the specific issues dealt with above in terms of sources, opinions and the Health Access Regulations, section 5 of the Data Protections Acts sets out a number of exemptions to the access rights. The provisions of section 4 do not apply if:

♦ The information is kept for the purpose of preventing, detecting or investigating offences, apprehending or prosecuting offenders, or assessing or collecting any taxes or duties; but only in cases where allowing the right of access would be likely to prejudice any such activities.

♦ The information is kept for certain anti-fraud functions; but only in cases where allowing the right of access would be likely to impede any such functions.

♦ Granting the right of access would be likely to impair the security or the maintenance of good order in a prison or other place of detention.

♦ Granting the right of access would be likely to harm the international relations of the State.

♦ The information concerns an estimate of damages or compensation in respect of a claim against the data controller, where granting the right of access would be likely to harm the interests of the data controller.

♦ The information would be subject to legal professional privilege in court.

♦ The information is kept only for the purpose of statistics or carrying out research; but only where the information is not disclosed to anyone else (except in circumstances provided for in the Acts), and where the results of the statistical work or research are not made available in a form that identifies any of the individuals involved.

- ◆ The information is back-up information.
- ◆ The information is kept by the Data Protection Commissioner or Information Commissioner for the purposes of their functions.

All of the above exceptions could be relevant, in certain circumstances, to personal health information. For example, an individual contemplating suing a hospital over a particular incident may be interested to establish whether the hospital has formulated an estimate of potential damages or a settlement figure should a case be brought. Similarly, where legal proceedings have been commenced or are threatened against a medical practitioner, documents or other information generated for the purpose of those proceedings may be subject to a claim for legal privilege and do not have to be produced to the patient. In this example, withholding access to certain personal health information is authorised by law.

The Data Protection Acts provide that, in general, its subject access provisions will prevail over all existing legal restrictions on the disclosure of information. However, section 5(3) allows this provision to be overridden by Regulations made by the Minister for Justice, Equality & Law Reform, where he or she is satisfied that the information involved is of such a nature that the existing prohibition on disclosure ought to prevail over the right of access. Such Regulations can be made only where the Minister is of the view that it is in the interests of the data subjects concerned or any other individuals.

The Regulations made under this section to date deal with the Adoption Index and the Ombudsman.[414] Specifically:

- ◆ The Index kept by the Registrar of Births, Deaths & Marriages tracing the connection between entries in the Adopted Children's Register and the Register of Births
- ◆ Information obtained by the Ombudsman during an investigation.

Separate Regulations under section 5(1)(d) of the Acts have also been made by the Minister for Justice, restricting access to personal data

---

[414] Data Protection (Restriction of Section 4 Regulations) 1989 (S.I. No.81 of 1989).

kept by persons or bodies with statutory functions designed to prevent financial loss to members of the public through (a) dishonesty, incompetence or malpractice in the provision of financial services or the management of companies or (b) the conduct of persons who have been adjudicated bankrupt.[415] The restriction applies only where access to the data would be likely to prejudice the proper performance of those functions.

What to Tell the Individual if Information is Restricted

It is worth noting that, where a data controller relies on a subject access exemption, there is an implicit obligation to inform the individual making the subject access request that such an exemption is being relied on.[416]

He or she must also be advised that they can appeal the matter to the Data Protection Commissioner. Ideally, in such situations, a healthcare provider or other party keeping personal health information should tell the individual which provision is being relied upon to refuse access and give reasons accordingly.

This creates a potentially serious dilemma. A person holding personal health information that relies on an exemption to withhold access may well consider it highly problematic to have to reveal that he or she is relying on a particular exemption. For example, advising a patient that to give the information would be likely to cause serious harm to him or her is unlikely to reassure the patient and could cause more distress – if not harm – than actually releasing it.

Commercially-sensitive Evaluative Information

This provision allows a data controller not to release information that will reveal the formulae, or fine details, of the evaluative process the provider uses in its commercially-sensitive business decisions.

In these situations, a healthcare service provider will not need to provide direct access to evaluative information, but will need to

---

[415] Data Protection Act 1988 (Section 5(1)(d)) (Specification) Regulations 1989 (S.I. No. 84 of 1989) were repealed and replaced by Data Protection Act 1988 (Section 5(1)(d)) (Specification) Regulations 1993 (S.I. No. 95 of 1993).

[416] The Freedom of Information Acts are much more explicit on the procedures to be followed when access is denied or restricted (see **Chapter 13**).

explain its decision to the individual. For example, a private nursing home's process for assessing prospective residents may involve recording commercially-sensitive information on an individual's record. The nursing home may choose to withhold information that reveals the financial calculations undertaken in reaching its decision, but will still need to provide access to the raw facts and opinions that were inputted into their evaluative process and a general explanation to the individual about how the decision was reached.

This provision applies in very limited circumstances, and should therefore be applied with care.

Discuss Accessed Information with the Patient

In all cases, however, the patient should agree on the form of the access and has the right to insist on direct access to his or her information, if desired.

In the health sector, it may be helpful to provide the individual with an opportunity to discuss their health information, when access is sought. This may prevent the information being misunderstood or taken out of context. It may also save unnecessary hurt or distress for the individual, if the information is potentially upsetting.

Requests for Corrections, etc.

Where the request for alteration is straightforward and not in dispute – for example, amending an address or telephone number – healthcare data controllers should agree to the change as a matter of course. In other cases, particularly as regards whether the information is excessive or not relevant, the applicable healthcare professional should exercise his or her professional judgement and explain the reasoning to the patient, as well as outlining that the patient may bring the matter to the Data Protection Commissioner for resolution if they are still not satisfied.

More complex issues are likely to arise when an individual challenges an opinion, evaluation or diagnosis that is contained in their health record, and seeks to have this corrected.

There may be important medical and legal reasons for retaining a complete record. Therefore, if an individual asks to have certain details amended or corrected, the healthcare service provider should generally attach comments to the record noting the correct information rather than permanently erasing details from the health record.

Where the individual and the healthcare service provider disagree on whether the information is incorrect, the provider must take reasonable steps to attach to the information a statement outlining the individual's claims that the information is not accurate, up-to-date or complete. Indeed, as a rule, with every request for alteration or correction, etc. (even where no action is subsequently taken), medical practitioners should annotate the record to indicate the nature of the request and whether they agree with it.

However, there may be situations when an individual will feel very strongly that they do not want certain health information, which is agreed to be incorrect, misleading and damaging, to remain on the medical record. An example of this might be where an agreed incorrect diagnosis of a psychiatric condition has been noted on the record.

If, in exceptional circumstances, a healthcare service provider decides that there are greater risks in leaving certain information on the record than in erasing it, erasure or deletion of the relevant part of the health record may be appropriate. However, this should not be done without fully considering potential legal or medical implications. Accordingly, it is expected that permanently erasing information from an individual's record would only be appropriate in limited circumstances.

Where information has been materially and significantly enhanced, corrected, amended, blocked or deleted, there is a requirement to notify any person to whom it was disclosed in the previous 12 months, unless such notification proves impossible or involves disproportionate effort.

USE OF THE SUBJECT ACCESS RIGHT BY THIRD PARTIES

The Nature of this Issue

Since data protection is essentially about privacy, and especially given that the subject access rights in the legislation are intended to allow data subjects access information about themselves in order to ensure that it is kept in accordance with the principles, it is interesting that third parties have sought to take advantage of the rights of access to obtain information on individuals (*albeit* with the consent of the individuals concerned). However, the practice has been noted, especially its use by prospective employers.

In response to a Parliamentary Question in 1999 dealing with the clearance system operated by his Department of Justice, Equality & Law Reform in relation to access to children by part-time workers and students, the Minister replied that:

> "I am informed by the Garda authorities that they were recently advised by the Data Protection Commissioner that section 4 of the Data Protection Act 1988, does not provide for the disclosure of personal data to third parties, irrespective of whether the individuals in question had consented to allow the Garda to respond to the prospective employer and the Garda authorities have, on the advice of the Data Protection Commissioner, ceased to do so.
>
> The Data Protection Commissioner has also advised that section 4 of the Data Protection Act 1988, does not provide for a situation whereby an employer may request that a prospective employee himself should make a request under section 4 of the Act and insist on receiving from the individual concerned a copy of material received on foot of such a request. The Data Protection Commissioner's view is that the essence of data protection law is that it enhances privacy by putting the individual in control of his or her information, and that access sought by an individual on foot of a request to that individual from a prospective employer may be regarded as an unanticipated use of what was intended by the Oireachtas to be a key aid for individuals in protecting their privacy."[417]

---

[417] Dáil Éireann, Vol.499, 27 January, 1999, Written Answers: Health Service Staff.

Data Protection Commissioner's View on Enforced Subject Access

In his *Annual Report* for 2003, the Commissioner set out his views on this matter:

> "The "right of access" – which is the key aid provided by section 4 of the Data Protection Acts to assist a data subject in defending his privacy interests – should not be used in a manner which brings about the disclosure to third parties of information which might not otherwise be available to them. That is why the Data Protection (Amendment) Act 2003 has a provision included to prevent employers forcing data subjects to allow them to access their personal data held by the Gardaí in particular or by any other organisation i.e. "enforced subject access".[418]

The Commissioner felt that "enforced subject access" under section 4 has consequences that go beyond access by employers to details of criminal convictions kept by An Garda Síochána. For example, enforced subject access, if left unchecked, raises the issue of access by other third parties – for example, landlords, insurance companies or sporting organisations requiring applicants for housing, insurance cover or club membership to access their data in respect of bank records, medical records, DNA databases, etc. as a prerequisite to acceptance of their application. He concluded:

> "It is for this reason that it appears to me, as a matter of public policy, that it is as important that the practice of enforced subject access be outlawed as it is to ensure the controlled availability of details of a person's previous criminal convictions for particular purposes."[419]

---

[418] Data Protection Commissioner (2004), *Appendix 3*. This provision has not been implemented pending the setting up by the Gardaí of a national clearance system.

[419] This is especially so, since Irish legislation makes no provision for "spent convictions" and the indefinite retention of minor convictions does not accord with the data protection principle regarding retention for as long as is necessary for the purpose for which it was obtained.

This provision of the Act should be implemented as early as possible following the establishment of suitable vetting systems by the Gardaí.

Disclosures under Section 8(h) & "Enforced Access"

Data may be released by a data controller to a third party under section 8(h), which provides that the restrictions on disclosure of personal information provided for in the Acts do not apply in circumstances where the data subject has given consent. Where a data subject has given such consent, the data controller has *discretion* in the matter as there is no obligation on it to accede to the request. The Commissioner recommends that the data controller should be guided by proportionality, having regard to the circumstances.[420] Should a data controller decide to make the data available, it may rely on section 8(h). In certain circumstances, such as life or health insurance, this could amount to "enforced subject access", if appropriate regard is not had to proportionality, as the individual may have little option but to agree to the insurance company's wishes.

CASE STUDY ON ACCESS TO PERSONAL HEALTH INFORMATION

This case study is featured in the 2004 *Annual Report* of the Data Protection Commissioner.[421] It deals with employment matters, claims of legal privilege and access to health information in the workplace.

> An employee of a major national company had been requested to attend a doctor nominated by the employer in the context of his on-going sick leave. His employment was subsequently terminated and he made an access request under section 4 of the Data Protection Acts for a copy of the medical report. The company refused him access, on the grounds that the employee had initiated legal proceedings against the company, and that the report was privileged, and that it did not have to be released as section 5(1) (g) applied.

---

420 Data Protection Commissioner (2004), *Appendix 3*.
421 Data Protection Commissioner (2005), *Case Study 1*.

This section provides that the right of access under section 4 of the Acts does not apply to personal information:

"(g) in respect of which a claim of privilege could be maintained in proceedings in a Court in relation to communications between a client and his professional legal advisers or between those advisers."

The Data Protection Commissioner pointed out that there are two main categories of legal professional privilege recognised by Irish Courts:

♦ Confidential communications between an individual and their lawyer seeking or giving legal advice and documents created by either party to provide or to obtain such advice are privileged.

♦ Documents created by either lawyer or client in anticipation or furtherance of litigation are also privileged. Therefore, communications between an individual and their lawyer that provide legal advice or assistance, and documents created to obtain or produce such advice or assistance, are privileged, if given or created in anticipation or furtherance of litigation.

In determining whether privilege could be claimed, the Commissioner considered the purpose of the referral to the doctor, and specifically whether it was in anticipation of legal proceedings or to obtain legal advice or whether the purpose was to determine fitness for work. The complainant stated that he had been requested by letter to attend the doctor to have his condition assessed due to his on-going sick leave – no reference was made to attendance being requested in connection with any court proceedings. The company, however, sought to claim that the report had been sought on legal advice and in anticipation of possible future legal proceedings.

The Commissioner found that, while there may indeed have been a possibility of legal proceedings in relation to other matters, the first formal notification of court proceedings was sent by the data subject's solicitors many months later. He also found that the purpose of the medical examination should be clear to the data subject at the time that he attends the doctor. The employee in this case was clearly under the impression that the referral was related to assessing his fitness for work only. It is an important data protection principle that another purpose cannot be introduced retrospectively. He added that information about the purpose is required to be provided to the employee (data subject) pursuant to section 2(D)(i) and (ii) of the Acts, otherwise personal data is not treated as "fairly processed".

The Commissioner concluded that, while privilege is an important feature of court proceedings, it should not be used as a veil to seek to restrict access where it cannot be justified. As section 5(1)(g) relates to personal information in relation to communications between a client and his or her professional legal advisers or between those advisers, he decided, in this case, that a copy of a medical report prepared for a specific personnel purpose could not be considered as such a "communication" that would attract privilege.

Separately, the Commissioner also considered the impact of the Data Protection (Access Modification) (Health) Regulations 1989.

Other Cases

In another employment-related case, the Commissioner established that a data controller cannot avoid dealing with an access request for an employee's medical report on the premise that it has been returned to the author of the report.

To deal with such requests, organisations should have a clear procedure in place. The request may be for (i) the report itself and / or (ii) the data on the medical file. When an access request for medical data is received, the Company Doctor / Medical Officer should be immediately advised and should make the data available unless it is considered "harmful" to so do.

On a related question, it is sometimes considered that the employee's consent is needed for referral to a company doctor. Generally, an employer will have the right under the contract of employment to refer an employee for a medical report. Processing of personal data in a medical report involves sensitive data and section 2(B)(i) of the Acts provides that a data controller must obtain "explicit" consent from a data subject before sensitive data may be processed. Alternatively, section 2B(ii) provides for processing which "is necessary for the purpose of exercising or performing any right or obligation which is conferred or imposed by law on the data controller in connection with employment". Relying on freely-given consent implies that an employee has a right to refuse referral. Given the employer's rights under the contract of employment, this may not fully reflect the entirety of the rights and obligations involved. Therefore when the employee agrees to attend the doctor, what is important is that the employee clearly understands that he or she is required to attend the medical assessment for a particular purpose – for example, to determine whether he or she is fit to return to work – and attends on that basis alone. On the other hand, if the purpose is connected with anticipation of or defence of legal proceedings, then the employee should know that this is the basis for the referral.

13
FREEDOM OF INFORMATION & DATA PROTECTION

INTRODUCTION

Freedom of information, like data protection, is an international concept. Sweden has the oldest FOI law, going back to 1766, and Colombia, in South America, has the second oldest, dating from 1888. The US introduced its FOI law in 1966, Australia in 1982, Canada in 1985, but Britain did not so until 2000.[422] Ireland did so in 1997.

At a European level, the EU Charter of Fundamental Rights gives a right of access to documents of the European Parliament, Council and Commission.[423]

The Council of Europe issued a *Recommendation on Access to Information held by Public Authorities*[424] based on:

> "... the importance in a pluralistic, democratic society of transparency of public administration and of the ready availability of information on issues of public interest".

Other relevant international instruments include:

♦ Article 19 of the Universal Declaration of Human Rights.

♦ Articles 6, 8 & 10 of the European Convention on Human Rights & Fundamental Freedoms.

---

[422] The Freedom of Information Act 2000 did not apply to Scotland, which introduced its own FOI statute in 2002.

[423] Article 42.

[424] Recommendation No. R (81) 19 of The Committee of Ministers to Member States, adopted by the Committee of Ministers on 25 November 1981.

♦ The United Nations Convention on Access to Information, Public
Participation in Decision-making & Access to Justice in
Environmental Matters.[425]

While there are many quotes that capture the nature and goal of
freedom of information, the American President James Madison
perhaps summed it up best when he observed:

> "Knowledge will forever govern ignorance, and a people
> who mean to be their own governors must arm themselves
> with the power knowledge gives. A popular government,
> without popular information or the means of acquiring it, is
> but a prologue to a farce or a tragedy or perhaps both."[426]

Freedom of information (FOI) law in Ireland is not just about open
government. It also has significant implications for privacy protection,
in particular rights of access and correction for individuals to publicly-
held records containing information about them. This chapter
concentrates mainly on this personal information privacy aspect and
how it compares and contrasts with data protection law.

FOI LEGISLATION IN IRELAND

The Freedom of Information Acts 1997 & 2003 give individuals legal
rights to:

♦ Access both personal and non-personal (organisational and
corporate) records (section 6, *Right of Access to Records*).

♦ Have personal records amended or deleted where the
information is incorrect, incomplete or misleading (section 17,
Amendment of Records relating to Personal Information).

♦ Seek reasons for decisions that affect them (section 18, *Right of
Person to Information regarding acts of Public Bodies affecting the
Person*).

As with the Data Protection Acts, there are exemptions provided for in
FOI law, which means that there are specified circumstances when the

---

[425] Adopted in Aarhus, Denmark, on 25 June 1998.
[426] In a letter to W.T. Barry, 4 August 1822.

requested information will not be released – for example to protect confidentiality, international relations, etc. In most cases where exemptions are relied on to withhold information, the reasons must be clearly explained to the individual making the access request. However, in other cases, there is a "neither confirm nor deny" provision.

FOI law also requires public bodies to put substantial amounts of information about themselves into the public domain by way of manuals. "Section 15 manuals" must give information about the structures, organisation, functions, powers, duties and services and the classes of records held by them. "Section 16 manuals" must give information regarding rules, procedures, practices, guidelines, interpretations and precedents used by the public body.

The introduction in 1997 of FOI legislation was accompanied by other statutes that were intended to bring greater transparency to public life. These included the Ethics in Public Office Act 1995, which required the disclosure of the interests of politicians and senior public servants, with a view to avoiding potential conflicts of interests. This was extended in 2001, by the Standards in Public Office Act, to enable standards of desirable conduct by those in public life to be specified in *Codes of Conduct* published under the legislation, and to require production of evidence of tax compliance by Parliamentarians and senior public servants. The Electoral Acts of 1997 to 2004 are designed to bring transparency to the relationship between, on the one hand, political parties and individual politicians and, on the other, their supporters, whether individual or corporate, where that support takes the form of donations of money, property, goods or services.[427]

Freedom of Information Acts 1997 to 2003

The Freedom of Information Bill 1996[428] – subsequently the 1997 Act – was introduced in the Seanad, with the sponsoring Minister stating:

---

[427] It was hoped that these Acts would help to obviate the need for further Special Tribunals of Inquiry such as Moriarty and Flood (now Mahon).

[428] Earlier Freedom of Information Bills had been introduced in the Seanad, without success, reflecting the reality that legislative initiatives in the Irish Parliament by any one other than the Government invariably require Government support to be successful.

"Freedom of information gives every person a legal right to ask for and get access to records held by public bodies. It creates a new legal right for citizens to see public files. It recognises in law that public bodies should be directly accountable to the public they are there to serve. Freedom of information overturns the presumption of official secrecy set out in the Official Secrets Act 1963, and replaces it with the legal presumption that the public has a right to know. The Bill contains a mandate for the public service to provide the public with access to information to the greatest extent possible consistent with the public interest and the right to privacy. This Bill will mark a permanent change in the way public business is done. Giving people a legal right to know what public bodies do and what information they have is extremely important because public services touch every aspect of our lives — as parents, patients, residents, when we pay tax or draw a pension ... The Bill requires public bodies to give reasons for the decisions they make to the individuals concerned. When a public body refuses a grant, a medical card or welfare payment or says a child is not a priority for orthodontic care, those affected will have a legal right to the reason for that decision ... When this Bill is in force, every person will have a legal right to correct any personal information on them in public files where it is incorrect, incomplete or misleading."[429]

The Freedom of Information Act 1997 commenced on 21 April 1998 for Government Departments and Offices, and certain other Government bodies, and on 21 October 1998 for local authorities and Health Boards. Since that time, a substantial number of additional public bodies have been prescribed by Regulations of the Minister for Finance. These include voluntary hospitals and major service providers in the intellectual and physical disability fields.[430]

---

[429] Freedom of Information Bill 1996, Seanad Éireann, Second Stage, Vol.149, 19 December 1996.

[430] A full list of public bodies to which the FOI Act applies is available on the FOI Central Policy Unit website at http://www.foi.gov.ie.

It is worth noting that the Freedom of Information (Amendment) Act 2003 did not enjoy the same public enthusiasm or support as the original statute. It introduced a range of changes:[431] many of these were minor but some altered the emphasis of the Act. From our particular concern with personal health information, it is worth noting that, while there was some pulling back on access to Government records, FOI law has "remained relatively sharply focused on access to records of individuals".[432]

Fees for Access

The Freedom of Information Act 2003 introduced "up-front" fees for the making of certain FOI requests.[433] The fees are applicable to the initial request, the request for internal review and the review by the Information Commissioner. In broad terms, requests for personal information will not attract a fee (in relation to the initial request or any subsequent internal review or review by the Information Commissioner). Equally, there is no fee for an application for amendment of a record, or for the reasons for a decision affecting the individual. However, requests for joint personal information or reports in which one might have a deep personal interest (such as access to industrial schools reports, for example) will attract the applicable prescribed fees. Specifically, there is a lack of clarity on this issue of fees that the Information Commissioner has drawn attention to on her website:

> "The phrase that is used in the Act for a request or application to be exempt from a fee is that it *contain only personal information relating to the requester* (my emphasis). The

---

[431] The key changes introduced provisions: (i) for more restrictive access to records relating to Government business; (ii) for strengthened deliberative process exceptions; (iii) that records may now be refused if they could be expected to prejudice the inquiries or investigations of any public body – not just the body that is the subject of the request; and (iv) for a mandatory class exemption for particular records, eliminating the need to identify a specific harm that might arise from their disclosure.

[432] Information Commissioner (2003).

[433] In July 2003, the Minister for Finance made regulations which set the amount of these fees.

phrase '... relating to ...' is open to varying interpretations which can raise a variety of scenarios. In particular, does the Act require the payment of a fee where the requester is the parent or guardian of a minor and the records sought are those of the minor? Or is payment required where the requester is the spouse or next of kin of a deceased person and the records sought are those of the deceased person? Secondly, does the legislation require the payment of a fee where the requester is seeking records which constitute personal information relating to both the requester and another individual or individuals?"[434]

Further, requesters can also be charged for the time spent searching and retrieving records (€20.95 per hour),[435] and for any photocopying costs incurred by the public body in providing material to the requester (4 cent per sheet).[436] Requesters cannot be charged for the time spent on deciding whether or not to grant their request.

In an investigation into the effect of the 2003 Amendment Act,[437] the Commissioner's Office found that overall usage of the Act had fallen by over 50 per cent, while requests for non-personal information had declined by 75 per cent. Most recently, in an address to Civil Service Assistant Secretaries, the Commissioner posed the question:

"... fees for requests and appeals to my Office were introduced, which are unparalleled in any other country that has an Information Commissioner. Whose interests does this serve? It seems to suggest that the people are seen as adversaries and nothing more than lip-service is being paid to the principles of open, fair and accountable government."[438]

---

[434] http://www.oic.ie.

[435] Disregarded, if only personal information is contained in the record, except where the grant of the request relates to a significant amount of records.

[436] Disregarded, if only personal information is contained in record, and it would not be reasonable, having regard to the means of the requester, to apply a charge.

[437] Information Commissioner (2004).

[438] Ombudsman & Information Commissioner (2005).

Enforcement

Similar to the Data Protection Acts, the Freedom of Information Acts provide for an independent enforcement authority – in this case, the Information Commissioner – who has powers similar to a High Court judge. These include the power to issue binding rulings, to overturn decisions to withhold information, to examine all the documents in any case, and to send for and examine witnesses.

The practice has developed that the Information Commissioner is also appointed to the Office of Ombudsman.

PERSONAL INFORMATION UNDER FOI LAW

Personal information is defined in the Freedom of Information Acts as:

"… information about an identifiable individual that:

(a)   would, in the ordinary course of events, be known only to the individual or members of the family, or friends, of the individual, or

(b)   is held by a public body on the understanding that it would be treated by it as confidential …"

Without prejudice to the generality of the definition, 12 examples are given in the Acts for illustrative purposes, as follows:

♦ Information relating to the educational, medical, psychiatric or psychological history of the individual.

♦ Information relating to the financial affairs of the individual.

♦ Information relating to the employment or employment history of the individual.

♦ Information relating to the individual in a record falling within section 6(6)(a) – that is, a personnel record that meets certain specified conditions.

♦ Information relating to the criminal history of the individual.

♦ Information relating to the religion, age, sexual orientation or marital status of the individual.

- ◆ A number, letter, symbol, word, mark or other thing assigned to the individual by a public body for the purpose of identification or any mark or other thing used for that purpose.

- ◆ Information relating to the entitlements of the individual under the Social Welfare Acts as a beneficiary (within the meaning of the Social Welfare (Consolidation) Act 1993) or required for the purpose of establishing whether the individual, being a claimant (within the meaning aforesaid), is such a beneficiary.

- ◆ Information required for the purpose of assessing the liability of the individual in respect of a tax or duty or other payment owed or payable to the State or to a local authority, a health board or other public body or for the purpose of collecting an amount due from the individual in respect of such a tax or duty or other payment.

- ◆ The name of the individual, where it appears with other personal information relating to the individual or where the disclosure of the name would, or would be likely to, establish that any personal information held by the public body concerned relates to the individual.

- ◆ Information relating to property of the individual (including the nature of the individual's title to any property).

- ◆ The views or opinions of another person about the individual.

In her first *Annual Report*, the present Information Commissioner, in considering the impact of the changes brought about by the 2003 statute, concluded:

> "The right to access personal information was not affected by the changes and does not attract an up-front fee. Many, many people are still using the Act to obtain information about their medical records, their employment, and a range of other matters personal to themselves ..."[439]

Clearly, therefore, FOI legislation remains extremely important to accessing personal information (held by public bodies). This makes consistency with the Data Protection Acts all the more important, since

---

[439] Information Commissioner (2004).

it is *prima facie* illogical to have differing rights of access to personal information under both codes.

Personal Information & Pre-Commencement Records

Section 6(5)(b) of the 1997 Act created a right of access to records created prior to the commencement of the Act,[440] if the records relate to personal information about the person seeking access.

The Freedom of Information Bill 2003 contained a provision, proposing to replace the phrase "relate to" with the word "contain".[441] This would have meant that pre-commencement records could be accessed only if they "contain" personal information about the person seeking access to them. The proposed change in wording sparked a major debate of substance. The Information Commissioner stated:

> "It is clear that records that 'relate to' personal information as currently provided encompasses a broader category of records than records which 'contain' personal information."[442]

The Commissioner referred to a High Court judgement arising from one of his decisions[443] that elaborated on the nature of this area. The Court found that, in determining whether a record relates to personal information about the requestor, one must see whether there is a sufficiently substantial link between the requestor's personal information and the record in question. Where the record does not name the requestor, or has no express reference to the requestor, a substantial link will be established if the record relates to something in which the requestor has a substantial personal interest, as distinct from something in which he or she has an interest as a member of the general community or of a large scale class of the same.

Ultimately, given the strength of opposition in the Oireachtas to the intended change, the Minister for Finance decided to drop the amending provision. Notwithstanding this, the definitional and scope

---

[440] For most public bodies, this was 21 April 1998.

[441] Section 4 of the 2003 Bill.

[442] Information Commissioner (2003a), p.10.

[443] *EH & the Information Commissioner*, High Court, 21 December 2001.

issues involved were important and may have to be revisited at some future date.

APPLICATION OF FOI LAW TO THE HEALTH SECTOR

At a conceptual level, the 1997 and 2003 Freedom of Information Acts should be viewed in the wider context of modernising the culture of the Irish public service, of which the health service is a crucial element. At a more practical level, FOI legislation has major operational implications for the public health system.

Freedom of Information: Impact on Doctors & Other Healthcare Professionals

The first, and most important, point to make is that freedom of information has no impact on doctors and other healthcare professionals in relation to records generated on a wholly private basis. It does, however, apply to records created in cases where the healthcare professional is carrying out the service on behalf of a public body – for example, the provision of medical card services or services under a public immunisation programme, or services received in a public hospital.

In such cases, FOI gives the persons receiving the service a statutory right of access to their own medical records, but only insofar as the records were created under, or relate to, the applicable public healthcare programmes. It also gives those persons a right to be given reasons for an act that affects them, and to be told of any findings of fact made for the purposes of such an act. These rights are exercised by way of a request to the relevant health agency that provided the service, or on whose behalf the service was provided.

Decisions on access are made within public bodies by designated decision-makers.[444] In general, doctors employed by the Health Service Executive or a public hospital tend not to be designated decision-makers for access requests. Further, GMS Scheme (medical card) GPs

---

[444] Section 4 of the Freedom of Information Acts 1998 to 2003 allows for the delegation of certain functions by heads of public bodies.

cannot be designated, as they are not members of staff of the public body concerned, as required by the legislation.

Access Requests under the Freedom of Information Acts

Under section 7 (Requests for Access to Records) of the FOI Acts, access requests should be made in writing and addressed to the head of the public body concerned. The request should:

♦ State that it is being made under the FOI Acts.

♦ Contain sufficient particulars in relation to the information concerned to enable the record to be identified by the public body on the basis of taking reasonable steps.

♦ Make clear whether the requestor requires access to be given in one of the particular forms specified in section 12 (Manner of Access to Records).

Section 12 provides the following formats by which access may be given:

♦ A copy of the record.

♦ A transcript of the information concerned.

♦ A computer disk or other electronic device containing the information.

♦ A reasonable opportunity to inspect the record.

♦ In cases where the record is of sound or visual images, a reasonable opportunity to hear or view the record.

♦ In cases where the information is in shorthand or other code, the information may be provided in de-codified form and in written form or such other form as may be determined.

♦ Any other form or manner as may be determined.

♦ Any combination of the above.

However, section 12 also provides specified exceptions to the need to provide the information in the format requested.

In practice, requests need not necessarily be made to the head of the public body – for example, for hospital records, application can be made to the Hospital Manager. Sufficient information should be provided to assist in locating files and other records. Proof of identity should also be provided, since this is important to protect confidentiality, especially where medical records are involved.

Acknowledgement of a request must be made within 10 working days and a full reply should, in normal circumstances, be issued within 20 working days. FOI law requires that all replies must clearly explain the decisions made, identify the sections of the Acts used in reaching those decisions and outline the applicant's entitlements to internal review and appeal.

Access & Joint or Third-Party Information

In the Oireachtas debates on the then Freedom of Information Bill 1996, it was stressed:

> "… that personal privacy is strongly protected by this Bill. People will not be able to see private information about other people".[445]

In that regard, in addressing circumstances where public interest and privacy issues conflicted the Bill initially provided that the public interest *"shall"* override the right to privacy but this was changed at Committee Stage in the Seanad to *"may"* to better protect privacy.

Consistent with the above, Section 28 (Personal Information)[446] of the Freedom of Information Acts protects the privacy of individuals by allowing the withholding of personal information held by a public body from third party access. The purpose is to protect the privacy rights of third parties in cases of joint personal information, while ensuring that there was no unreasonable restriction on the provision of personal information that relates solely to the requester.

The exceptions to this rule are:

---

[445] Minister of State at the Department of Enterprise & Employment, Seanad Éireann, 29 January 1997.

[446] The specific provision is subsection 5(B) of section 28. It superseded Freedom of Information Act 1997 (Section 28(1)) (Amendment) Regulations, 1998 (S.I. No.521 of 1998). Those Regulations related to requests for records containing joint personal information – for example, information not only about the requester, but also a third party. The purpose of the regulations was to confirm that, in such circumstances, subject to public interest or other considerations specified in section 28, third-party information would remain protected.

♦ Where disclosure of a record is necessary for the protection of a third party.

♦ Where the release would benefit the record subject.

♦ Where it is decided that the public interest in its release outweighs the privacy rights of the subject.

A decision to rely on any of these exceptions ultimately only can be made on a case-by-case basis, but the existence of policy guidelines can certainly be of assistance in making decisions more structured and consistent. In every instance, consultation procedures, provided for in section 29 (Procedure in relation to Certain Requests under Section 7 to which Section 26, 27 or 28 applies), must be followed when a public body is contemplating release of personal information on any of these grounds.

Denying Access to Medical Records under Freedom of Information

The previous chapter on data protection subject access rights paid considerable attention to the freedom of information rules on release of information given in confidence, or information that might identify the source of certain information. Accordingly, it is not intended to repeat those issues here except to point out that they are, of course, most relevant.

In addition, there is specific reference in section 28(3) to medical, psychiatric and social work records, with provision for denying access where, in the opinion of the public body, to release the record might be prejudicial to the subject's physical or mental health, well-being or emotional condition. This arrangement parallels, but is not identical to, the corresponding provisions in data protection law. Importantly, the obligation on the public body to refuse access is discretionary under the Freedom of Information Acts, whereas it is mandatory under the Data Protection Access Regulations. There is also a difference in the degree of potential harm to the requester justifying denial of access, with freedom of information law requiring a lower threshold.

Further, where access is denied under section 28(3), the public body is required to advise (under subsection 4) the individual that access may be provided through a nominated health professional.[447]

Access & Correction by Parents, Guardians & Next-of-Kin

Another access area where problems can arise is that of a parent's right of access to a child's records. However, unlike the data protection statutes, the freedom of information legislation make express provision for such access through regulations.

The FOI Acts also provide for access to the records of deceased individuals. In such cases, access to the personal information of the deceased may be granted:

- ♦ To the personal representative who is administering the estate of the deceased.

- ♦ To a person who is performing some legal function in relation to the individual or the estate of the individual.

- ♦ To the spouse (including a divorced spouse or cohabitee), or next of kin or such other person as the head of the public body involved considers appropriate.

It was felt appropriate that access issues in relation to next-of-kin and parents in respect of their children should be subject to regulations to be made by the Minister for Finance:

> "... because such issues are sufficiently sensitive that it would be inappropriate to put it into primary legislation".[448]

---

[447] In section 28, "health professional" means a medical practitioner, within the meaning of the Medical Practitioners Act 1978, a registered dentist, within the meaning of the Dentists Act 1985, or a member of any other class of health worker or social worker standing prescribed, after consultation with such (if any) other Ministers of the Government as the Minister for Finance considers appropriate. Social workers and clinical psychologists were so prescribed by the Freedom of Information Act 1997 (Classes of Health Professionals) Regulations 2001 (S.I. No.368 of 2001).

[448] Minister of State at the Department of Enterprise & Employment, Seanad Éireann, Committee Stage, 29 January 1997.

Interestingly, the examples used (in the Oireachtas debates on the FOI Bill 1996) for both areas related to health:

♦ A dying person not wanting his or her next of kin to know the cause of death due to its sensitivity (AIDS).

♦ A parent's entitlement to see a child's medical records, if their child is using contraception.

Speaking in 1998, prior to the making of Regulations, the Information Commissioner claimed that:

> "... in most cases, there will be no problem; either the child will have given consent, is of an age that the consent may be deemed to have been given or it may be decided that the public interest is best served by the release of the record". [449]

Despite this positive view, he conceded that:

> "... some important issues do arise in this context regarding the autonomy of a minor and also regarding the best interests of a child or minor. Should, for example, the privacy rights of a 15-year old prevail over parental expectation? Will there not be instances where the best interests of the child are not served by the provision of the child's records to a parent? Hopefully, some of these difficulties will be resolved under regulations which may be made at a future date."

In 1999, Regulations were made under the 1997 statute to allow the exercise of the right of access to records by parents, guardians and next-of-kin, on behalf of relatives who were unable to exercise their rights directly.[450] However, the other two FOI rights (namely, to have personal records amended or deleted and to seek reasons for decisions that affect them) could not be exercised in this way. This was

---

[449] Information Commissioner (1998).

[450] Freedom of Information Act 1997 (Section 28(6)) Regulations 1999 (S.I. No.47 of 1997). There are also detailed *Guidance Notes* on Access to Records by Parents / Guardians and Access to Records Relating to Deceased Persons (as approved by the FOI Inter-Departmental Working Group, March 1999) – available from the Department of Finance's FOI Central Policy Unit website, http://www.foi.gov.ie.

addressed in the 2003 Act, section 12 of which permits the Minister for Finance to make Regulations dealing with:

♦ The making of an application under section 17 of the 1997 Act (Amendment of Records relating to Personal Information) for the correction of personal information by the parents, guardians or next of kin of an individual if the individual belongs to a class specified in the regulations.

♦ The making of an application under section 18 of the 1997 Act (Right of Person to Information regarding acts of Public Bodies affecting the Person) for reasons where decisions have to be provided to the parent or guardians or next of kin of a person, if the person belongs to a class specified in the regulations.

In each case, as with requests for access to records, such classes will encompass minors, the intellectually disabled and deceased persons. These changes were suggested by the Information Commissioner. The relevant Regulations were made in 2003.[451]

While unfortunate, it is understandable that difficulties relating to parental access under FOI tend to arise mainly where the parents are themselves in dispute with each other. Perhaps the most significant of these parent cases is McK *v* the Information Commissioner.[452] This case involved a father seeking access to certain written hospital records relating to his daughter, arising out of her admission to that hospital in January 2000. The case went to the High Court, on appeal against the Commissioner's decision to affirm the decision of the hospital to refuse access to the records sought in Case Number 000128: *Mr X & the Adelaide & Meath Hospital*. The High Court found in favour of the appellant. It held that, in reaching the decision made in this case, the Information Commissioner had misconstrued the relevant statutory provisions of the FOI Acts, by failing to recognise that the decisions of the parent of minors are presumed to be in the best interests of that

---

[451] Freedom of Information Act 1997 (Section 17(6)) Regulations 2003 (S.I. No.265 of 2003) and Freedom of Information Act 1997 (Section 18(5A)) Regulations 2003 (S.I. No.266 of 2003).

[452] McK *v* The Information Commissioner, High Court Judgment, 14 January, 2004.

minor,[453] in the absence of evidence to the contrary. The judgment has been appealed to the Supreme Court by the Office of the Information Commissioner.

Access & "Confirm or Deny" Provisions

Section 21 of the 2003 FOI Act provides for two amendments to section 26 (Information Obtained in Confidence) of the 1997 Act. The first amendment makes it clear that the protection available for information, obtained in confidence, applies across public bodies. The second amendment will permit a public body to refuse to confirm or deny the existence of a record, if the record is covered by the exemption in section 26(1)(a) of the 1997 statute, where the mere acknowledgment of the existence or non-existence of the record could undermine or reveal the sensitive information contained in the record. In the Seanad, the Minister for Finance stated that it:

> "... is essential that such a prudent provision should be included in relation to the text of information obtained in confidence".[454]

Section 23 of the 2003 Act provides for the insertion of a similar refusal to confirm or deny provision into section 28 (Personal Information) of the 1997 Act. This extends the power to refuse to confirm or deny the existence of a record containing personal information, where the acknowledgment of the existence or non-existence of the record concerned could undermine the exemption or reveal the sensitive personal information contained in the record. The use of the "confirm or deny provision" is subject to a public interest test. Of course, one of the key issues with such a provision is that someone requesting information must be aware that the provision has been invoked or else he or she will not be in a fair position to appeal. Consequently, it was interesting that, in the Dáil, the Minister of State at the Department of

---

[453] The Freedom of Information Act 1997 (Section 28(6)) Regulations 1999 (S.I. No.47 of 1999) provide that access to a record containing personal information about a child may be granted to a parent or guardian of the child where the granting of access would be in the best interests of the child.

[454] Freedom of Information Bill 2003, Seanad Éireann, Report Stage, 20 March 2003.

Enterprise, Trade & Employment (who was taking the Bill in the absence of the Minister for Finance) confirmed that the requestor is explicitly informed that the exemption is invoked.[455] The particular relevance of the confirm or deny provision to medical records is highlighted immediately below.

Access & Personal Safety

Any legislation that provides for the release of information creates the need to consider how such a release could impact on the privacy of another person.

A report in the *Irish Medical News* cited the Information Commissioner as advising that:

> "... doctors who give out personal medical information to patients who have requested it under freedom of information legislation could, without exercising due care, expose themselves to a professional negligence charge."[456]

The article was based on a 2003 submission that the then Information Commissioner had made in the context of a review of the 1997 Act, where he called for consideration of including a "public safety" clause in any revised FOI legislation.[457] This would allow for records not to be released by doctors, if doing so would create a risk to the welfare or life of someone other than the person requesting the information concerned, including doctors who have treated the person or other health professionals who have expressed an opinion on the person. In the submission, he outlined the frequency and importance of the subject:

> "... issues of personal safety have arisen in a very small number of cases which have come before me for review. However, where this issue does arise, it is a very serious matter as it would be quite unacceptable that the FOI Acts

---

[455] Freedom of Information (Amendment) Bill 2003, Seanad Éireann, Committee Stage, Vol.171, 12 March 2003.

[456] "Doctors may be sued under FOI", *Irish Medical News*, 27 February 2003.

[457] Information Commissioner (2003b), p.59.

should have the effect of putting anyone's personal safety at risk." [458]

In his *Annual Report* for 2002, the Information Commissioner explained that his:

> "... initial consideration of this issue related to the release of psychiatric records and to fears that in certain rare cases access to records might prompt a violent reaction from the requestor directed at a family member or, indeed, a medical professional".[459]

Interestingly, after further consideration, he concluded in a discussion paper published on his website in February 2003:

> "It is clear the FOI Act, while not having a specific exemption to ensure the personal safety of third parties or their property, does have a number of provisions which might be invoked to achieve the same purpose. Ultimately, a specific 'personal safety' exemption might be useful; but even with such a provision, it remains the case that informing the requestor that such a provision (or one of the section 23 options outlined above[460]) is being invoked creates difficulties. This is because the requester will be put on notice that some people are in fear of him / her. Finding a solution to this dilemma will require considerable further thought."[461]

In the event, section 18 of the 2003 Act does provide a specific "public safety" exception, which provides explicit protection for a record which, if released, could reasonably be expected to endanger the life or safety of any person.[462] The full effect of the new provision is to permit a public body to refuse to confirm or deny the existence of a record that could endanger life or safety if, by confirming or denying the

---

[458] Information Commissioner (2003b), p.59.

[459] Information Commissioner (2003c), p.20.

[460] Section 23 creates a number of access exceptions for reasons of law enforcement and public safety.

[461] Information Commissioner (2003c).

[462] Section 18 amends section 23 *(law enforcement and public safety)* of the 1997 Act.

existence of the record, it could actually have the effect which the exemption seeks to avoid. It also provides that, if the provision is used, that fact need not be quoted to the requestor. This was considered important, in view of the fact that circumstances may arise where it is the requester's propensity to violence that is at issue.[463]

INFORMATION COMMISSIONERS' CRITICISMS OF THE OPERATION OF FOI IN THE HEALTH SECTOR

From time to time, the Information Commissioner has commented adversely on the operation of FOI in the health sector. These criticisms should not be construed as indicating that the health sector receives undue negative comment from the Information Commissioner but, since this book is concerned with health information, it is right to look at some of the specific and general criticisms made. The instances set out below are all taken from the Information Commissioner's 2004 *Annual Report*,[464] unless otherwise stated.

National Maternity Hospital, Holles Street, Dublin

The Commissioner, under the heading *Problematic Reviews*, looked at a case involving Holles Street Hospital, Dublin.[465] This case concerned records relating to a Post Mortem Inquiry (the Dunne Inquiry) held by the Hospital. The records included the submissions of the Hospital to the Inquiry, as well as its correspondence with the Inquiry and with third parties. Medical records of deceased patients or correspondence with their next-of-kin were not included within the review's scope. In drawing attention to this case, the Commissioner stated that she was concerned to highlight not the findings of the review but:

♦ The behaviour of the Hospital in relation to the provision to her Office of the records, the subject of the review

---

[463] Freedom of Information (Amendment) Bill 2003, Select Committee on Finance & the Public Service (3 April 2003).

[464] Information Commissioner (2005).

[465] National Maternity Hospital, Holles Street, Dublin: Case No.030830.

♦ The approach adopted by the Hospital as to how she should conduct the review.

She stated:

"On both counts, I regard the attitude of the Hospital as falling well short of the standard of reasonableness one is entitled to expect from a publicly-funded body engaging in a process with a statutory office such as that of the Information Commissioner. I would go so far as to say that the behaviour of the Hospital in this case amounted to obstruction of my Office in the performance of its functions. For the future, I believe the Hospital would do well to reflect on the nature of the instructions it gives its solicitors. It would do well, also, to reflect on whether it is justified in incurring what must be substantial legal costs in engaging solicitors to represent it in a way which hinders rather than helps the overall FOI review process.

For completeness, it is important to point out that Holles Street Hospital has rejected some of the criticisms made.[466]

Difficulties in Accessing Medical Records

The Information Commissioner observed that her "predecessor drew attention on a number of occasions to difficulties incurred by members of the public in accessing their medical records from hospitals". She shared this concern and was very conscious of the importance of patients being able to access their medical records in a quick and efficient manner.

Two cases were identified to demonstrate some of the difficulties encountered by requesters in accessing records: the first illustrated the confusion and delay caused by the manner in which the request was handled by the hospital;[467] the second raised questions about the

---

[466] "Holles Street hits back at criticism by Information Commissioner", *Irish Medical News*, June 2004.

[467] St. James's Hospital, Dublin: Case No.010215.

adequacy of search procedures and medical record management by public bodies.[468]

Losing Medical Records

In his *Annual Report* for 2001, the then Information Commissioner felt obliged to comment on the problem of medical records that go missing:

> "Quite often, a request for records is refused because the records in question cannot be found. However, there seems to be a particular problem in the case of medical records which go missing or get mislaid. A person's medical records are amongst the most sensitive of personal records and great care should be taken to ensure the safe holding of such records. Apart from their sensitive nature, there is also the very practical consideration that they can be of considerable clinical value in relation to the ongoing care of a patient; they can be of great importance in relation to any case of medical negligence or other such litigation; and they may be of value to the family of a patient after he or she has died. Despite their undoubted importance, I find that the incidence of lost medical records seems to be greater than for other categories of records held by public bodies."[469]

Records' Management by General Practitioners

In the 2004 *Annual Report*, the Commissioner was concerned that there were a number of shortcomings in relation to the management of GPs' records. She referred to the GMS Scheme contract, where doctors are required to keep adequate clinical records. However, this requirement is not elaborated, especially as regards the nature of the records to be kept, the period of retention, the treatment of records of deceased persons, and the absence of proper implementation mechanisms for

---

[468] Adelaide & Meath Hospital, Tallaght, Dublin: Case No.040177.

[469] Information Commissioner (2002), *Medical Records*, p.23. As well as commenting on the matter generally, he identified three cases concerning what happened medical records after the hospitals involved closed.

records where a GP contractor dies, resigns or retires from the GMS scheme.

The Commissioner acknowledged that, while many GPs keep adequate records and have proper record management practices, this arises more from the professionalism and initiative of the individual GP rather than from any agreed contractual arrangement applied consistently by all medical card doctors. She believed that the absence of binding standards is a source of frustration and upset to many medical card holders and their families. She expressed the view that GPs also would welcome clarity as to what is expected of them in this area and called on the HSE to address the issue of GP record-keeping in a comprehensive fashion, adding that any such arrangements should form part of the standard contract under which GPs treat medical card patients.

COMPARISONS, CONTRASTS, CONFLICTS & OVERLAPS BETWEEN FOI & DATA PROTECTION

It is evident that there are similarities and differences in substance and perspective between freedom of information and data protection.

The essential principle of data protection is the protection of individual privacy and the putting in place of safeguards where personal information is collected, used, disclosed or transferred to other persons and / or other countries. It imposes obligations on all individuals, agencies or organisations that keep personal information, and not just public bodies.

The essential principle of FOI, on the other hand, is that there should be access to records held by, or under the control of, public bodies "to the greatest extent possible consistent with the public interest and the right to privacy."[470] It is driven by a desire to make government more open, transparent and accountable and to strengthen the democratic right to freedom of expression, which is automatically impeded once access to information is restricted.

---

[470] Long title to the Freedom of Information Act 1997.

In 1992, anticipating the introduction of FOI legislation, the Data Protection Commissioner felt that it should not be "an occasion of conflict and tension", since both data protection and FOI are derived from human rights principles. However, he did feel that:

> "... the provisions of any freedom of information legislation must take into account those already existing for the protection of personal data. Access to information law must be fully co-ordinated with existing 'data protection' law, so that the entire corpus of information law will be as coherent as possible."[471]

Speaking in 2002, the then Information Commissioner felt that:

> "... there is a clear overlap between the two pieces of legislation in relation to public bodies which are subject both to freedom of information and data protection, since both provide for the protection of personal data or information and for access to that information in specified circumstances. But the form that protection takes differs as between the two regimes."[472]

He added that:

> "the argument that there is potential for conflict between the two regimes largely hinges on two considerations:
>
> (i) the definitions of personal data or information in the two Acts are very different, and
>
> (ii)   the release of personal information to a third party on grounds of public interest even where it breaches the privacy rights of the individual concerned."

On (i), since the Information Commissioner's comments, the Data Protection Act 2003 has narrowed considerably the practical differences between the two pieces of legislation. Data protection law now covers personal information in manual and electronic formats. On

---

[471] Data Protection Commissioner (1993), p.8.
[472] Information Commissioner (2002a).

the other hand, not all manually-recorded personal information is actually covered by the data protection legislation, due to the particular definitions used. In addition, freedom of information does not identify certain classes of personal information as sensitive and deserving of additional protection.

On (ii), further, the notion of the public interest now has found its way explicitly into the data protection regime and is referred to most notably in section 4 (Right of Access), where its inclusion is expressly targeted on health records.[473]

Public Interest Considerations under Freedom of Information

Indeed, the fact that data protection law now expressly includes numerous references to the public interest[474] makes the interpretation of that concept under freedom of information law all the more relevant. In the Information Commissioner's *Annual Report* for 2003, the then Commissioner stated:

> "In very general terms I take it that the public interest is that which supports and promotes the good of society as a whole (as opposed to what serves the interests of individual members of society or of sectional interest groups). In this sense I take it that the term 'public interest' broadly equates with the term 'the common good'."[475]

In March 2002, he had pointed out that, under the Freedom of Information Acts, there is a tension between the right of access of third parties to personal information about other individuals and the privacy rights of those individuals.[476] This tension is not simply

---

[473] See **Chapter 7** for more detail on this point.

[474] There are actually 9 references in total, all added by the 2003 Amendment Act. They can be found in Sections 2A(i)(c)(iv) (Processing of Data); 2B(1)(b)(x) (Conditions for Processing of Sensitive Personal Data); 4(1)(a)(iii) and 4(8) (Right of Access); 6A(2) (Right of Data Subject to Object to Processing); 11(4)(a)(v) and 11(5) (Restriction on Transfer of Personal Data Outside of State); 22A(1)(b) and 22A(3) (Journalism, Literature & Art).

[475] Information Commissioner (2004).

[476] Information Commissioner (2002a).

between freedom of information and data protection rights, but also internally within the former. The Freedom of Information Acts provide that, when deciding whether or not to release personal information to a third party on public interest grounds, the public body has to consider whether:

> "... on balance, the public interest that the request should be granted outweighs the public interest that the right to privacy of the individual to whom the information relates should be upheld."

The Commissioner's approach to the disclosure to third parties of personal information about other people is to favour the protection of privacy:

> "... unless I am satisfied that there are other considerations which clearly outweigh that interest. Where the arguments for and against release are finely balanced I would, therefore, tend to come down against release in order to protect privacy".[477]

He contrasted this with his public interest approach, where the information involved was not *personal*:

> "... without proper scrutiny, there can be no real accountability. Given the emphasis in the Long Title of the Act on release of information being to the greatest extent possible and the requirement in section 34 (*Review by Commissioner of Decisions*) of the FOI Act that public bodies must show to the satisfaction of the Information Commissioner that refusals to release are justified, I tend where public interest arguments for and against release are finely balanced to come down in favour of release. But I approach the exemption for personal information which is clearly designed to protect privacy somewhat differently."[478]

---

[477] As above.
[478] As above.

Using Rights under Both Codes

There is specific provision in the Data Protection Acts 1998 to 2003 that:

> "... a right conferred by this Act shall not prejudice the exercise of a right conferred by the Freedom of Information Act 1997".[479]

In moving this provision in the Dáil, the Minister of State at the Department of Justice, Equality & Law Reform gave the following example:

> "If a person fails to obtain access to personal data under the Data Protection Act, perhaps because it is manual data not recorded in a relevant filing system, he or she may, depending on the circumstances, have a right to gain access to that data under the 1997 Act."[480]

He added that the reason for including this provision expressly was clarity:

> "If somebody made an application for information under the Freedom of Information Act and could not get what he or she wanted under that Act, his or her entitlements under the Data Protection Act were unclear. This makes it clear that the two Acts are separate. If one cannot gain access to information under one Act, one may be able to do so under the other."

This raises the question, especially for public bodies, such as hospitals and the HSE, whether there is a moral or professional obligation on them to advise an individual seeking access to his or her medical records under one Act that they might enjoy more access under the other code.

---

[479] Section 1(5)(a).
[480] Select Committee on Justice, Equality, Defence & Women's Rights, 12 February 2003.

Freedom of Information & the National Health Information Strategy

Chapter 10 discussed the information governance ideas in the National Health Information Strategy, which relate as much to FOI as they do to data protection. The Strategy saw FOI law as "a significant driver of equity and other strategic goals"[481] and, in that regard, added that the extension of FOI to the remaining statutory bodies in the health sector and the routine inclusion of new agencies or administrative structures would be significant in terms of accountability and in delivering equity in access to information. However, it also felt that, with the application of FOI, several policy issues of active concern have arisen, specifically in regard to access to quality assurance records held in the context of clinical audit, peer group review and accreditation processes. It was considered that the changes in data protection law, brought about by the 2003 Act, would offer a timely opportunity for health agencies to review records management and access practices.

Interestingly, the Strategy also stated that:

> "... harmonisation of freedom of information and data protection access will be addressed through appropriate administrative and legislative measures".[482]

Action 17 of the Strategy asserts that:

> "... access to data will be made as seamless as possible for members of the public. Common access procedures will be adopted where feasible and provide for indirect access via a nominated health professional where appropriate."

It will be interesting to see how this can be achieved, in practice, without significant changes to either current FOI or data protection rules. There is also the matter of having to meet, at the very least, the requirements of the EU Data Protection Directive.

---

[481] Department of Health & Children (2004), *Chapter 12*.
[482] Department of Health & Children (2004), *Chapter 12*.

Co-operation between Data Protection & Freedom of Information Commissioners

The supervisory structures for data protection and freedom of information differ between countries. In the UK, the Information Commissioner is an independent official appointed by the Crown to oversee both the Data Protection Act 1998 and the Freedom of Information Act 2000.[483] That type of regime is found in a number of jurisdictions.

In other instances, freedom of information law and data protection law are set out in the same statute, but in different parts that emphasise the distinctions between the two concepts. In Hungary, for example, the Protection of Personal Data & Disclosure of Data of Public Interest Act 1992 is a combined data protection and freedom of information law with one supervisory authority. In Canada, at a Federal level, the Information Commissioner investigates complaints from people who believe they have been denied rights under the Access to Information Act — Canada's freedom of information legislation – while the separate Privacy Commissioner deals with matters arising under the Privacy Act. However, the situation differs at a provincial level, where generally the same legislation and officer deals with both FOI and data protection.[484]

In Ireland, the Data Protection Acts provide that:

> "… the [Data Protection] Commissioner and the Information Commissioner shall, in the performance of their functions, co-operate with and provide assistance to each other."[485]

The nature of this co-operation and assistance is not spelt out.

---

[483] Scotland has its own Information Commissioner. See **Chapter 3** for more information on the FOI and data protection regimes in the UK.

[484] For example, in British Columbia, the same statute – Freedom of Information & Protection of Privacy Act 1996 – addresses both areas.

[485] Section 1(5)(b).

14
CONCLUSIONS

Privacy is a human right directly associated with a truly democratic society. Around the world, people share an appreciation of the value of privacy when it comes to information relating to them. Even if the precise notion of what is encompassed by the privacy concept varies from country to country, and even from person to person, it is clear that it has certain universal human rights themes. Since information is rightly associated with power, it is apparent that the unregulated collection, use, retention and disclosure of information on or about individuals seriously threatens their privacy. Accordingly, laws have been enacted to safeguard the privacy of individuals and to control personal information.

However, the global nature of contemporary technological information systems that are rapidly making physical frontiers increasingly irrelevant raises the question of whether traditional legislative approaches on their own can fully cope with some of the newer privacy challenges. We live in a world that is changing rapidly and, for the most part, these changes pose new and unrelenting challenges for privacy protection. Although the fundamental principles and objectives of privacy regulation will remain, in this new environment, there is an ongoing imperative to update and refine these principles to take into account the rapid development of technology, of world events and even attitudes to privacy itself. For governments, the courts and privacy regulators, the task is to respond with policies that are practical and flexible, while retaining and protecting fundamental human rights. There is no one single or simple answer to reconciling all the competing interests but, without an awareness of the issues, nothing meaningful or lasting can be achieved.

Clearly, fragmentary and opaque requirements of law, ethics and policy will need to be consolidated and supported by transparent and straightforward standards that clearly establish what constitutes responsible social behaviour in an Information Society. In such an environment, commitment by governments to greater public awareness and the continued evolution of workable enforcement mechanisms will be fundamental.

Personal health information will become increasingly valuable as a clinical, management, economic and business asset. This will generate greater pressures for more sharing and disclosure, and accelerate the potential for loss of control by the individual. Consequently, assurances on confidentiality, privacy and security will need to be matched by rigorous sanctions and independent enforcement. Even more, there is an onus on everyone who keeps personal health information to have a genuinely pro-active policy of making individuals aware of the policies and procedures applied in relation to managing such information. This can range from a simple patient information leaflet to a major publicity campaign. The starting point for both, however, should be an internal examination of the extent to which current practices meet proper privacy standards and the adoption, wherever possible, of privacy-enhancing technologies.

As Donna Shalala said in 1997:

> "Yet, as we know from past experience, national legislation alone will not inspire trust in one's rights or commitment to one's responsibilities. It's going to take education. Every single health care professional, every public health official, every pharmacist – every single person who comes in contact with health care records must understand why it's important to keep them safe, how they can keep them safe, and what will happen to them if they don't."[486]

Most of all, society and the individuals that comprise it need to appreciate that real and desirable progress in healthcare does not have to be at the expense of privacy. On that note, perhaps it is best to leave the final word to Joe Meade, the former Data Protection Commissioner:

---

[486] Testimony of Donna Shalala, Secretary, U.S. Department of Health & Human Services before the Senate Committee on Labor & Human Resources, 11 September 1997.

"In the current information era, the concepts of privacy and data protection are, on occasions, put forward as a barrier to progress. On the contrary, I feel strongly that for the information society to succeed it is vital that good data protection practices are in place."[487]

---

[487] Data Protection Commissioner (2003).

APPENDIX 1
TRANSFERRING PERSONAL HEALTH INFORMATION ABROAD

In line with the Council of Europe Data Protection Convention, the Data Protection Act 1988 was concerned to ensure that personal data could not be sent out of Ireland to countries that did not provide an adequate level of protection. In **Chapter 3**, we saw that the EU Data Protection Directive was part of the Internal Market process, intended to facilitate the free flow of information within the Community. We also saw that it has had a major impact on the transfer of personal information from within the Community to outside countries. Accordingly, the data transfer provision in the 1988 Act was deleted and replaced in the 2003 Act by a new section that fully reflects the EU rules.

This specifies conditions that must be met before personal data may be transferred to third countries – that is, states outside of the European Economic Area (EEA). The rules can be summarised as follows:

1.   The general rule is that personal data cannot be transferred to third countries unless the country ensures an adequate level of data protection. The EU Commission has prepared a list of countries that are deemed to provide an adequate standard of data protection.

2.   If the country does not provide an adequate standard of data protection, then the Irish data controller must rely on one of eight alternative measures, including the consent of the data subjects, and the use of approved contractual provisions.

3.   The Data Protection Commissioner retains the power to prohibit transfers of personal data to places outside of Ireland, if he or she considers that data protection rules are likely to be contravened, and that individuals are likely to suffer damage or distress as a result.

Adequate Standard of Data Protection

The "adequacy" test relates to all of the circumstances surrounding a proposed transfer of personal information, including the nature of the data, the purposes for the transfer, the laws in force in that country, and the security measures in place. The EU Commission maintains a list of approved countries that are regarded as satisfying this requirement. If a country appears on this "approved list", then Irish data controllers may transfer personal data to such countries, in the same way as if the transfer were being made within Ireland, or within the EEA.[488]

The Act makes it clear that any EU findings about the adequacy or inadequacy of a third country's data protection regime are definitive, and cannot be second-guessed by national data protection authorities or by data controllers.

The Act also envisages situations where a Member State's Data Protection Commissioner may consider that a third country does not ensure an adequate level of data protection. In such situations, the Commissioner is required to inform the EU Commission, and the other data protection authorities throughout the EU, of his opinion. If the Irish Data Protection Commissioner were to form such a view of a third country, it would be reasonable and prudent for Irish data controllers to regard such a view as authoritative, until such time as the view had been modified by the EU Commission.

---

[488] To date (June 2005), only Switzerland, Guernsey, Argentina and Isle of Man have been approved in full. Canada has been approved for certain types of personal data. The "Safe Harbour" arrangement – a voluntary but enforceable code of good data protection practice, established by the US Department of Commerce – has also been approved, to facilitate transfers of personal data to US organisations that have signed up to the arrangement. (Transfers of personal data to other US organisations, which have not signed up to the Safe Harbour arrangement, are subject to the same restrictions as transfers to other unapproved third countries.) The EU Commission website gives full information about which third countries have been approved for data protection purposes, and about the Safe Harbour arrangement. Further details about the Safe Harbour arrangement, including a list of US companies that have signed up to the arrangement, are also available at the US Department of Commerce website.

Transferring Personal Data to Non-Approved Third Countries: The Eight Alternative Measures

If a country does not appear on the EU Commission's "approved list", then Irish data controllers must rely upon alternative measures. If a data controller can point to one or more of the following eight alternatives, then the transfer of personal data to the third country may proceed:

(i)   The transfer of personal data is required or authorised by law.

(ii) The data subject (the individual to whom the personal data relates) has given his or her consent[489] to the transfer.

(iii) The transfer is necessary for the performance of a contract to which the data subject is party; or the transfer is necessary for the taking of steps – at the request of the data subject – with a view to his or her entering into a contract with the data controller.

(iv) The transfer is necessary to conclude a contract (or to perform a contract) between the data controller and someone other than the data subject, in cases where the contract is entered into at the request of the data subject, or where the contract is in the interests of the data subject.[490]

(v)   The transfer is necessary for obtaining legal advice or for legal proceedings.

(vi) The transfer is necessary to prevent injury or other damage to the data subject's health, or to prevent serious damage to his or her property, or to protect his or her vital interests in some other way – provided that it is not possible to inform the data subject, or obtain his or her consent, without harming his or her vital interests.[491]

---

[489] The Data Protection Commissioner has indicated that he will have regard to relevant provisions of the 1995 EU Directive, which refers to the "unambiguous consent" of individuals in this context. The Directive also requires that "consent" must be freely given and informed. Accordingly, it may not be sufficient to offer individuals an "opt-out".

[490] The Commissioner has advised that, in order to rely fully upon the third and fourth of the eight alternative provisions above, it would be advisable to inform data subjects, in the context of concluding the contract, that their personal data may need to be transferred to third countries for the above purposes.

[491] The Commissioner has stated that, understandably, data protection considerations are sometimes outweighed by other considerations, such as the protection of life. This provision allows data controllers to transfer personal data to third countries in such situations. However, before relying on this provision, data controllers must first establish whether it is possible to obtain

(vii) The personal data to be transferred are an extract from a statutory public register – a register established by law as being available for public consultation, or as being available for consultation by persons with a legitimate interest in its contents. In the latter case, the transfer must be made to a person having such a legitimate interest, and subject to compliance by that person with any relevant conditions.

(viii) The transfer is authorised by the Data Protection Commissioner, where the data controller can point to adequate data protection safeguards, such as approved contractual provisions. The EU Commission has approved "model contracts" to assist data controllers in this regard, and such contracts would automatically fall under this provision.[492]

---

the person's consent. Only if this is not possible – for example, due to urgency – can this provision be invoked.

[492] The Data Protection Commissioner also has the power to endorse "model contracts" specific to Irish circumstances, as well as the power to approve particular contracts or other arrangements that provide satisfactory safeguards. In practice, it is likely that most transfers to "unapproved" third countries will be on the basis of model contracts.

APPENDIX 2
PERIODS OF RETENTION OF
PERSONAL HEALTH RECORDS

The periods set out below are minimum recommended periods.

Acute Hospitals & Residential Services Records

Records	Retention Period
Medical Records, including X-ray films & reports, Pathology reports, A&E records	
General (Adult)	8 years after last contact.
Obstetrics	25 years after last contact.
Children & young persons	Until the patient's 25th birthday; or 26th birthday, if young person was 17 at conclusion of treatment; or 8 years after patient's death if death occurred before 18th birthday.
Mental Health patients	20 years after cessation of treatment; or 8 years after the patient's death, if patient died while still receiving treatment.
Oncology patients	8 years after conclusion of treatment, especially when surgery only involved.[493]
Patients involved in clinical trials	15 years after conclusion of treatment.
Donor patients	11 years post-transplantation.
Deceased patients	8 years after death.

---

[493] Consider also BFCO(96)3 issued by the Royal College of Radiologists, which recommends permanent retention on a computer database when patients have been given chemotherapy and radiotherapy.

Community Health & Welfare Services

Records	Retention Period
Child & Family Services	
Personal records created under Child Care Act 1991	Indefinitely.
Case records & registers – Fostering / Placement of children with relatives / children in residential care	Indefinitely.
Community Medical Services (AMOs)	8 years after last contact, except where the records have been created in accordance with Child Care legislation, in which case they should be held indefinitely.
Dental Records	
Adults	8 years after last contact.
Children & young persons	Until the patient's 25th birthday; or 26th birthday, if young person was 17 at conclusion of treatment; or 8 years after patient's death if death occurred before 18th birthday.
Deceased persons	8 years after death.
Dental X-ray films & reports	As for dental records.
Environmental Health Records	
Environmental Health complaints	Indefinitely.
Food Alerts	1 year.
Food & Drug Sampling reports	2 years.
Food Hygiene (Inactive)	3 years.
Food Sampling & Bacteriological	Retain indefinitely.
Housing	5 years.
Housing Aid for the Elderly	Indefinitely.
Planning	10 years.
Psychology	
Clinical records	8 years after last contact, except where the records have been created in accordance with Child Care legislation, in which case they should be held indefinitely.

Records	Retention Period
Public Health Nursing	
Records	8 years after last contact, except where record is created under Child Care legislation, in which case they should be held indefinitely.
Social Work	
Relating to Child Care legislation	Indefinitely.
Housing, Welfare, etc.	8 years from last contact.
Deceased	8 years after death.
Allied Health Professionals / Paramedics	
Addiction Counselling	As for medical records.
Audiometry	As for medical records.
Chiropody / Podiatry	As for medical records.
Dietetics	As for medical records.
Home Help / Home Care Assistants	As for medical records.
Occupational Therapy	As for medical records.
Pharmacy	As for medical records.
Physiotherapy	As for medical records.
Speech & Language Therapy	As for medical records.
Other	As for medical records.

TABLE OF STATUTES

Luxembourg

TABLE OF CASES

BIBLIOGRAPHY

American Medical Association (2004). *Code of Ethics*, 2004/2005 edition. Chicago, IL: American Medical Association.

An Bord Altranais (Irish Nursing Board) (1998). *Code of Professional Conduct for Each Nurse & Midwife*. Dublin: An Bord Altranais.

Anderson, R. (2001). "Undermining data privacy in health information", *British Medical Journal*, 322:442-443.

Appavu, S.I. (1999). "Unique Patient Identifiers: What are the Options?" *Journal of AHIMA*, October, 70(9):50-54, 56-57.

Article 29 Working Party (2004). *Genetic Data*, Working Document. 12178/03/EN, WP 91, 17 March 2004. Brussels. Available at http://www.europa.eu.int/comm/justice_home/fsj/privacy.

ASTM International (2000). *A Standard Guide for Properties of a Universal Healthcare Identifier*, E1714-00. West Conshohocken, PA: ASTM International.

Attorney-General (Australia) (2003). Keynote address to 25th *International Conference of Data Protection and Privacy Commissioners*, Sydney, 12 September. Available at http://www.privacyconference2003.org/presentations.

Australian Privacy Charter Group (1994). *The Australian Privacy Charter*. Sydney: Law School, University of New South Wales.

Beskow *et al.* (2001). "Informed consent for population-based research involving genetics", *Journal of the American Medical Association*, 286(18), 2315-2321.

Brandeis, L.D. & Warren, S.D. (1890). "The Right to Privacy", 4 *Harvard Law Review* 193, at 195.

Brennan, N. (2003). *Report of the Commission on Financial Management & Control Systems in the Health Service* (The Brennan Report). Dublin: Department of Health & Children.

Burke, K.C. (1981). "Secret Surveillance & the European Convention on Human Rights", 33 Stanford Law Review 1113, 1122.

Calcutt, D. (1990). *Report of the Committee on Privacy and Related Matters*, Cmnd. 1102, p.7. London: HMSO.

Canadian Institute for Health Information (2000). *Unique Identifiers for Health Services Recipients in Canada: A Background Paper*. Toronto: Canadian Institute for Health Information.

Canadian Medical Association (1998). *Health Information Privacy Code*. Ottawa: Canadian Medical Association.

Canadian Standards Association (1996). *Model Code for the Protection of Personal Information* (CAN/CSA-2830). Mississauga, Ontario: Canadian Standards Association.

Central Statistics Office (2004). *Information Society Statistics – Ireland 2004*. Cork: Central Statistics Office.

Comptroller & Auditor General (2002). *Annual Report 2001*. Dublin: Office of the Comptroller & Auditor General.

Confidentiality & Security Advisory Group for Scotland (2002). *Protecting Patient Confidentiality, Final Report to Scottish Ministers*. Edinburgh: Scottish Executive Health Department.

Cotturri, G., Inglese, S.A., Moro, G., Roffiaen, C. & Scattolon, C. (2002). *European Charter of Patients' Rights*. Rome: Cittadinanzattiva-Active Citizenship Network.

Cousins, G., McGee, H., Ring, L., Conroy, R., Kay, E., Croke, D. & Tomkin, D. (2005). *Public Perception of Biomedical Research: A Survey of the General Population in Ireland*. Dublin: Health Research Board.

Data Protection Commissioner (1990). *Annual Report 1989*. Dublin: Office of the Data Protection Commissioner.

Data Protection Commissioner (1991). *Annual Report 1990*. Dublin: Office of the Data Protection Commissioner.

Data Protection Commissioner (1992). *Annual Report 1991*. Dublin: Office of the Data Protection Commissioner.

Data Protection Commissioner (1993). *Annual Report 1992*. Dublin: Office of the Data Protection Commissioner.

Data Protection Commissioner (1994). *Annual Report 1993*. Dublin: Office of the Data Protection Commissioner.

Data Protection Commissioner (1995). *Annual Report 1994*. Dublin: Office of the Data Protection Commissioner.

Data Protection Commissioner (1996). *Annual Report 1995*. Dublin: Office of the Data Protection Commissioner.

Data Protection Commissioner (1997). *Annual Report 1996*. Dublin: Office of the Data Protection Commissioner.

Data Protection Commissioner (1998). *Annual Report 1997*. Dublin: Office of the Data Protection Commissioner.

Data Protection Commissioner (1999). *Annual Report 1998*. Dublin: Office of the Data Protection Commissioner.

Data Protection Commissioner (2002). *Annual Report 2001*. Dublin: Office of the Data Protection Commissioner.

Data Protection Commissioner (2003). *Annual Report 2002*. Dublin: Office of the Data Protection Commissioner.

Data Protection Commissioner (2004). *Annual Report 2003*. Dublin: Office of the Data Protection Commissioner.

Data Protection Commissioner (2005). *Annual Report 2004*. Dublin: Office of the Data Protection Commissioner.

Deloitte & Touche (2001). *Value for Money Review of the Irish Health System*. Dublin: Deloitte & Touche.

Department of Communications & Department of Justice (Canada) (1972). *Privacy & Computers: Report of a Task Force established by the Department of Communications and the Department of Justice*. Ottawa: Information Canada.

Department of Communications, Marine & Natural Resources (2003). *Guidance Notes on the Transposition into Irish Law of EU Directive 2002/58/EC*. Dublin: Department of Communications, Marine & Natural Resources.

Department of Health & Children (1999). *Children First: National Guidelines for the Protection and Welfare of Children*. Dublin: Department of Health & Children.

Department of Health & Children (2001). *Quality & Fairness: A Health System for You* (National Health Strategy). Dublin: Stationery Office.

Department of Health & Children (2001a). *Primary Care: A New Direction* (Primary Care Strategy). Dublin: Stationery Office.

Department of Health & Children (2001b). *Making Knowledge Work for Health: A Strategy for Health Research*. Dublin: Stationery Office.

Department of Health & Children (2004). *Health Information: A National Strategy* (National Health Information Strategy). Dublin: Stationery Office.

Department of Health & Human Services (USA) (1998). *Unique Health Identifier for Individuals*, White Paper. Available at http://aspe.hhs.gov/admnsimp/nprm/noiwp1.htm.

Department of Health (1966). *The Health Services & their Future Development*, White Paper. Dublin: Department of Health.

Department of Health (1992). *Charter of Rights for Hospital Patients*. Dublin: Department of Health.

Department of Health (UK) (1998). *General Principles in the Use of the NHS Number*. London: Department of Health / NHS Executive / NHS Number & Tracing Service Programme (available at www.nhsia.nhs.uk/nnp/pages/default.asp).

Department of Health (UK) (2001). *The Health & Social Care Act 2001: Sections 60 & 61: Background Information*, An Information Note. London: Department of Health.

Department of Health (UK) (2002). *Treatment of Family History Information in Health Records* (Paper Hrdg 05/2002). London: Department of Health.

Department of Health (UK) (2003). *Confidentiality: NHS Code of Practice*. London: Department of Health.

Department of Health (UK) (2005). *The Care Record Guarantee: Our Guarantee for NHS Care Records in England*. London: Department of Health.

Department of Health, Social Services & Public Safety (2002). *Health & Personal Social Services: Protecting Personal Information*, Consultation paper. Belfast: Department of Health, Social Services & Public Safety.

Department of Health, Social Services & Public Safety (Northern Ireland) (2003). *Health & Personal Social Services: Protecting Personal Information – Responses to a Consultation Paper*. Belfast: Department of Health, Social Services & Public Safety.

Department of Justice, Equality & Law Reform (1997). *Transposition into Irish Law [of EU Data Protection Directive]*, Consultation Paper. Dublin: Department of Justice, Equality & Law Reform.

Department of Social & Family Affairs (2004). *Code of Practice on the Personal Public Sector Number*, February. Dublin: Department of Social & Family Affairs.

Economist (1996). "We know you're reading this", *The Economist*, February 10, pp.27-28.

EUROPA (2003). *Eurobarometer*. Brussels: Commission of the European Communities. http://europa.eu.int/comm/public_opinion/archives/ebs/ebs_196_data_protection.pdf.

European Commission (2003). *First report on the implementation of the Data Protection Directive* (95/46/EC), 15 May 2003, COM(2003) 265 Final. Brussels: European Commission.

European Commission (2004). *E-Health – Making Healthcare Better for European Citizens: An Action Plan for a European e-Health Area*. Brussels: European Commission. Adopted 30 April. Available at http://www.europa.eu.int/information_society/activities/health/index_en.htm.

Eysenbach, G. (2001). What is eHealth? [editorial]. *Journal of Medical Internet Research*, 3(2):e20.

Favier, M. & Boland, M. (undated). *Computerising Your Practice*. Dublin: Irish College of General Practitioners.

Federal Privacy Commissioner (Australia) (2001). *Guidelines on Privacy in the Private Health Sector*. Canberra: Office of the Federal Privacy Commissioner.

Federal Privacy Commissioner (Australia) (2001a). *Annual Report to Parliament*. Canberra: Office of the Federal Privacy Commissioner.

Government of Ireland (1937). *Bunreacht na hÉireann* (The Constitution of Ireland). Dublin: Government Publications.

Hauch, J.M. (1994). "Protecting Private Facts in France: The Warren & Brandeis Tort is Alive & Well & Flourishing in Paris", 68 *Tul. L. Rev.* 1219, May.

Information Commissioner (1998). "FOI & Doctors". *Irish Medical Times*, 20 November.

Information Commissioner (2002). *Annual Report 2001*. Dublin: Office of the Information Commissioner.

Information Commissioner (2002a). "Data Protection & Freedom of Information: Is There a Contradiction?". Presentation to the Institute of Management Consultants in Ireland, March.

Information Commissioner (2002b). *Use & Disclosure of Health Data: Guidance on the Application of the Data Protection Act 1998*. Dublin: Office of the Information Commissioner.

Information Commissioner (2003). Address to the Second Annual Conference on the Freedom of Information, School of Law, Trinity College, Dublin, 12 September.

Information Commissioner (2003a). *The Application & Operation of Certain Provisions of the Freedom of Information Act 1997*. Dublin: Office of the Information Commissioner.

Information Commissioner (2003b). *Annual Report 2002*. Dublin: Office of the Information Commissioner.

Information Commissioner (2003c). *Refusal of FOI Requests to Ensure "Personal Safety"*, Discussion paper, available at http://www.oic.ie.

Information Commissioner (2004). *Annual Report 2003*. Dublin: Office of the Information Commissioner.

Information Commissioner (2005). *Annual Report 2004*. Dublin: Office of the Information Commissioner.

Information Commissioner (UK) (2002). *Use & Disclosure of Health Data: Guidance on the Application of the Data Protection Act 1998*. Wilmslow: Office of the Information Commissioner.

Information Society Commission (2004). *An eHealthy State? An Assessment of the Adoption of eHealth in Ireland.* Dublin: Information Society Commission.

Irish Council for Bioethics (2005). *Human Biological Material: Recommendations for Collection, Use & Storage in Research.* Dublin: Irish Council for Bioethics.

Kerkin, S. (1998). *Disclosing Children's Health Information: A Legal & Ethical Framework.* Address to the Consent in Child Health Workshop (6 August). Available at www.privacy.org.nz/media.

Law Reform Commission (1998). *Report on Privacy: Surveillance and the Interception of Communications*, LRC57-1998. Dublin: Law Reform Commission.

Leahy, A.L. & Wiley, M.M. (1998). *The Irish Health System in the 21st Century.* Dublin (now Cork): Oak Tree Press.

Lennon, P., Meade, B. & Boland, R. (2003). *Managing & Protecting the Privacy of Personal Health Information in Irish General Medical Practice* (the "GPIT Guide"). Dublin: Department of Health & Children.

Lindop, N.. (1978). *Report of the Committee on Data Protection*, Cmnd 7341. London: HMSO.

Madden, D. (2002). "Implementation of the Data Protection Directive 1995", *Irish Medical News*, 11 March.

Matthiessen-Guyader, L. (ed.) (2005). *Survey on National Legislation & Activities in the Field of Genetic Testing in EU Member States.* Brussels: Commission of the European Community, Directorate E: Biotechnology, Agriculture & Food.

McBride, A. & Burr, K. (1997). *Towards a Health Identification System in Canada: Uniquely Identifying & Cross-referencing Individuals across Jurisdictions.* Toronto: Canadian Institute for Health Information.

McDougall, J. (1998). *Well-Read: Developing Consumer Health Information in Ireland.* Wexford: Library Association of Ireland.

McDowell, M. (2005). Address to the Irish Society for European Law's meeting on The European Convention on Human Rights & the Media, Dublin, May.

McMahon, B. & Binchy, W. (1990). *Irish Law of Torts.* Dublin: Butterworths.

Meade, B. (2001). "Securing your computerised medical records". *Irish Medical News*, 15 January.

Medical Council (2004). *Guide to Ethical Conduct & Behaviour*, Sixth Edition. Dublin: Medical Council.

Ministry of Health (New Zealand) (1996). *Health Information Strategy for the Year 2000.* Wellington: Ministry of Health.

Molony, B. (2004). *Data Protection in VHI Healthcare.* Presentation at conference on Data Protection, organised by National GPIT Group, 31 January.

MORI Ireland (2005). *Technology Tracker*, January. Dublin: MORI Ireland.

National Freedom of Information Liaison Group (Health Boards) (1999). *Policy for Health Boards on Record Retention Periods*. Dublin: Department of Health & Children.

National Health Information Management Advisory Council (Australia) (1999). *Health Online: A Health Information Action Plan for Australia*. Canberra: Department of Health & Ageing.

National Health Service Information Authority (UK) (2002). *Share with Care: People's Views on Consent and Confidentiality of Patient Information*. Birmingham: National Health Service Information Authority.

O'Mathúna, D., Scott, P.A., McAuley, A., Walsh-Daneshmandi, A. & Daly, B. (2005). *Health Care Rights & Responsibilities: A Review of the European Charter of Patient Rights*. Dublin: Patients Rights Research Team, School of Nursing and School of Law & Government, Dublin City University.

OECD (1980). *Guidelines Governing the Protection of Privacy and Transborder Flows of Personal Data*. Paris: OECD.

Ombudsman & Information Commissioner (2005). "Public Trust in the Civil Service: Room for Improvement". Address to the Annual Conference of Assistant Secretaries, 3 March.

Peto, J., Fletcher, O. & Gilham, C. (2004). "Data protection, informed consent, and research", *British Medical Journal*, May.

President's Advisory Commission on Consumer Protection & Quality in the Healthcare Industry (1997). *Consumer Bill of Rights*. Washington, D.C.: President's Advisory Commission on Consumer Protection & Quality in the Healthcare Industry.

Privacy Commissioner (Canada) (2000). *Annual Report 1999-2000*. Ottawa: Office of the Privacy Commissioner.

Privacy Commissioner (Canada) (2002). *Annual Report 2001*. Ottawa: Office of the Privacy Commissioner.

Privacy Commissioner (New Zealand) (1998). *Information Protection in Healthcare: Knowledge at What Price?*. Address to *Health Summit 1998*, 15 July. See also http://privacy.org.nz/media.

Privacy Commissioner (New Zealand) (2000). *New Zealand Health Information Privacy Code*. Auckland, NZ: Office of the Privacy Commissioner (New Zealand).

Privacy Commissioner (New Zealand) (2001). *News from the Office of The Privacy Commissioner*, Issue No.39, February/April.

Prospectus Consultants (2003). *Audit of Structures & Functions in the Health System*. Dublin: Prospectus Consultants.

Radwanski, G. (2001). "Patient Privacy in the Information Age", Presentation at *E-Health 2001: The Future of Healthcare in Canada*, Canadian Medical Association, Toronto, 29 May.

Radwanski, G. (2002). "Privacy in Health Research: Sharing Perspectives & Paving the Way Forward", Address to Canadian Institutes of Health Research, November 14.

Rits Group (2000). *Information Security Survey 2000*. Dublin: Rits Group. Also at http://www.rits.ie.

Robins, J. (1997). *Reflections on Health: Commemorating 50 years of the Department of Health, 1947 to 1997*. Dublin: Institute of Public Administration.

Ryssdal, R. (1992). "Data Protection & the European Convention on Human Rights in Council of Europe". Presentation at *Data Protection, Human Rights & Democratic Values: XIII Conference of the Data Commissioners*, 2-4 October 1991, p.41-43.

Shalala, D. (1997). *Protecting Privacy of Health Information*. Address to National Press Club, Washington, D.C., 31 July.

Slane, B. (1999). "Health Information: Some Issues at the Close of the 20th Century", Notes for an address to the 7th Annual New Zealand Medico-Legal Conference, February.

Standing Committee on Justice & of the Solicitor General (Canada) (1987). *A Review of the Access to Information Act & the Privacy Act*, Report of the Standing Committee on Justice and of the Solicitor General, Canada. Ottawa: Department of Justice.

Task Force on Quality in Australian Healthcare (1996). *Quality in Healthcare Study*, Final report. Canberra: Commonwealth of Australia.

Thomas, R. (2004). *Show & Tell: Is Market Competitiveness Hindered by Data Protection Law?* Presentation by the Information Commissioner at the Royal Society of Arts, London (8 June).

Tu, J.V. *et al.* (2004). "Impracticability of informed consent in the registry of the Canadian Stroke Network", *The New England Journal of Medicine*, 350(14), 1414-1421.

Wanless, D. (2004). *Securing Good Health for the Whole Population*, Final Report. London: HM Treasury.

Westin, A. (1967). *Privacy & Freedom*. New York: Athaneum.

Wren, M.-A. (2003). *Unhealthy State: Anatomy of a Sick Society*. Dublin: New Island.

Younger, K. (1972). *Report of the Committee on Privacy*, Cmnd 5012. London: Home Office.

USEFUL WEBSITES

Useful Irish websites

BUPA	http://www.bupa.ie
Comhairle	http://www.comhairle.ie
Department of An Taoiseach	http://www.taoiseach.gov.ie
Department of Health & Children	http://www.doh.ie
Department of Justice, Equality & Law Reform	http://www.justice.ie
Department of Social Community and Family Affairs	http://www.welfare.ie
Health Research Board	http://www.hrb.ie
Health Service Executive	http://www.hse.ie
Information Society Commission	http://www.isc.ie
Ireland's National Education and Research Network	http://www.heanet.ie
Irish College of General Practitioners	http://www.icgp.ie
Irish Council for Bioethics	http://www.bioethics.ie
Irish Health	http://www.irishhealth.com
Irish Hospital Consultants Association	http://www.ihca.ie
Irish Internet Association	http://www.iia.ie
Irish Medical Directory	http://www.imd.ie
Irish Medical Organisation	http://www.imo.ie
Law Reform Commission	http://lawreform.ie
My GP	http://www.mygp.ie
National Cancer Registry	http://www.ncri.ie
National GPIT Group	http://www.gpit.ie
National Healthlink Project	http://www.healthlink.ie
National Standards Authority of Ireland	http://www.nsai.ie
OASIS	http://www.oasis.gov.ie
Office of the Data Protection Commissioner	http://www.dataprivacy.ie
Office of the Information Commissioner	http://www.oic.gov.ie
Oireachtas (Parliament)	http://www.oireachtas.ie
REACH	http://www.reach.ie
Royal College of Surgeons in Ireland	http://www.rcsi.ie

VHI   http://www.vhi.ie
Vivas   http://www.vivashealth.ie

European Union Data Protection Authorities

Austria	http://www.dsk.gv.at/
Belgium	http://www.privacy.fgov.be/
Cyprus	http://www.dataprotection.gov.cy/
Czech Republic	http://www.uoou.cz/
Denmark	http://www.datatilsynet.dk/
Estonia	mailto:urmas.kukk@dp.gov.ee
Finland	http://www.tietosuoja.fi/
France	http://www.cnil.fr/
Germany	http://www.bfd.bund.de/
Greece	http://www.dpa.gr/
Hungary	http://abiweb.obh.hu/dpc/index.htm
Ireland	http://www.dataprotection.ie/
Italy	http://www.garanteprivacy.it/
Latvia	http://www.dvi.gov.lv/
Lithuania	http://www.ada.lt/
Luxembourg	http://www.cnpd.lu/
Malta	http://www.dataprotection.gov.mt/
Netherlands	http://www.cbpweb.nl/
Poland	http://www.giodo.gov.pl/
Portugal	http://www.cnpd.pt/
Slovakia	http://www.dataprotection.gov.sk/
Slovenia	mailto:jernej.rovsek@varuhrs.si
Spain	http://www.agpd.es/
Sweden	http://www.datainspektionen.se/
United Kingdom	http://www.informationcommissioner.gov.uk/

EFTA Data Protection Authorities

Iceland	http://personuvernd.is/
Liechtenstein	http://www.sds.llv.li/
Norway	http://www.datatilsynet.no/
Switzerland	http://www.edsb.ch/

Other European Data Protection Authorities

Guernsey	http://www.dataprotection.gov.gg/
Isle of Man	http://www.gov.im/odps
Jersey	http://www.dataprotection.gov.je/

Romania   http://www.avp.ro/

Some Data Protection Authorities Outside of Europe

Australia   http://www.privacy.gov.au/
Canada   http://www.privcom.gc.ca/
New Zealand   http://www.privacy.org.nz/

EU Supervisory Bodies

European Data Protection   http://www.edps.eu.int/
   Supervisor
European Joint Supervisory   http://europoljsb.ue.eu.int/
   Body
Schengen Joint Supervisory   http://www.schengen-
   Authority   jsa.dataprotection.org/
Eurojust   http://www.eurojust.eu.int/jsb.htm

Other International Organisations of Interest

Council of Europe   http://www.coe.int
European Union   http://europa.eu.int
United Nations   http://www.un.org

INDEX